D1257669

elementary theory
of structural
strength

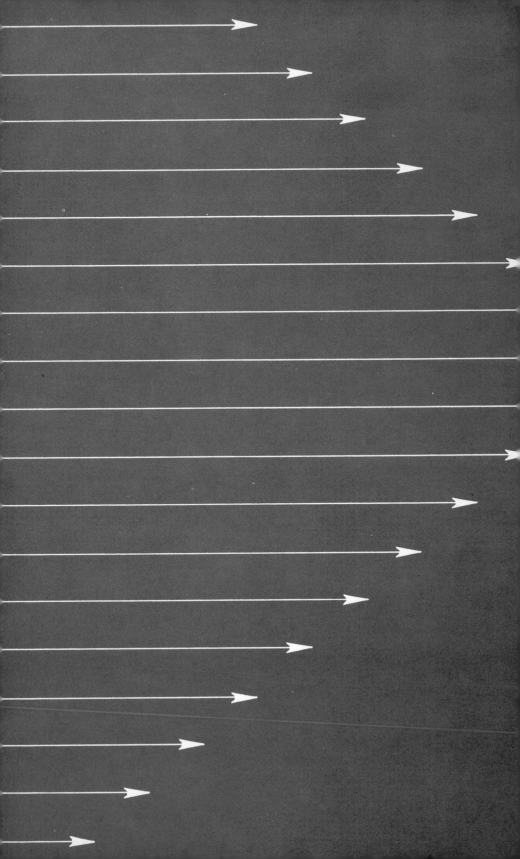

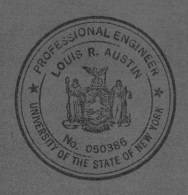

elementary theory

of structural

strength

F. Panlilio

Professor, Mechanical Engineering Department, Union College

John Wiley & Sons, Inc., New York • London

to my wife, Elsie,
and
to our daughters, Misty and Lisa—
here is what I have to show
for those countless hours of togetherness
we have done without

PREFACE

Writing yet another treatise on a subject well covered by a plethora of books is somewhat like putting out still another body style of automobile amid an already staggering array of choices. Undoubtedly, books are written for many different reasons; a common one is probably that of the author being dissatisfied with certain aspects of existing works—this, coupled with a conviction that he has something to contribute.

This book is in part an outgrowth of a nagging dissatisfaction with the treatment of the subject variously known as strength of materials, mechanics of materials, resistance of materials. This discontent has led to the development of an approach to the subject which is hereby offered for consideration as a small contribution to the teaching of strength theory.

I like the word "strength" for its terse cogency and have used it freely; indeed, it forms the central theme of the book. My dissatisfaction comes from the fact that strength has not been used as meaningfully as I feel its pithiness suggests it could be used. Worse than leaving the meaning implicit has been the actual misuse of the term. Example: When an author writes of "a beam of uniform strength," he means really a beam of variable strength which is everywhere stressed to the same maximum. Within the limitations of language, and of my own command of it, I have tried to define strength and have used it in that sense. In the hope of instilling in the student a proper appreciation of the strength concept, I have introduced the notion of utilization factors and have touched upon optimization.

I have deemphasized statical indeterminateness and stressed constraint redundancy instead. I believe that constraint redundancy is *very* germane to strength and have treated it accordingly. Statical indeterminateness (I have used it, but most sparingly) would certainly be appropriate for a chapter heading in a book entitled, say, "How to Solve Problems in Structural Mechanics." The usual treatment of this topic has been largely unsatisfactory to me for the one reason that the physical significance of redundancy has seldom been brought out, if at all. I have long had the feeling that statical indeterminateness has provided little more than a convenient excuse for demonstrating the niceties of certain mathematical techniques. It is really a simple matter to comment, even only as an afterthought, on why indeterminate structures are *purposely* made that way.

Equally as basic a reason as the preceding, for my soft-pedaling statical indeterminateness, is that of consistency. I have not classed multimaterial tension and compression members and torsion members as indeterminate, just as I have not multimaterial beams (they never are), because they are no more indeterminate than a simple tension member. As soon as we consider the distribution of internal forces, we have indeterminateness. Hence we should not assume, for instance, that one-half of a tension bar's cross section transmits one-half of the tension load, unless we *explicitly* point out that this *assumption* is needed to break the deadlock of indeterminateness.

At the risk of having them loom as a stumbling block, I have introduced in Chapter 2, as part of the background material, the fundamental differential equations (only in cartesian form) of equilibrium and compatibility. I see no other way out if the student is to be made aware of (1) what is the problem, when are solutions possible, and when are possible solutions correct, and (2) what are the bases of strength theory? This also explains why I have chosen to present the general statement of Hooke's law first, from which are then derived the special cases. Of the several topics in this chapter, I ask the reader to pay special attention to the discussion of signs. Modesty aside and ignorance confessed, I must say that I am not aware of any previous exposition of this dichotomy in the sign conventions and of why signs are so often a source of difficulty.

In Chapters 3 to 8, the one item that probably deserves special mention is the singularity function. Beam loading presents such a good opportunity for introducing the technique of handling stepwise continuous functions that it would be a shame not to use it. Furthermore, this treatment of the subject paves the way and furnishes as good a motivation as any, especially to nonelectrical engineers, for the later study of the Laplace transformation, now fast becoming standard in required mathematics courses.

In regard to columns, two things have long impressed me. One is the artificial, therefore needless, separation of the centrally loaded from the eccentrically loaded member; the other is the near absolute silence on the most important one among the salient aspects of column behavior, namely, that a column is most sensitive to errors of one kind or another in the vicinity of the critical slenderness and becomes less so away from this region. It is inevitable therefore (1) that the centrally loaded column is presented as a special case of the eccentrically loaded member, and later it is remarked that the eccentrically loaded member may just as validly be considered a special case of a centrally loaded column; and (2) that empiricism in column design is discussed.

The variation of stress at a point comes late in the book. I am convinced that this variation should be presented only once, but fully and correctly. To confine the discussion to the one family of planes in two-dimensional problems could be misleading. Example: To tell the student that, when the two nonzero principal stresses have the same sign, the maximum shear stress is one-half of their difference, is a disservice to him because this is incorrect. Somehow, it is never easy for the student to reconcile the two ideas: that, in dealing with two-dimensional stress, one need not confine the discussion to two dimensions only.

Elegant as tensor notation is, I am not quite ready to say that it properly belongs here where the emphasis has been on strength. If, however, we were studying the mechanics of continua, then, certainly, the tensor should be used right from the start, beginning with the cartesian, to provide background, and building up to the general tensor. Nevertheless, some of the essential characteristics of cartesian tensors are pointed out; in fact, on the basis of the properties that are common to the strain and the stress tensors, the transformation equations for strain are derived from those previously obtained for stress.

As an alternative and powerful method of handling deflections, Castigliano's theorem is discussed. The sequence of presentation is not the usual one in that reciprocity of deflections is taken up first, in quite a general form, and then, as a concomitant, Castigliano's second theorem is brought out. The significance of what is commonly referred to as the Theorem of Least Work is explained from the supplementary view of differentiation relative to independent variables.

In keeping with the emphasis on strength, I have treated the role of ductility in one separate and final chapter. Once again, the significance of constraint redundancy is brought out, this time coupled with the added benefits of material ductility. And, of course, an introduction to limit design is a natural. For the last topic, the riveted connection is used to illustrate limit analysis; I have long believed that this is the only logical way of presenting this subject.

It is a foregone conclusion that not everybody will be pleased. No doubt some will miss temperature effects; others, stress concentration, fatigue, and dynamic effects. I can only say that I have had to omit some topics in order that I might do justice to the exposition of an introductory viewpoint: the concept of optimum load-carrying capacity.

In these days of the feverish rush to get on the science bandwagon, when it seems the fashion to subserve engineering to science, some will look upon this work as a needless manicuring of an old viewpoint. Of course, I am prejudiced when I say that to me it represents a great deal more than this—in a small way I have tried here, as others have been trying elsewhere, again to draw attention to the engineer's sense of values and way of thinking, to the vitally necessary art of making meaningful assumptions and extrapolations.

This book, which presupposes a solid background in statics, would probably appear too lengthy for a three-hour course; but this is only because I have not spared words in explaining fundamental concepts. Paucity of words is not necessarily a virtue in a textbook, and I am asking the student to read many paragraphs uninterrupted by equations (he should do more of this, anyway). If desired, Chapters 10 to 13 may be skipped for a brief course.

Some of the problems are much more than mere exercises; they form an extension of the theory. The answers to most of the even-numbered ones are given at the end of the book. Experience has shown that nothing is more frustrating to a student, in trying to develop facility at this one of the many roles he is expected to play (that of being a computist), than not having any kind of guide or yardstick by which to gage whether or not he is in the "right ball park."

The influence of the many treatises on the subject is obvious—this book owes its very existence to them. I have learned much from my teachers, in particular, the late J. A. Van den Broek, of whose sense of values I hope I have retained a measure; for this I am truly grateful. My debt to many students in more than twenty years of teaching is a very real one: from their fresh viewpoints and unintentionally probing questions I have profited. Among several I cite John E. Edinger, Union, 1960, and Martin P. Einert, Union, 1961, for the many constructive comments they made on the class notes which were the rough draft of this book.

I acknowledge with appreciation the steadfast encouragement and moral support of my colleagues at Union College: Professors Joseph

Modrey, Gardner M. Ketchum, and Raymond Eisenstadt, and Anthony Hoadley who read portions of the manuscript. The grant by the Trustees of Union College, through President Carter Davidson, of a sabbatical leave is sincerely appreciated; without that break this book would have been further delayed. I also want to express my gratitude to Carole Walck for typing the bulk of an earlier version of the manuscript for class use, to my former students Paul Snyder and Robert Marquez for preparing many of the sketches for reproduction, and to Dr. J. H. Smith of the Knolls Atomic Power Laboratory for a number of suggestions. Special thanks are due to Professors Lucien A. Schmit, Jr., of Case Institute of Technology and Samuel T. Carpenter of Swarthmore College for their critical reviews of the final manuscript, and to John Wiley and Sons, Inc., for special considerations during production of the book. Finally, I sincerely thank my wife, to whom this work is dedicated, for her monumental patience (many times sorely tried) at my being such a slow worker.

No effort has been spared to see to it that there are no errors as to both content and typography; for those that surely must have escaped hours of proofreading, I cheerfully assume sole responsibility. May I hope that they will be called to my attention by discerning readers:

FILADELFO PANLILIO

Schenectady, New York
January, 1963

CONTENTS

1 Introduction   1

    1.1   Analysis and Design, 1
    1.2   Strength, 3
    1.3   Force and the Free-Body Diagram, 3
    1.4   Internal Forces Exposed by the Method of Sections, 5

2 Foundations of the Subject   11

    2.1   Stress, 11
    2.2   Equations of Equilibrium, 17
    2.3   Strain, 20
    2.4   Equations of Compatibility, 25
    2.5   Hooke's Law, 26
    2.6   Strain Energy, 31
    2.7   The Basic Problem, 32
    2.8   The Engineering Approach. Saint-Venant's Principle, 34
    2.9   Principle of Superposition, 36
    2.10 Units. Symbols, 36
    2.11 Sign Conventions, 37

3 Tension and Compression   41

    3.1   Simple Tension, 41
    3.2   Strength Properties of Materials, 47

3.3   Simple Compression, 51
3.4   The Strength of an Axially Loaded Member, 53
3.5   Factor of Safety, 55
3.6   Tension or Compression Bars That Are Not Two-Force
      Members, 61

4 Torsion   **72**

4.1   Simple Shear, 72
4.2   Solid Round Shafts, 76
4.3   Hollow Round Shafts, 85
4.4   Strength Properties in Torsion, 88
4.5   Rotating Shafts, 92
4.6   Solid Shafts of Noncircular Cross Sections, 98
4.7   Closely Coiled Helical Spring, 101
4.8   Thin-Walled Tubes in Torsion, 106

5 Bending: Shear Force and Moment   **111**

5.1   Introduction, 111
5.2   Types of Beams, 111
5.3   Shear Force and Moment, 113
5.4   Shearing-Force and Bending-Moment Equations, 116
5.5   The Concept of Beam Loading, 121
5.6   Differential Relations between Bending Moment, Shear
      Force, Load Intensity, and Position, 122
5.7   Singularity Functions, 125
5.8   Shear-Force and Bending-Moment Diagrams, 136

6 Bending: Beam Strength   **142**

6.1   Load-Carrying Capacity, 142
6.2   Strength in Bending, 142
6.3   Significance of the Beam Formula, $M = \sigma I/c$, 148
6.4   Strength in Shear, 153
6.5   Shear Stresses in Wide-Flange Sections, 160
6.6   Further Significance of the Beam Formula, $\tau = VQ/It$,
      164
6.7   Applications, 167
6.8   Efficiencies of Symmetrical Beam Sections, 177
6.9   Beams of Variable Cross Sections, 178
6.10 Beams of Two or More Materials, 183

7 **Bending: Beam Deflections**   **194**

  7.1 Introduction, 194
  7.2 Deformations in a Transverse Plane, 194
  7.3 Deformations in a Longitudinal Plane. The Bernoulli-
       Euler Equation, 197
  7.4 Beam Deflections, 199
  7.5 Differential Equation of the Elastic Curve, 200
  7.6 Differential Relations between y, θ, M, V, q, and x, 201
  7.7 The Double Integration Method, 203
  7.8 Deflections Due to Shear. Warping of Transverse
       Sections, 210
  7.9 Deflections of Variable Cross Section Beams, 216

8 **Redundantly Supported Members**   **221**

  8.1 Redundant Constraints. Statical Indeterminateness,
       221
  8.2 Axially Loaded Members, 225
  8.3 Torsion Members, 230
  8.4 Beams of One Span, 234
  8.5 Continuous Beams, 241
  8.6 The Three-Moment Equation, 244

9 **Column Action**   **255**

  9.1 The Short Post, 255
  9.2 The Column, 260
  9.3 Column Behavior, 264
  9.4 The Euler Column, 267
  9.5 Elastic Deformation, 273
  9.6 Independent and Dependent Variables, 275
  9.7 End Conditions, 275
  9.8 The Problem of Column Design, 281

10 **Variation of Stress at a Point**   **285**

  10.1 Introduction, 285
  10.2 State of Stress at a Point, 285
  10.3 Variation of Stress, 287
  10.4 General Three-Dimensional Stress, 297
  10.5 Plane Stress, 300
  10.6 Pure Shear in Plane Stress, 307

Contents

10.7   Mohr's Circle for Stress, 308
10.8   Mohr's Circle for the General Case of Plane Stress, 316

11   Variation of Strain at a Point   **324**

11.1   Introduction, 324
11.2   Plane Strain, 324
11.3   Principal Strains in the Three-Dimensional Case, 330
11.4   Mohr's Circle for Strain, 331
11.5   Strain Gage Rosettes, 336
11.6   Stress and Strain.   Hooke's Law, 340
11.7   Relations between Mohr's Two Circles in Plane Stress, 344

12   Theories of Failure.   Combined Loading   **348**

12.1   Introduction, 348
12.2   The Maximum Normal-Stress Theory, 349
12.3   The Maximum Shear-Stress Theory, 351
12.4   The Maximum Distortion-Energy Theory, 353
12.5   Combined Loading: Uniaxial Stress, 357
12.6   Combined Loading: Biaxial Stress, 363
12.7   Thin-Walled Pressure Vessels, 367

13   Energy Concepts   **375**

13.1   Energy Stored in a Strained Member, 375
13.2   Reciprocity of Static Deflections, 378
13.3   Castigliano's Theorem, 382
13.4   Deflections by Energy Methods, 383
13.5   Application to Redundantly Supported Systems, 390

14   The Role of Ductility in Static Loading   **397**

14.1   Introduction, 397
14.2   Tension and Compression, 398
14.3   Torsion, 407
14.4   Bending, 413
14.5   Column Action, 428
14.6   Limit Design, 435
14.7   The Riveted Connection, 441

Appendix Tables: Rolled Steel Shapes   453

    I   American Standard **I** Sections, 454
   II Wide-Flange Sections (Abridged Listing), 456
  III Equal-Leg Angles (Abridged Listing), 460

Answers to Even-Numbered Problems   463

Index   471

INTRODUCTION

This book is concerned with the subject of structural strength, which in its widest sense means the strength of entire structures such as buildings, bridges, automobile frames, spacecraft frames. In the more limited scope which is both desirable and proper for an introductory text, it is confined to a theory of strength of the elements which constitute a structure. To gain some perspective and develop a proper appreciation of the nature of the subject, the student is invited to take a look back at some aspects of the background material.

1.1 Analysis and Design. In *statics*, the subject that is basic and preparatory to this one, there is a group of problems on frames and trusses that require determination of tension and compression forces in the component parts of these structures induced by specified loads. One important assumption tacitly made is that the dimensional changes caused by the loads are so slight as to be negligible. Furthermore, it is generally implied that the component parts possess the necessary load-carrying capacities which enable the entire structure to withstand the given loads. The process involved in the solution of such problems is one of *analysis*. If the problems were so changed as to necessitate calculation of the proper sizes for the component parts in order that the structure as a whole could safely carry the given loads, then the process involved in their solution would be one of *design*.

Analysis and design are inverse processes. To analyze a structure means to solve either one of two problems: (1) from given or assumed dimensions, forms, and material properties, to determine the internal

1

forces and accompanying dimensional changes produced by given or assumed loads—a process that may be described as a *force-and-deformation analysis;* (2) from given or assumed dimensions, forms, material properties, and prescribed limitations on the induced internal forces and dimensional changes, to determine the load-carrying capacity of the structure—a process that may be called a *strength analysis.*

On the other hand, to design a structure is to determine, from given or assumed loads and major dimensional limitations, the appropriate sizes and forms of the component parts (sometimes also the proper material to use when there are two or more materials to choose from) in order that the structure will function effectively, safely, and economically.

Let us consider, for example, the horizontal bar supporting a load as represented in Fig. 1.1. If all the dimensions of the bar, the kind of material it is made of, and the magnitude of the load W are assumed known, the maximum deflection or sag can be found in a deformation analysis. If it were desired to calculate the maximum value that W may have without the deflection exceeding a given amount, then the answer would follow from a strength analysis. Finally, if, say, the cross-sectional dimensions of the bar are not fixed and we would answer such questions as what these dimensions should be and which is the most economical of several available cross sections so that, under the given load, the maximum deflection shall not exceed a prescribed amount, then we would have a problem in design.

One of the most important objectives of the engineer is to design structures and machines for the prospective benefit of his fellowmen. In order to achieve his goal, he must necessarily be conversant with methods of analysis. An analysis may precede a design as a preliminary step; another analysis may follow the design as a final step. The intermediate step, however, which is the solution of the design problem proper, requires something else in addition to analysis. This means that a knowledge of analysis alone is not adequate, because separating analysis and design is a gap that can be bridged effectively only by a strength theory.

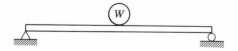

FIG. 1.1

The object of this book is to develop such a theory of strength. In common with all physical theories, this is based on certain assumptions; these have to do with mechanical properties of materials that have been determined in testing laboratories. Since the subject matter of this book is not intended for a laboratory course, in which properties as such are studied, only brief mention is made of those properties and the manner of their determination as are pertinent to the theory.

1.2   Strength. The strength of a structure is one primary measure of its usefulness. The layman, and certainly the beginning student, would most likely understand by "the strength of a structure" its load-carrying capacity. In this book we approach the subject matter with this basic thought in mind, and we shall endeavor to use the word "strength" always with this connotation.

On the strengths of its individual components depends that of the entire structure. Governing such dependence is a functional relationship that may be simple or complex. Before we can determine the strength of the whole, we must first know the strength of each part. In much that follows, we will discuss the strengths of the basic structural elements: tension and compression members, shafts, beams, columns.

1.3   Force and the Free-Body Diagram. Partly by way of review, we define force as the mechanical action of one body on another body. Engineering mechanics recognizes only two types: (1) action from a distance, without benefit of contact between the interacting bodies, in which case the force is distributed throughout a volume; and (2) action through the medium of contact, in which case the force is distributed over the surface area of contact between the interacting bodies. Actions of the first type are called *body forces*, of which the earth pull is the most familiar example; those of the second type are called *contact forces*, which then comprise all forces not of the first type.

In problems involving the effects forces have on the supports of bodies at rest or on the state of motion of bodies not at rest, extensive use is made of the *free-body diagram*. When the actions on a "free" body of the bodies imagined removed are represented, the point of application of each force may be located anywhere along its action line (or of each moment, anywhere in its plane or any parallel plane). This *principle of transmissibility* is valid so long as only the "external" effects of forces are dealt with. Then the point of application is not a significant attribute of the action.

When dealing with "internal" effects of forces, however, we may no longer apply the transmissibility principle without restriction. Although even more extensive use is made of the free-body diagram, where the effects dealt with involve induced internal forces and concomitant dimensional changes, the location of the application point of a force (or a moment) becomes significant. Force and moment vectors must then be *localized*. The number of important characteristics of force as well as of moment must accordingly be increased from three to four, thus: magnitude of the force, orientation of its action line, sense, *and* point of application; magnitude of the moment, aspect of its plane of action, sense, *and* site of application.

As an example, let us consider the simple symmetrical truss shown in Fig. 1.2. The load P is applied at pin B in case (a) and at pin D in case (b). An analysis of pin D in each case reveals that, whereas in (a) member BD experiences no internal force and hence tends to remain of the same length, in (b) member BD is subject to axial tension forces at its ends, equal to P in magnitude, and hence will elongate. Thus, although the reactions at A and C, which are external effects of the load, do not depend on its point of application (they are each equal to $P/2$ in both cases), the "stress" in BD, which is an internal effect, most definitely depends on the location of the application point of the load P.

The beam in Fig. 1.3 provides another example. In case (a) the moment load M is applied between supports, whereas in case (b) it is applied at the overhanging end of the beam. In either case, the reactive forces at the supports are each equal to M/L. It is observed, however, that in (a) the bent beam displays one point of inflection, part of it being downwardly concave and part upwardly concave, whereas in (b) it is downwardly concave throughout its length, displaying no point of inflection.

Therefore, we repeat: in the analysis of internal effects, to which practically all of strength theory is devoted, it is imperative that force and moment vectors be localized in all representations.

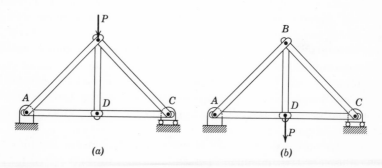

(a)   (b)

Fig. 1.2

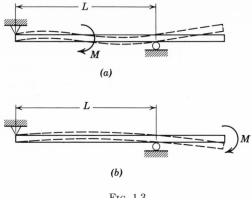

(a)

(b)

FIG. 1.3

1.4   Internal Forces Exposed by the Method of Sections.   The analysis of internal-force distribution in a load-carrying member usually begins with the isolation of part of the member.   This is accomplished by the simple expedient of "passing a section" across or through the body, after which the part of interest is represented as an isolated free body.   This is nothing new in the experience of the student, since in his study of elementary trusses he passed cutting sections freely, isolating individual joints in the "joint-to-joint method" or several joints with their interconnecting members in the "method of sections."

It cannot be overemphasized that, except for one's lack of imagination, there are absolutely no limitations on the selection of a free body.   In the actual construction of the free-body diagram, however, there is one cardinal rule which may never be violated without inviting trouble: *Whenever a discrete body or part of a body is considered removed, its AC-TION on the part or parts which remain MUST be substituted for its bodily presence.*   Failure to observe this rule invariably leads to incorrect free-body diagrams and faulty interpretation of the situation, as well as as to results which can only be accidentally correct.

To illustrate the method of sections as well as to emphasize further the limitations of the principle of transmissibility, let us consider the bent supporting a cylinder as shown in Fig. 1.4a.   Figure 1.4b represents the free-body diagram of the entire system, bent and cylinder together. The double subscript notation indicates the interacting bodies; for instance, V_{PB} denotes the vertical component of the action which the pin P (removed) exerts on the bent B.   The solid line vector labeled R_{PB} may be used alternatively, in lieu of the horizontal and vertical components, to denote the resultant action of the pin P on the bent B.   The

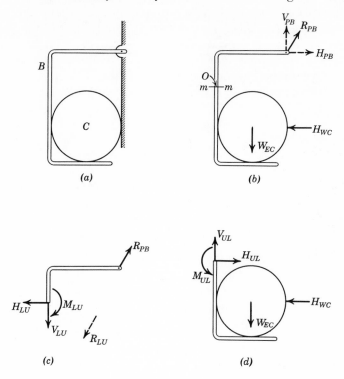

Fig. 1.4

earth pull on the cylinder C is designated W_{EC}, the principal symbol W being used because of our familiarity with the notion of weight. It is assumed that the bent itself has negligible weight. Suppose now it is required to investigate the internal-force system at some location O in the bent. The obvious thing to do is to expose this force system by passing through O a plane such as m-m and isolate, say, the upper part of the bent. There is, however, an infinite number of cutting planes that may be passed through O, all with different aspects; therefore the problem arises as to which cutting plane to use. For reasons that will become clear later, a "transverse" plane such as m-m in Fig. 1.4b is to be preferred to all others. Of course, the word transverse implies that the thickness of the piece is much smaller than its length, for otherwise it is a vague term.

The free-body diagram of the upper part of the bent is shown in Fig. 1.4c, in which the earth pull on the piece is ignored. The action of the removed lower part of the bent is clearly one of contact, transmitted across the plane m-m; it is, therefore, desirable to localize this action to the vicinity of O. To be sure, the *resultant* action of the lower on the upper part reduces to the statically equivalent single force R_{LU}, shown as a dashed line vector in Fig. 1.4c. Such representation, however, would contribute nothing toward developing the "feel" for the contact action involved; certainly, contact action should be shown at the site of contact.

The "microscopic" view of these internal forces, now become external by the technique of isolation, is considered in succeeding chapters. The gross representation we are at this stage justified in making is that shown in Fig. 1.4c. This consists of (a) the totality of those forces that prevent translation in the vertical direction; (b) the totality of those forces that prevent translation in the horizontal direction; and (c) the totality of those forces that prevent rotation about O. They are labeled, respectively, V_{LU}, H_{LU}, and M_{LU}, where the subscripts stand for the lower and the upper parts of the bent; these actions are sometimes called *stress resultants*.

It is equally proper to use the free-body diagram of the lower portion of the system, as shown in Fig. 1.4d. The components, V_{UL}, H_{UL}, and M_{UL}, of the action of the upper on the lower part are equal in magnitude but opposite in sense to their corresponding partners in Fig. 1.4c. For the purpose of calculating these unknown stress resultants either free-body diagram is valid.

Illustrative Example.   Figure 1.5a represents a pin-connected frame, essentially a planar structure. It is desired to evaluate the components of the internal-force system at the section m-m of member B caused by the load shown. The weights of the individual members may be ignored, and the horizontal floor as well as all the pins may be assumed smooth.

ANALYSIS.   Although it is obviously desirable to consider the member in question as soon as possible in the analysis, as a general rule it is good practice to treat the entire structure as a free body first, especially if it is immediately clear that the associated force system is solvable completely or, at least, in part. In Fig. 1.5a are shown dashed line vectors representing the unknown floor reactions. Since the force system classifies as planar parallel, we note that there are available two independent equilibrium equations; and, since there are only two unknown quantities involved, we conclude that the system is completely solvable and proceed at once to calculate the unknowns.

From the equilibrium equation,

$$\Sigma M_5 = 0 = -9R_{FA} + 3(500),$$

we find

$$R_{FA} = \tfrac{500}{3} \text{ lb},$$

and, from

$$\Sigma F_V = 0 = R_{FA} + R_{FC} - 500,$$

there follows

$$R_{FC} = \tfrac{1000}{3} \text{ lb}.$$

The free-body diagram of member B is now considered (Fig. 1.5b). Observe that, since four unknowns are involved but only three independent equilibrium equations may be written for this general planar force system, a complete solution is not possible. If, however, advantage is taken of the fact that three of the four unknown forces intersect at point

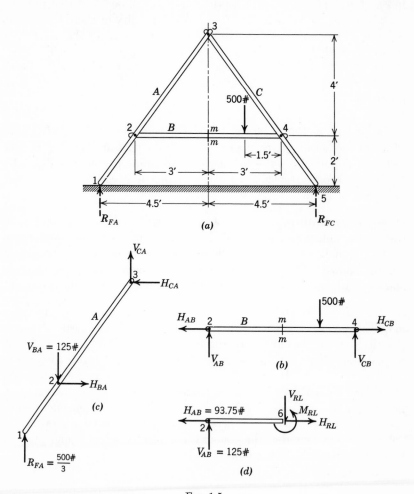

Fig. 1.5

4 (or at point 2), a partial solution can be accomplished, thus:

$$\Sigma M_4 = 0 = -6V_{AB} + 1.5(500),$$

whence $\qquad\qquad V_{AB} = 125$ lb.

The component V_{CB} may now be found, if desired, from

$$\Sigma F_V = 0 = V_{AB} + V_{CB} - 500,$$

which gives $\qquad\qquad V_{CB} = 375$ lb.

Beyond the conclusion that the axial forces H_{AB} and H_{CB} are equal in magnitude, which follows from the third independent equation $\Sigma F_H = 0$, these two forces remain undetermined. Hence recourse must be made to another free-body diagram. Quite aside from the fact that there are no other choices left, either member A or member C is a logical next choice for investigation because A involves the unknown H_{BA} (the reactive partner of H_{AB}) and C involves H_{BC} (the reactive partner of H_{CB}). Figure 1.5c shows the free-body diagram of member A, with the previously determined forces indicated; this is a completely solvable system. Since the force we are immediately interested in is H_{BA}, we determine this directly by considering moments about point 3, thus:

$$\Sigma M_3 = 0 = -4.5(\tfrac{500}{3}) + 3(125) + 4H_{BA}.$$

This yields $\qquad\qquad H_{BA} = 93.75$ lb,

with sense correctly shown. Hence $H_{AB} = 93.75$ lb also, with sense as shown in Fig. 1.5b.

There is now sufficient information for solving the original problem. At this point there is no need for completing the analysis of the force system in Fig. 1.5c, although this can easily be done. (The student should demonstrate to himself that this is so.) We come finally to the free-body diagram of the left half of member B, separated from the right half by the transverse cutting plane m-m; this is shown in Fig. 1.5d. The internal-force system now become external is represented by its three components: an axial force H_{RL}, a transverse force V_{RL}, and a pure moment M_{RL}, where the subscripts signify that these actions are exerted by the right part, which has been removed, on the left part, which has been retained as the free body. This force system is completely solvable. Thus, from

$$\Sigma F_V = 0 = 125 - V_{RL},$$

we find $\qquad\qquad V_{RL} = 125$ lb.

From $\qquad\qquad \Sigma F_H = 0 = -93.75 + H_{RL},$

we get $\qquad\qquad H_{RL} = 93.75$ lb.

Finally, from $\Sigma M_6 = 0 = -3(125) + M_{RL}$,

we obtain $M_{RL} = 375$ ft-lb.

Since all three initially unknown co nponents came out with plus signs, their senses are correct as originally assumed in Fig. 1.5d.

Note that the right half of member B would serve equally as well in the analysis. If it were considered, one should obtain V_{LR}, H_{LR}, and M_{IR} with the same magnitudes as in the foregoing but with senses opposite to those shown in Fig. 1.5d, since these are the reactive partners of the previous three components. In practice one learns to consider as a free body that part of the member which involves the least number of forces and moments, known as well as unknown, since it is generally true that fewer actions usually means fewer terms to write in the summations.

PROBLEMS

1.1. In Fig. 1.5a, determine the components of the internal-force system at a transverse section of member A, 4 ft from pin 3.

1.2. In Fig. 1.5a, determine the moment component of the internal-force system at a transverse section of member C, x ft from pin 3, $0 < x < 5$.

1.3. Repeat Prob. 1.2 for the range $5 < x < 7.5$.

1.4. In Fig. 1.5a, suppose each of the three uniform bars weighs 10 lb/ft. Determine the components of the internal-force system at the midsection of member B.

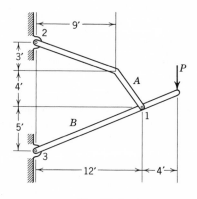

FIG. P1.5

1.5. Find one set of components of the internal-force system at the bend of member A.

1.6. In Fig. P1.5, determine the resultant action of member A on pin 1.

FOUNDATIONS OF THE SUBJECT

2.1 Stress. The most basic concept we will be using is that of stress. In the simplest qualitative terms, *stress is the intensity of internal force.* Force is a vector quantity and as such has direction; intensity implies an area of distribution.

Imagine a solid subjected to the action of a force system in equilibrium. Some of the forces may be surface distributed, whereas others may be volume distributed; all these forces are assumed exerted on the body by agents external to it. Let a cutting plane be passed, dividing the body into two parts (Fig. 2.1a) and let one part be isolated (Fig. 2.1b). The forces exerted by the part removed on the part being considered constitute a system of contact forces transmitted across this section.

Let us consider a small area ΔA on this exposed section and let ΔF represent the resultant of the contact forces transmitted across ΔA. This resultant can have any orientation relative to the plane. Dividing ΔF by ΔA, we obtain a ratio representing the average intensity at which ΔF is distributed across ΔA. Let us call this the *average stress on* ΔA and use for it the symbol S_{ave}, thus:

$$S_{\text{ave}} = \frac{\Delta F}{\Delta A}. \qquad (a)$$

Observe that, since ΔF is a vector quantity and ΔA is a scalar, S_{ave} is necessarily a vector quantity with the same direction as ΔF. Let us

11

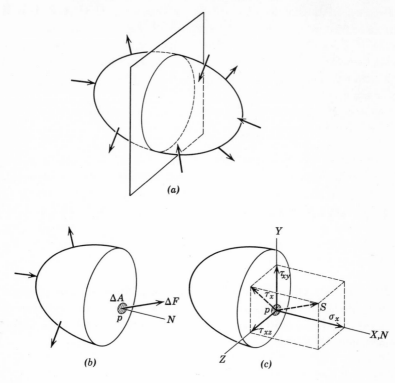

Fig. 2.1

now assume that the substance of the body is structureless so that, as we examine an ever decreasing ΔA, we do not detect any changes in the character of the surface.   In more sophisticated language, we say that we *assume the material to be a continuum*.   This assumption also implies that the contact forces transmitted across the section are assumed to be continuously distributed and that there are no concentrated *finite* forces among them.   We can therefore say that, as we take ΔA ever smaller, making it approach a point in the limit, the corresponding ΔF also becomes ever smaller and also approaches zero.   The limit of the ratio of these two infinitesimals, which we now assume to exist because of continuity, is then defined as the *stress on the plane at the point p to which ΔA converges*.   Thus

$$S_p = \lim_{\Delta A \to 0} \left(\frac{\Delta F}{\Delta A} \right) = \frac{dF}{dA}. \tag{b}$$

Because dA lies in the plane of the section, its aspect remains fixed as represented by the outward normal N in Fig. 2.1b. On the other hand, dF does not necessarily remain fixed in direction, possibly differing from ΔF slightly in both magnitude and direction. Without loss of generality, however, we may assume that the vector representing S_p is the same as that representing S_{ave}.

Suppose now that across the original body we pass another cutting plane of different aspect, through the same point p, and repeat the process just described. We will then obtain a second value of S_p in the form defined by Eq. b. Like the first one, this second S_p is also a vector quantity; the two vectors, however, will not necessarily be identical. Hence we will have a second value of the stress at point p. Since there is an infinity of planes that can be passed across the body, all containing the point p, it follows that there is an infinity of values possible for S_p. Therefore the expression "the stress at a point" is vague, if not meaningless, *unless the plane is specified on which the point in question is imagined to lie.*

Thus, at any point in a stressed body, with every aspect of plane through the point there is associated a pair of vectors: one representing the stress, the other (a unit vector) representing the aspect of the plane. Accordingly, Eq. b should be rewritten in the symbolic form

$$\mathbf{S_n} = \frac{d\mathbf{F}}{dA}. \qquad (c)$$

This necessary association of the unit vector **n** with the stress vector **S** confers on the concept known as stress a higher pedigree, so to speak, than that of an ordinary vector. Stress is an example of a *tensor* quantity. Although we may treat the stress at a point p *on some particular plane* as any ordinary vector quantity, which can be manipulated according to the parallelogram law (for instance, it may be resolved into components in the usual manner), the total concept known as "the stress at point p," which is a tensor quantity, may not be so treated. It is, however, proper to consider a particular stress vector $\mathbf{S_n}$ with its associated normal N as a *component* of the stress tensor for the point.

The stress vector is not convenient to handle by our elementary techniques; hence let us resolve it into a set of rectangular components. The most convenient set is that of which one component is normal and another is tangent to the plane. The normal component is then called *normal stress*, designated by the symbol σ, whereas the tangential component is called *shear stress*, denoted by τ. The components σ and τ

combine vectorially to give **S** according to the equation

$$|\,\mathbf{S}\,| = \sqrt{\sigma^2 + \tau^2}. \tag{d}$$

If we now construct a right-handed system of cartesian axes with the point p as origin, and so orient the axes that one of them, say the X axis, coincides with the normal N, Fig. 2.1c, σ will be collinear with this axis; on the other hand, τ will not necessarily coincide with either of the two remaining axes. Let us therefore further resolve τ into two rectangular components in the directions of the Y and Z axes. This immediately creates the need for systematic notation. Accordingly, let a subscript denote the direction of the plane's normal, thus: σ_x stands for the normal stress on a plane whose normal is the X axis, and τ_x for the shear stress on that same plane. Furthermore, let a second subscript denote the particular direction of each of the two components of the shear stress, thus: τ_{xy} stands for the Y component and τ_{xz} for the Z component of τ_x. Equation d now becomes

$$|\,\mathbf{S_i}\,| = \sqrt{\sigma_x{}^2 + \tau_{xy}{}^2 + \tau_{xz}{}^2} \tag{e}$$

where **i** is the unit vector in the X direction, normal to the plane in question. These three stresses, σ_x, τ_{xy}, and τ_{xz}, are components of the stress tensor for the point p.

A normal stress component directed in the sense of the outward normal is called a *tensile* stress; when directed in the sense of the inward normal, it is called a *compressive* stress. There are no special names for the shear stress components.

Does the above suggest that the stress tensor for a point can have any number of components? Yes, it does. This is analogous to the well-known fact that a vector can have any number of components. Not all these components, however, are necessary, and a minimum number of them suffices for a complete specification of the tensor. For the present this is explained qualitatively as follows. The most elementary solid with plane faces that can be cut out of a body which will completely surround a particular point is a tetrahedron. Each of the four faces then transmits a force ΔF. In order that the force ΔF on some one face can be evaluated, each of the other three ΔF forces must be known. This is because a concurrent system of forces in space may not involve more than three unknowns for determinateness (the three unknowns may be the magnitude of the desired force and its two direction angles or, equivalently, three rectangular components of this force). If any one of the other three ΔF's is not known, then the fourth one cannot be

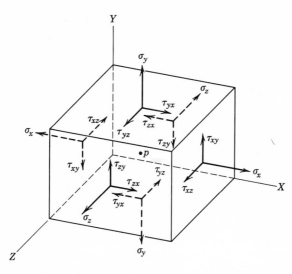

Fig. 2.2

found; hence all three are necessary. On the other hand, if all three are known, then the fourth can always be uniquely determined; hence the three ΔF's are sufficient. Equation e now appears to suggest that nine stress components are necessary, since each ΔF is determined first as the product of the stress on the plane by the differential area ΔA (Eq. a) and since each stress vector may in turn be represented by its three rectangular components. We shall now show that of these nine only six components are necessary for the complete specification of the stress tensor for the point.

A small rectangular parallelepiped surrounding the point p is shown in Fig. 2.2. The dimensions of the figure are so small that they vanish in the limit. This being so, for every pair of parallel faces there need be shown only one set of values for the three stress components; that is, if σ_x, τ_{xy}, and τ_{xz} are used for one face, then the same values are used for the opposite (parallel) face, etc. Hence the following nine vectors are represented: σ_x, σ_y, σ_z, τ_{xy}, τ_{xz}, τ_{yx}, τ_{yz}, τ_{zx}, and τ_{zy}. The senses of all stress components are assumed. It is clear that equilibrium of the block as regards translation in each of three perpendicular directions is automatically satisfied, as illustrated by the following equation:

$$\Sigma F_x = \sigma_x(\Delta y)(\Delta z) - \sigma_x(\Delta y)(\Delta z) + \tau_{yx}(\Delta x)(\Delta z) - \tau_{yx}(\Delta x)(\Delta z)$$

$$+ \tau_{zx}(\Delta x)(\Delta y) - \tau_{zx}(\Delta x)(\Delta y) = 0.$$

Since the block must also be in equilibrium as regards rotation, the equation

$$\Sigma M_z = 0 = -\sigma_x(\Delta y)(\Delta z)\frac{\Delta y}{2} + \sigma_x(\Delta y)(\Delta z)\frac{\Delta y}{2} + \sigma_y(\Delta x)(\Delta z)\frac{\Delta x}{2}$$

$$- \sigma_y(\Delta x)(\Delta z)\frac{\Delta x}{2} + \tau_{xy}(\Delta y)(\Delta z)\Delta x - \tau_{yx}(\Delta x)(\Delta z)\Delta y$$

$$- \tau_{zx}(\Delta x)(\Delta y)\frac{\Delta y}{2} + \tau_{zx}(\Delta x)(\Delta y)\frac{\Delta y}{2}$$

$$+ \tau_{zy}(\Delta x)(\Delta y)\frac{\Delta x}{2} - \tau_{zy}(\Delta x)(\Delta y)\frac{\Delta x}{2}$$

must likewise be satisfied. This yields the following significant result:

$$\tau_{xy} = \tau_{yx}. \tag{2.1a}$$

The other two equilibrium equations, $\Sigma M_x = 0$ and $\Sigma M_y = 0$, give, respectively,

$$\tau_{yz} = \tau_{zy} \tag{2.1b}$$

and

$$\tau_{zx} = \tau_{xz}. \tag{2.1c}$$

We state these results in words, thus: *On perpendicular planes at a point in a stressed body, the shear stress components normal to the common line of intersection of the planes must exist concomitantly, if at all, and are equal in magnitude and similarly directed relative to this line, either both toward it or both away from it.*

Therefore only six cartesian components are necessary for a complete specification of the stress tensor. That these are also sufficient is shown quantitatively in Chapter 10.

From the foregoing, we may now interpret the phrase "the stress at a point" to mean the stress tensor for that point and represent it by its nine cartesian components (of which only six are distinct) in the symbolic matrix

$$S = \begin{bmatrix} \sigma_x & \tau_{xy} & \tau_{xz} \\ \tau_{yx} & \sigma_y & \tau_{yz} \\ \tau_{zx} & \tau_{zy} & \sigma_z \end{bmatrix}. \tag{2.2}$$

Observe that the above matrix is symmetrical about its principal diagonal. This interesting circumstance is expressed in the statement that the cartesian stress tensor is symmetric. It must be noted, however, that these nine components of stress are only one set of an infinite number of sets possible by which the stress at a point may be specified; in terms of other (noncartesian) components, the specification is not necessarily symmetric. In Chapter 10 we discuss in considerable detail the variation of stress at a point as the aspect of the plane in question changes.

2.2 Equations of Equilibrium. Let it be assumed that the stress, which in general varies from point to point in a stressed body, is a continuous function of position and, furthermore, that its derivatives exist and are themselves continuous. Using the cartesian components of stress, we now derive the equations which must be satisfied at every point of the body. We confine the derivation to conditions of equilibrium; hence, the final equations will be called the equations of equilibrium. There are two such sets of equations, one for interior points and another for points on the bounding surface of the body.

Figure 2.3 shows a small rectangular parallelepiped of dimensions Δx by Δy by Δz, containing some interior point of interest. The stress

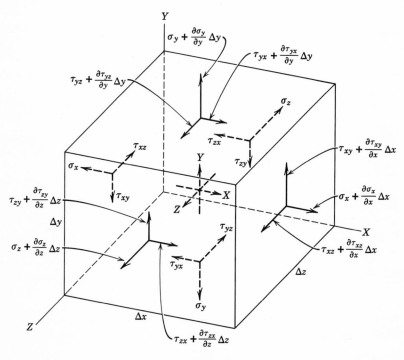

FIG. 2.3

components shown on any one face are the average values for the small area; these converge to the correct values for the point as the small area shrinks. We now take into account the slight differences between the corresponding stress components on parallel faces. For instance, on the two faces whose normal is in the X direction, the difference between the normal stresses (both assumed tensile) represents the change in this component owing to the change in the X coordinate; expressed mathematically, this difference is $(\partial\sigma_x/\partial x)\Delta x$. Furthermore, we now consider also any body forces acting on the little parallelepiped. Let the resultant body force per unit volume be represented by its three rectangular components X, Y, and Z.* The senses of all stress components shown in Fig. 2.3 are assumed positive according to the following convention.

At a face, to be known as a positive face, whose outward normal is in the positive sense of a coordinate axis, each stress component thereon shall be considered positive if its vector points to the positive sense of the axis corresponding to the subscript; at a face, to be known as a negative face, whose outward normal is in the negative sense of a coordinate axis, each stress component thereon shall be considered positive if its vector points to the negative sense of the axis corresponding to the subscript.

The following equilibrium equation may now be written:

$$\Sigma F_x = 0 = -\sigma_x(\Delta y)\Delta z + \left(\sigma_x + \frac{\partial\sigma_x}{\partial x}\Delta x\right)(\Delta y)\Delta z - \tau_{yx}(\Delta z)\Delta x$$

$$+ \left(\tau_{yx} + \frac{\partial\tau_{yx}}{\partial y}\Delta y\right)(\Delta z)\Delta x - \tau_{zx}(\Delta x)\Delta y$$

$$+ \left(\tau_{zx} + \frac{\partial\tau_{zx}}{\partial z}\Delta z\right)(\Delta x)\Delta y + X(\Delta x)(\Delta y)\Delta z,$$

from which is obtained the differential equation

$$\frac{\partial\sigma_x}{\partial x} + \frac{\partial\tau_{yx}}{\partial y} + \frac{\partial\tau_{zx}}{\partial z} + X = 0. \qquad (2.3a)$$

---

* In demonstrating the equality of the cross shear stresses with the aid of Fig. 2.2, we did not have to consider the body forces for the following reason. Since body forces are proportional to some linear dimension raised to the third power, whereas surface forces are proportional to such dimension raised to only the second power, as the little block shrinks to a point any body forces will approach zero faster than surface forces. Therefore, when the spatial variation of the stresses is *not* being considered, body forces are safely ignored.

Similarly, $\Sigma F_y = 0$ and $\Sigma F_z = 0$ yield, respectively,

$$\frac{\partial \sigma_y}{\partial y} + \frac{\partial \tau_{zy}}{\partial z} + \frac{\partial \tau_{xy}}{\partial x} + Y = 0 \tag{2.3b}$$

and $\qquad \qquad \dfrac{\partial \sigma_z}{\partial z} + \dfrac{\partial \tau_{xz}}{\partial x} + \dfrac{\partial \tau_{yz}}{\partial y} + Z = 0. \tag{2.3c}$

Since, for concurrent forces in space only three independent equilibrium equations may be written, Eqs. 2.3 represent necessary and sufficient conditions for equilibrium at interior points.

Let us turn our attention next to some point on the surface of the body. Figure 2.4 shows a small rectangular tetrahedron with the point of interest lying on the inclined surface. Unless there is some geometric singularity (which we are precluding) at the point in question, the curved surface in the immediate neighborhood of the point will approach the tangent plane in the limit; hence, we replace this portion of the curved surface by a small part of the tangent plane and consider this as that face of the tetrahedron which is inclined to the other three mutually perpendicular faces defined by the cartesian axes. The outward normal to the curved surface at the point of interest is assumed to have the direction cosines l, m, and n. Then, if the area of the inclined face is ΔA, the areas of the three faces, representing the projections of ΔA, are given

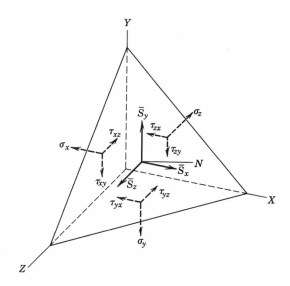

Fig. 2.4

by $l(\Delta A)$, $m(\Delta A)$, and $n(\Delta A)$. It is assumed further that the local intensity $\overline{S}$ (continuous at the point) of the surface forces exerted on the body by external agents is represented by its three rectangular components $\overline{S}_x$, $\overline{S}_y$, and $\overline{S}_z$. All stress components on the three mutually perpendicular faces are taken positive. Applying the conditions of equilibrium to the tetrahedron, we write

$$\Sigma F_x = 0 = -\sigma_x l(\Delta A) - \tau_{yx} m(\Delta A) - \tau_{zx} n(\Delta A) + \overline{S}_x(\Delta A),$$

from which we obtain

$$l\sigma_x + m\tau_{yx} + n\tau_{zx} = \overline{S}_x. \tag{2.4a}$$

The other two equations, $\Sigma F_y = 0$ and $\Sigma F_z = 0$, lead, respectively,

to
$$m\sigma_y + n\tau_{zy} + l\tau_{xy} = \overline{S}_y \tag{2.4b}$$

and
$$n\sigma_z + l\tau_{xz} + m\tau_{yz} = \overline{S}_z. \tag{2.4c}$$

Equations 2.4 state the necessary and sufficient conditions for equilibrium at boundary points of the body.

For bodies in equilibrium, a correct system of stresses satisfies Eqs. 2.3 at interior points and Eqs. 2.4 at boundary points. Stresses that do not satisfy these equations cannot be correct since they violate equilibrium; not all stresses which satisfy them, however, are correct. Equations 2.3 and 2.4 constitute necessary, but not sufficient, conditions for the *correctness* of stress systems. The sufficiency criterion depends on deformations, presently to be described.

PROBLEMS

2.1. From Fig. 2.3, derive Eqs. 2.3b and 2.3c. What orderly relations between the various subscripts do you notice in Eqs. 2.3?

2.2. From Fig. 2.4, derive Eqs. 2.4b and 2.4c. What orderly relations between the various subscripts and between the direction cosines do you notice in Eqs. 2.4?

2.3. If a system of stresses satisfies Eqs. 2.3 and 2.4, is it necessarily correct? For an interior point, explain your answer in terms, say, of the stresses on a set of parallel faces of a unit cube.

2.3   Strain. The other basic concept in our subject is *strain*, defined as *the intensity of deformation*. A body deforms when its various points suffer unequal displacements distinct from those due to rigid-body motion. We distinguish between two kinds of strain.

The first is *linear strain;* it represents the change in the distance between two neighboring points of a body, from the undeformed to the deformed state, averaged over their original distance apart. Thus, if this original distance is ΔL and the new distance is $\Delta L'$, so that the change is $\Delta e = \Delta L' - \Delta L$, then the *average* linear strain in ΔL is

$$\epsilon_{\text{ave}} = \frac{\Delta e}{\Delta L}. \qquad (a)$$

Assuming a homogeneous continuum, we let ΔL approach zero; we then define the limit of the ratio as *the linear strain at the point in the direction of* ΔL, thus:

$$\epsilon = \lim_{\Delta L \to 0} \left(\frac{\Delta e}{\Delta L} \right) = \frac{de}{dL}. \qquad (b)$$

This (Lagrangian) definition is valid only for very small strains, the order of magnitude of, say, one in 1000. It is not intended for finite strains involved in processes like metal forming.

The second kind is angular strain, commonly called *shear strain;* it has to do with the change in the angular "distances" between lines in the body. Because we seek to establish the idea of shear strain at a point, we consider at the outset two lines intersecting at the point in question; these define a plane. Aside from the displacements of this plane due to rigid-body motion, these lines in general undergo different angular shifts. Following the pattern set for linear strain, we might now say that this difference in the angular displacements divided by the original angle between the two lines should be defined as the average angular strain. If we did this, however, a difficulty would immediately arise, because two angles are involved at the point. Although these angles are always related because they are supplementary, nevertheless this way of defining angular strain would result in two values instead of one. We would, therefore, look askance at such an approach that leads to a nonunique definition. We resolve this difficulty by considering instead two lines through the point which form a right angle in the unstrained body. Furthermore, we no longer need to take the original angle ever smaller in the limiting process because the two intersecting lines already define the point. We now define *shear strain at the point on a plane, in the directions of two perpendicular lines,* as *the change in the original right angle between them.* If α denotes the new angle in radian measure, then the shear strain γ is

$$\gamma = \left| \frac{\pi}{2} - \alpha \right|. \qquad (c)$$

To make these definitions of strain meaningful, it is best to relate them to the actual linear displacements of the point. Toward this end, let us focus attention on point A in the unstrained body whose coordinates are x, y, and z, relative to a fixed reference frame; on neighboring point B with coordinates $x + \Delta x$, y, and z; on neighboring point C with coordinates x, $y + \Delta y$, and z; and on neighboring point D with coordinates x, y, and $z + \Delta z$. (See Fig. 2.5a.) Figure 2.5b shows the projections A_1, B_1, and C_1 on the x-y plane of the three points A, B, and C. As the body deforms, point A displaces to A', B to B', C to C', and D to D'. The displacement of A (the vector $\mathbf{AA'}$) has the three scalar components u, v, and w in the directions of the X, Y, and Z axes. Similarly, the displacement of B (the vector $\mathbf{BB'}$) has the three components $u + (\partial u/\partial x)\Delta x$, $v + (\partial v/\partial x)\Delta x$, and $w + (\partial w/\partial x)\Delta x$; that of C the components $u + (\partial u/\partial y)\Delta y$, $v + (\partial v/\partial y)\Delta y$, and $w + (\partial w/\partial y)\Delta y$; and that of D the components $u + (\partial u/\partial z)\Delta z$, $v + (\partial v/\partial z)\Delta z$, and $w + (\partial w/\partial z)\Delta z$. Along with material continuity, that of the displacements and their derivatives is assumed. The projections on the x-y plane of the points A', B', and C' are shown in Fig. 2.5b as A_1', B_1', and C_1'.

By definition, the linear strain in the X direction is $(A'B' - AB)/(AB)$. Since the strains as defined are limited to very small quantities, the length $A'B'$ (which is virtually $A_1'B_1'$) is, except for higher-order terms, $A'B' = \Delta x + (\partial u/\partial x)\Delta x$. Therefore the linear strain at the point A in the X direction is

$$\epsilon_x = \lim_{\Delta x \to 0} \frac{\Delta x + (\partial u/\partial x)\Delta x - \Delta x}{\Delta x} = \frac{\partial u}{\partial x}. \qquad (2.5a)$$

Similarly, the linear strain at A in the Y direction is

$$\epsilon_y = \lim_{\Delta y \to 0} \frac{\Delta y + (\partial v/\partial y)\Delta y - \Delta y}{\Delta y} = \frac{\partial v}{\partial y}, \qquad (2.5b)$$

and the linear strain at A in the Z direction is

$$\epsilon_z = \lim_{\Delta z \to 0} \frac{\Delta z + (\partial w/\partial z)\Delta z - \Delta z}{\Delta z} = \frac{\partial w}{\partial z}. \qquad (2.5c)$$

Now let us examine the change in the right angle $\underline{/BAC}$. The new angle $\underline{/B'A'C'}$ differs from its x-y projection $\underline{/B_1'A_1'C_1'}$ only by higher-order quantities. Hence the change in the angle $\underline{/BAC}$ is approximately equal to the sum of the two small angles: one between the lines $A_1'B_1'$ and A_1B_1, the other between the lines $A_1'C_1'$ and A_1C_1. Since very small angles may be assumed equal in radian measure to either their sines or their tangents, the angle between $A_1'B_1'$ and A_1B_1 is approximately $\partial v/\partial x$; similarly, the angle between $A_1'C_1'$ and A_1C_1 is approxi-

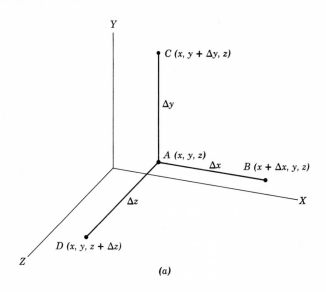

(a)

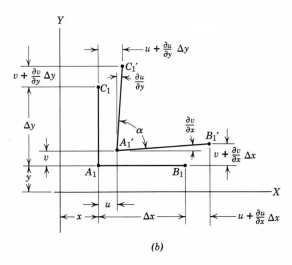

(b)

FIG. 2.5

mately $\partial u / \partial y$. Therefore the change in the original right angle $\underline{/BAC}$, which by definition is the shear strain in the X and Y directions, is (see Fig. 2.5b)

$$\gamma_{xy} = \frac{\partial u}{\partial y} + \frac{\partial v}{\partial x} = \gamma_{yx}. \qquad (2.5d)$$

Similarly, the change in the original right angle $\underline{/CAD}$, which is the shear strain in the Y and Z directions, is

$$\gamma_{yz} = \frac{\partial v}{\partial z} + \frac{\partial w}{\partial y} = \gamma_{zy}, \qquad (2.5e)$$

and the change in the original right angle $\underline{/DAB}$, which is the shear strain in the Z and X directions, is

$$\gamma_{zx} = \frac{\partial w}{\partial x} + \frac{\partial u}{\partial z} = \gamma_{xz}. \qquad (2.5f)$$

It is customary and convenient to associate the *plus* sign with *elongations* and the *minus* sign with *contractions;* hence the sign convention for linear strains comes about naturally.   From Fig. 2.5b we find the clue to the sign convention regarding shear strains: since a positive $\partial v / \partial x$ and a positive $\partial u / \partial y$ result in a decrease of the original right angle $\underline{/BAC}$, *a shear strain which represents a decrease in the original right angle shall be given the plus sign,* and *a shear strain which represents an increase in the original right angle shall be given the minus sign.*

Equations 2.5 define the six cartesian components of strain that are necessary and sufficient for a complete specification of the state of strain at a point.   Like stress, strain is an example of a tensor quantity.   Thus the strain at a point may be represented by the deformation matrix

$$D = \begin{bmatrix} \epsilon_x & \dfrac{\gamma_{xy}}{2} & \dfrac{\gamma_{xz}}{2} \\[2ex] \dfrac{\gamma_{yx}}{2} & \epsilon_y & \dfrac{\gamma_{yz}}{2} \\[2ex] \dfrac{\gamma_{zx}}{2} & \dfrac{\gamma_{zy}}{2} & \epsilon_z \end{bmatrix}. \qquad (2.6)$$

Like the stress matrix, Eq. 2.2, the preceding is symmetrical with respect to its principal diagonal because, of the nine cartesian components of strain, only six are distinct.   The factor $\frac{1}{2}$ is there in order that the components of strain shall transform in a certain orderly manner when the frame of reference is altered. It is this transformation which actually defines a tensor; for the present this is of little concern to us. We discuss this to a limited extent in Chapter 11.

2.4 Equations of Compatibility. Continuity of displacements means that in the deformed body there are no gaps; even then, however, there could still be faults and kinks. It is but reasonable to require that there be no such geometric singularities. In other words, from whatever sense in the cartesian directions any point in a strained body is approached, there should be obtained (1) only one set of strain components and (2) only one set of rates of change in these strain components. Furthermore, as the point is approached, the order in which two directions may be chosen should make no difference either; hence there should also be obtained only one set of values for the second-order rates of change of the strain components at the point. All this is expressed mathematically by saying we *require that the strains themselves as well as their derivatives be continuous functions of position.*

The preceding suggests that we should find some significant relationships between the derivatives of the strains. Obviously, the simplest relationships must involve the lowest-order derivatives. Looking at Eqs. 2.5, we note that by differentiating the strains relative to the position coordinates it should be possible to eliminate the displacements themselves. Trying various combinations of derivatives and orders of differentiation, we find that the simplest groupings involve second-order derivatives; that is, it is not possible to eliminate the displacements u, v, and w by use of first-order derivatives only. For instance, differentiating ϵ_x twice with respect to y and ϵ_y twice with respect to x and then adding the results, we discover this is identically the same expression as that obtained by differentiating γ_{xy} once with respect to x and then once with respect to y, thus:

$$\frac{\partial^2 \epsilon_x}{\partial y^2} = \frac{\partial^3 u}{\partial x \partial y^2}, \tag{a}$$

$$\frac{\partial^2 \epsilon_y}{\partial x^2} = \frac{\partial^3 v}{\partial x^2 \partial y}, \tag{b}$$

and
$$\frac{\partial^2 \gamma_{xy}}{\partial x \partial y} = \frac{\partial^3 u}{\partial x \partial y^2} + \frac{\partial^3 v}{\partial x^2 \partial y}. \tag{c}$$

Therefore
$$\frac{\partial^2 \epsilon_x}{\partial y^2} + \frac{\partial^2 \epsilon_y}{\partial x^2} = \frac{\partial^2 \gamma_{xy}}{\partial x \partial y}. \tag{2.7a}$$

By similar manipulations, we obtain five other equations, as follows:

$$\frac{\partial^2 \epsilon_y}{\partial z^2} + \frac{\partial^2 \epsilon_z}{\partial y^2} = \frac{\partial^2 \gamma_{yz}}{\partial y \partial z}, \tag{2.7b}$$

$$\frac{\partial^2 \epsilon_z}{\partial x^2} + \frac{\partial^2 \epsilon_x}{\partial z^2} = \frac{\partial^2 \gamma_{zx}}{\partial z \partial x}, \tag{2.7c}$$

$$2\frac{\partial^2 \epsilon_x}{\partial y \partial z} = \frac{\partial}{\partial x}\left(\frac{\partial \gamma_{xy}}{\partial z} - \frac{\partial \gamma_{yz}}{\partial x} + \frac{\partial \gamma_{zx}}{\partial y}\right), \tag{2.7d}$$

$$2\frac{\partial^2 \epsilon_y}{\partial z \partial x} = \frac{\partial}{\partial y}\left(\frac{\partial \gamma_{yz}}{\partial x} - \frac{\partial \gamma_{zx}}{\partial y} + \frac{\partial \gamma_{xy}}{\partial z}\right), \tag{2.7e}$$

and
$$2\frac{\partial^2 \epsilon_z}{\partial x \partial y} = \frac{\partial}{\partial z}\left(\frac{\partial \gamma_{zx}}{\partial y} - \frac{\partial \gamma_{xy}}{\partial z} + \frac{\partial \gamma_{yz}}{\partial x}\right). \tag{2.7f}$$

No other combinations of second-order derivatives are possible which eliminate the displacements. Therefore these must be the simplest relations that will insure no gaps, no faults, and no kinks in the deformed continuum.

They are known as the *equations of compatibility* because they define the necessary and sufficient conditions that must be satisfied by a system of strains in order that the various parts of the deformed body continue to fit together smoothly. If a set of strains does not satisfy these equations, the strains cannot possibly be correct; on the other hand, strains that satisfy them are necessarily correct.

PROBLEMS

2.4. Show that for small strains, the change in volume per unit volume is approximately $\epsilon_x + \epsilon_y + \epsilon_z$. This is called the *volume strain* or *dilatation* e.

2.5. Is the following state of strain possible? $\epsilon_x = k(x^3 + y^3)$, $\epsilon_y = kxy^2$, $\gamma_{xy} = 3kxy^2$, $\epsilon_z = \gamma_{yz} = \gamma_{zx} = 0$.

2.5 Hooke's Law.

The first major physical basis for our subject is contained in a law which by courtesy is named after Robert Hooke. In its original form (1678) which we paraphrase here, Hooke's law asserted that the ability (force) of a springy body to restore itself to its natural state is proportional to how much it is displaced (deformation) from this state. It is often stated in the simplest possible form: *stress is proportional to strain*. Then, of course, arises the question: Which stress and which strain? We now give first a word description of the generalized

Hooke's law and then the mathematical relations that symbolize it. This description comes in two parts.

PART A. If a body is subjected to stress in one direction only, then *within limits* the resulting strain in that *same* direction is proportional to the stress, the degree of proportionality depending in general on the direction involved.

PART B. If a body is subjected to stress in one direction only, then within limits the resulting strain in *any other* direction is proportional to the stress, the degree of proportionality depending in general on the relative directions involved.

For our needs in this introductory course, we shall assume homogeneity and isotropy of the continuum, which means that it has uniform and nondirectional properties. For such a superidealized material, the preceding statements are added to as follows.

PART A. There is only one proportionality constant between each individually acting normal stress and its corresponding linear strain, and only one proportionality constant between each individually acting shear stress and its corresponding shear strain; these constants are independent of direction.

PART B. Normal stress in any one direction produces linear strains in all other nonparallel directions, the degree of proportionality between any one such strain and the given normal stress being dependent only on their relative directions and not at all on the absolute orientations of these directions in the body; no shear strains are produced, however, in any pair of perpendicular directions, one of which is parallel to the given normal stress. Moreover, shear stresses on any given pair of perpendicular planes do not produce linear strain in any direction parallel to or perpendicular to the given shear stresses; nor do these shear stresses produce shear strains in any plane parallel to the intersection of their planes.

Following are the equations that symbolize the preceding description of the *generalized Hooke's law for homogeneous and isotropic substances:*

$$\epsilon_x = \frac{1}{E}[\sigma_x - \nu(\sigma_y + \sigma_z)] \qquad \gamma_{xy} = \frac{2(1 + \nu)}{E}\tau_{xy}$$

$$\epsilon_y = \frac{1}{E}[\sigma_y - \nu(\sigma_z + \sigma_x)] \qquad \gamma_{yz} = \frac{2(1 + \nu)}{E}\tau_{yz} \qquad (2.8a)$$

$$\epsilon_z = \frac{1}{E}[\sigma_z - \nu(\sigma_x + \sigma_y)] \qquad \gamma_{zx} = \frac{2(1 + \nu)}{E}\tau_{zx}.$$

Solved for the stresses, equations 2.8a give

$$\sigma_x = \frac{E}{(1 + \nu)(1 - 2\nu)} [(1 - \nu)\epsilon_x + \nu(\epsilon_y + \epsilon_z)]$$

$$\sigma_y = \frac{E}{(1 + \nu)(1 - 2\nu)} [(1 - \nu)\epsilon_y + \nu(\epsilon_z + \epsilon_x)]$$

$$\sigma_z = \frac{E}{(1 + \nu)(1 - 2\nu)} [(1 - \nu)\epsilon_z + \nu(\epsilon_x + \epsilon_y)]$$

$$\tau_{xy} = \frac{E}{2(1 + \nu)} \gamma_{xy}$$

$$\tau_{yz} = \frac{E}{2(1 + \nu)} \gamma_{yz}$$

$$\tau_{zx} = \frac{E}{2(1 + \nu)} \gamma_{zx}.$$

(2.8b)

If there exists a family of parallel planes in the body such that all stress components on them either vanish or are so small as to be negligible, the body is said to be in a state of *plane stress*. An example is a thin flat plate bearing loads only in its plane. The special equations of Hooke's law for such a situation can be derived from the above by making the proper substitutions and performing some algebraic manipulations. On the other hand, if there is a family of parallel planes such that all strain components perpendicular to them vanish or are negligibly small, then the body is said to be in a state of *plane strain*. An example is a long cylinder constrained against either expanding or contracting in the longitudinal direction while it is subjected to forces that are uniformly distributed normal to its geometric axis. Again, special equations of Hooke's law may be derived from the foregoing. For immediate comparison as well as for future use, these special forms of Hooke's law are shown in Table 2.1. The Z direction is assumed to be stress free in the one case, strain free in the other. It is observed from Table 2.1 that, insofar as linear strains and normal stresses are concerned, plane stress is *not* the same as plane strain, although in both cases the same relations hold between shear strains and shear stresses.

Even simpler than either of these special cases is one we will make much use of; this is *uniaxial stress*, in which all stress components except a normal one are zero. Let this be σ_x; then $\sigma_y = \sigma_z = \tau_{xy} = \tau_{yz} = \tau_{zx} = 0$. By Eqs. 2.8a, we find the strain components to be

$$\epsilon_x = \frac{\sigma_x}{E}$$

$$(2.8e)$$

$$\epsilon_y = \epsilon_z = -\frac{\nu\sigma_x}{E}.$$

This simplest form of Hooke's law, probably familiar to every one since his earliest exposure to physics, brings out the significance of the two material constants, E and ν. The constant E, commonly known as the *modulus of elasticity* or *Young's modulus*, is an index of rigidity; that is, the larger this value the less will be the material strain under a given stress. The constant ν, called *Poisson's ratio*, reflects the transverse effects of normal stress. Note from Eqs. 2.8e that uniaxial stress does not result in uniaxial strain, since a stress-caused elongation in one direction is accompanied by contraction which is ν times as large in every transverse direction. This Poisson effect can be vividly demonstrated with an ordinary rubber band, which when stretched contracts markedly in its transverse dimensions.

TABLE 2.1

EQUATIONS OF HOOKE'S LAW FOR PLANE STRESS AND FOR PLANE STRAIN

Plane Stress	Plane Strain
$\epsilon_x = \dfrac{1}{E}\left(\sigma_x - \nu\sigma_y\right)$	$\epsilon_x = \dfrac{1+\nu}{E}\left[(1-\nu)\sigma_x - \nu\sigma_y\right]$
$\epsilon_y = \dfrac{1}{E}\left(\sigma_y - \nu\sigma_x\right)$	$\epsilon_y = \dfrac{1+\nu}{E}\left[(1-\nu)\sigma_y - \nu\sigma_x\right]$
$\epsilon_z = -\dfrac{\nu}{E}\left(\sigma_x + \sigma_y\right)$	$\epsilon_z = 0$
$\sigma_x = \dfrac{E}{1-\nu^2}\left(\epsilon_x + \nu\epsilon_y\right)$	$\sigma_x = \dfrac{E}{(1+\nu)(1-2\nu)}\left[(1-\nu)\epsilon_x + \nu\epsilon_y\right]$
$\sigma_y = \dfrac{E}{1-\nu^2}\left(\epsilon_y + \nu\epsilon_x\right)$ (2.8c)	$\sigma_y = \dfrac{E}{(1+\nu)(1-2\nu)}\left[(1-\nu)\epsilon_y + \nu\epsilon_x\right]$ (2.8d)
$\sigma_z = 0$	$\sigma_z = \dfrac{\nu E}{(1+\nu)(1-2\nu)}\left(\epsilon_x + \epsilon_y\right)$
$\gamma_{xy} = \dfrac{2(1+\nu)}{E}\tau_{xy}$	$\gamma_{xy} = \dfrac{2(1+\nu)}{E}\tau_{xy}$
$\tau_{xy} = \dfrac{E}{2(1+\nu)}\gamma_{xy}$	$\tau_{xy} = \dfrac{E}{2(1+\nu)}\gamma_{xy}$
$\gamma_{yz} = \gamma_{zx} = 0$	$\gamma_{yz} = \gamma_{zx} = 0$
$\tau_{yz} = \tau_{zx} = 0$	$\tau_{yz} = \tau_{zx} = 0$

The combination of E and ν in the form $E/[2(1 + \nu)]$ is called the *shear modulus* of elasticity and is designated G. Both E and G are expressed in units of force per unit area, the dimensions of stress; on the other hand, the pure number ν has no dimensions. Typical values of these constants for a few materials are given in Table 2.2.

Hooke's law expressly affirms the proportionality of strain to stress; hence it necessarily implies elasticity, defined as the ability of a body to recover its original shape upon removal of any deforming forces. The reverse, however, is not necessarily true; that is, elasticity does not imply Hooke's law. Soft rubber, alluded to before is an outstanding example of a highly elastic material which does not obey Hooke's law for large strains. Nevertheless, in view of the fortunate circumstance that most materials which are elastic also obey Hooke's law, elasticity has been used more or less synonymously with the law of proportionality. So

TABLE 2.2

TYPICAL VALUES OF ELASTIC CONSTANTS FOR METALS AT ROOM TEMPERATURE

Metal	Specific Weight, γ lb/in.^{3}	Elasticity Modulus (Tension or Compression), E 10^6 psi	Elasticity Modulus (Shear), G 10^6 psi	Poisson's Ratio, ν
Aluminum	0.0975	9.9	3.7	0.34
Aluminum alloys	.097	10.6	4.0	.32
Copper	.324	18	6.7	.35
Iridium	.809	75		
Iron	.284	28.5	11.1	.28
Carbon steels	.284	30	11.6	.28
Low alloy steels	.283	29	11.4	.27
Magnesium	.0632	6.5	2.5	.33
Magnesium alloys	.065	6.5	2.4	.34
Titanium	.1625	16	6.0	.34
Tungsten	.697	52		
Sintered tungsten carbide (3% Co)		105		.24

This is a composite table from the following sources:

C. J. Smithells, *Metals Reference Book*, Interscience Publishers, New York, 1955; L. S. Marks, *Mechanical Engineers Handbook*, McGraw-Hill Book Company, New York, 1958; *Metals Handbook*, American Society for Metals, Cleveland, 1961.

deeply ingrained in our thinking is this association that those instances where the word elasticity is obviously a misnomer have come to be accepted as normal. For example, the mathematical Theory of Elasticity is *not* a theory explaining the nature of elasticity but rather is one which explains the behavior of bodies made of materials that obey Hooke's law. Or consider the constant E, which is called the modulus of elasticity when it should properly be called merely a proportionality constant (perhaps, Hooke's modulus after Young, to put things in their proper perspective and to give credit where it is due). One simple way of achieving consistency in usage is to describe materials as being *linearly elastic*. Then we may use the words elasticity and proportionality interchangeably. Thus the limit of behavior according to Hooke's law may be referred to as either the elastic or the proportional limit.

PROBLEMS

2.6. Derive Eqs. 2.8c from Eqs. 2.8a and 2.8b.

2.7. Derive Eqs. 2.8d from Eqs. 2.8a and 2.8b.

2.8. Derive the equations of Hooke's law for uniaxial strain.

2.9. Using the equations of Hooke's law for uniaxial stress, express the compatibility conditions in terms of the nonzero stress component. What is the simplest correct form for this component?

2.6 Strain Energy. Because of the inherent resistance to deformation that is characteristic of them, elastic solids store energy when strained. If the work expended in deforming a solid is completely stored in it as energy of strain and is fully recoverable as useful work, the substance is considered to be perfectly elastic. A material that is linearly elastic is also perfectly elastic; let the material be so assumed.

Consider a small rectangular parallelepiped of dimensions Δx by Δy by Δz. As a uniform tensile stress σ_x is gradually applied, the dimension Δx gradually elongates to $(1 + \epsilon_x)\Delta x$. The work done by the pair of opposing forces, $\sigma_x(\Delta y)\Delta z$, during an infinitesimal deformation, $d(\epsilon_x \Delta x)$, is $\sigma_x(\Delta y)(\Delta z)d(\epsilon_x \Delta x)$. Since, by Hooke's law, $\epsilon_x = \sigma_x/E$, this work becomes

$$\Delta U = \frac{\Delta y(\Delta z)(\Delta x)\sigma_x \, d\sigma_x}{E} = \frac{\Delta V}{E} \sigma_x \, d\sigma_x.$$

Therefore the energy stored per unit volume is

$$\frac{dU}{dV} = \frac{1}{E} \int_0^{\sigma_x} \sigma \, d\sigma = \frac{\sigma_x^2}{2E} = \frac{\sigma_x \epsilon_x}{2}. \tag{a}$$

Similarly, if only σ_y is gradually applied, then $dU/dV = \sigma_y\epsilon_y/2$. There are four other such expressions, corresponding to the other four pairs of stress and strain components.

Suppose now that several or all stress components are applied gradually on the parallelepiped; then it can be shown that, for small strains, the total strain energy depends only on the final state of stress and not at all on the sequence in which the individual stress components are applied—it would be the same as if all stresses were applied simultaneously, attaining their full values at the same instant. The general expression for the strain energy per unit volume then becomes

$$\frac{dU}{dV} = \frac{1}{2}\left(\sigma_x\epsilon_x + \sigma_y\epsilon_y + \sigma_z\epsilon_z + \tau_{xy}\gamma_{xy} + \tau_{yz}\gamma_{yz} + \tau_{zx}\gamma_{zx}\right). \quad (2.9a)$$

Substituting Eqs. 2.8a in Eq. 2.9a, we obtain the equivalent expression

$$\frac{dU}{dV} = \frac{1}{2E}\left[\sigma_x{}^2 + \sigma_y{}^2 + \sigma_z{}^2 - 2\nu(\sigma_x\sigma_y + \sigma_y\sigma_z + \sigma_z\sigma_x)\right.$$
$$\left. + 2(1 + \nu)(\tau_{xy}{}^2 + \tau_{yz}{}^2 + \tau_{zx}{}^2)\right]. \quad (2.9b)$$

The unit strain energy is therefore a quadratic function of the stresses. Note that if the preceding is differentiated with respect to any stress component, there is obtained the corresponding strain component. For example,

$$\frac{\partial}{\partial\sigma_x}\left(\frac{dU}{dV}\right) = \frac{1}{E}\left[\sigma_x - \nu(\sigma_y + \sigma_z)\right] = \epsilon_x. \quad (2.10a)$$

From the manner in which Eq. 2.9b was derived from Eq. 2.9a, it should be clear that dU/dV may also be expressed as a quadratic function of the strains. Then differentiating it with respect to any strain component will give the corresponding stress component. Thus, for instance,

$$\frac{\partial}{\partial\epsilon_x}\left(\frac{dU}{dV}\right) = \sigma_x. \quad (2.10b)$$

PROBLEMS

2.10. Supply the missing algebra between Eqs. 2.9a and 2.9b.

2.11. Show that Eq. 2.10b is indeed valid.

2.7   The Basic Problem.   The fundamental problem in the mechanics of elastically deformed solids is the determination of the six components of stress which will completely define the state of stress at all points in the body. These stress components must satisfy equilibrium at interior points, Eqs. 2.3, and the boundary conditions at exterior points, Eqs. 2.4. Related to the stresses by Hooke's law, Eqs. 2.8, are the associated strain components; their correctness, hence also that of the stresses, hinges on the compatibility equations, Eqs. 2.7, being satisfied.

The concomitant problem is the determination of the three displacement components from the six strain components. Because there are twelve equations (Eqs. 2.5 and 2.7) that relate these nine quantities, the question of consistency arises. In general, there will be many sets of displacement components that will satisfy the equations defining the strain components, Eqs. 2.5; these will differ among one another only by amounts representing rigid-body displacements. In order for a set of displacement components to be unique, the constraints on the body must be known from which the boundary conditions in terms of displacements may then be specified.

The stress components may be determined mathematically either by direct quadratures or by trial and error. Owing to the form of the partial differential equations of equilibrium, Eqs. 2.3, solution by direct quadrature is quite impossible. If some simplifying assumptions are allowed, then direct quadrature becomes possible for simple geometrical shapes. The trial-and-error approach consists in trying various functional expressions of the stresses in terms of position on the equations of equilibrium, Eqs. 2.3 and 2.4. If these are satisfied, the associated strains are determined through Hooke's law and on these is then applied the test of compatibility. Needless to say, such an approach could be very tedious.

A variant of the trial-and-error approach is to try various expressions of the stresses in terms of position, on the equations of equilibrium, and then the equations of compatibility are brought in by the use of Hooke's law. The boundary conditions, which the solution being tried satisfies, are then determined by means of Eqs. 2.4. With a catalog of results available, a particular problem is "solved" by combining various cases until the correct boundary conditions are obtained. This technique of problem solving in reverse, whereby a solution is defined first and later the problem which it solves is determined, is known as the *inverse method*. By virtue of the fact that there is no limit to the number of combinations which may be made of algebraic and transcendental expressions as trial solutions, in theory at least any stress problem can be solved. The actual accomplishment of this can be extremely difficult, if not impossible, except for relatively simple boundary geometries and external force systems.

PROBLEMS

2.12. Are the following systems of stresses possible? (In other words, do they satisfy Eqs. 2.3?) What conditions at the boundaries of the prism do they satisfy? (Substitute the pertinent coordinates in the given equations.) Sketch

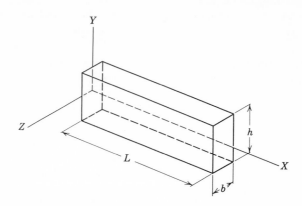

Fig. P2.12

the stress distributions on the periphery. Are they correct? (Or do the associated strains satisfy Eqs. 2.7?) Assume there are no body forces.

(a) $\sigma_x = d_3 y$, $\quad \sigma_y = \sigma_z = \tau_{xy} = \tau_{yz} = \tau_{zx} = 0$.

(b) $\sigma_x = c_3 x$, $\quad \sigma_y = \sigma_z = \tau_{yz} = \tau_{zx} = 0$, $\quad \tau_{xy} = -c_3 y$.

(c) $\sigma_x = d_4 xy$, $\quad \sigma_y = \sigma_z = \tau_{yz} = \tau_{zx} = 0$, $\quad \tau_{xy} = -(d_4/2)y^2$.

(d) $\sigma_x = c_4(x^2 - 2y^2)$, $\quad \sigma_y = c_4 y^2$, $\quad \sigma_z = \tau_{yz} = \tau_{zx} = 0$, $\quad \tau_{xy} = -2c_4 xy$.

2.8 The Engineering Approach. Saint-Venant's Principle.
No engineering material can be so homogeneous and isotropic as to warrant its being considered a real continuum. Glass, the one substance that can probably qualify, is not significant as a load-bearing material. Metals and metallic substances, which are by far the useful building blocks of technology, are by no means homogeneous and isotropic, although the randomness at which their constituent particles are oriented allows a useful approximation of homogeneity and isotropy. Since any solution to a stress problem, no matter how nearly "exact" it may be, is no more meaningful than the underlying assumptions of the theory allow it to be, one must often be content with solutions that are far from exact.

What might be called "the engineering approach" consists in making certain assumptions, among which are some that have to do with the manner in which the loaded body deforms, assumptions that are usually not part of the formal mathematical theory and which cannot always be rigorously justified. Using an assumed system of strains as a starting point, one then invokes Hooke's law; thus stresses enter the picture. The unknown stress values, often the numerically largest ones, are then evaluated strictly on the basis of equilibrium, helped along by additional simplifying assumptions.

The success of this approach naturally depends on the assumptions made. In the early stages of the art, when little was known concerning the nature of materials and the actual behavior of stressed bodies, much reliance had to be placed on judgment. Those who had special gifts of physical insight naturally achieved success and contributed significantly to the advancement of the subject. With an increasing number of solved (analytically or experimentally) cases and an increasingly accurate understanding of materials science becoming available to him, the modern engineer-analyst needs to develop more and more sophistication in order that he can better exercise judgment as to which of the many aids would be of utmost use to him. The assumption-making part of the process gives way to the technique known as extrapolation, which the engineer has often been accused (at times, with justification) of abusing.

In extrapolating the results of solved problems to beyond what immediately appear to be their legitimate bounds, the engineer leans heavily on a very useful concept, *Saint-Venant's principle*, named after one of the most famous elasticians. The gist of this principle is that statically equivalent force systems, individually applied at the same site in a given body which is supported in a prescribed manner, will produce the same stresses and strains at points far removed from the forces, the stress and strain distribution differing significantly only in the vicinity of the sites of application of the force systems. This means, for example, that if a uniformly distributed force system of 100 lb per sq. in. acting over a 2 sq. in. area of a body were replaced by the resultant of 200 lb, the stresses and strains due to each force system would differ less and less at increasing distances from the site of the distributed system.

Much of the confidence with which the engineer extrapolates from the known to the unknown stems from the knowledge that an actual test can always be made, or at least approximated, the results of which may then be compared with the predictions of his "theoretical" solution. So long as he must produce, as he is constantly expected to do, because "the customer is waiting and the goods must be delivered," the engineer must keep on making approximations, refining these as he gains in experience and new knowledge.

In much that follows, we will use this engineering approach even for those cases that can be solved formally. We do this by way of emphasizing the importance of assumptions, which all too often in engineering subjects we tend to gloss over or, worse yet, overlook.

Before we leave this article, there are two theorems from the formal mathematical theory that we should at least mention. One of them, the Existence Theorem, asserts the existence of a solution to a properly defined stress and strain problem. The engineer tends to look askance at such refinement; he senses from the purely practical viewpoint that a solution to a physical problem must exist. The other, the Uniqueness Theorem, says that if a solution is found which passes the various tests of equilibrium and compatibility, then it is the only solution; any other would be an approximate one. This is comforting to the analyst.

2.9   Principle of Superposition.   Prominent among our aids to analysis is the powerful tool of superposition. Expressed in a general way, this principle provides that

If an effect p is linearly proportional to its cause P, and an effect q to its cause Q, which necessarily means that Q in no way affects the influence of P on p, or P that of Q on q, then P and Q together will have an effect equivalent to p and q together.

For example, P and Q may be forces and p and q their moments; if the moment p is independent of Q and the moment q independent of P, then P and Q acting together, applied in any sequence, will result in a moment equal to the sum of p and q. When this is so, we say that superposition applies. On the other hand, if the moment p depends not only on P but also on whether or not Q has been previously applied, and, similarly, if the moment q depends not only on Q but also on whether or not P has been previously applied, then the moment of P and Q together will depend on the order in which the two are applied and, in general, will differ from the sum of p and q. In such a situation, we say that superposition does not apply.

This principle is in the nature of a postulate which we accept intuitively. Linearity between effect and cause is a necessary and sufficient condition for its applicability. Smallness of effect may be considered equivalent to linearity. We have seen this in the definition of strain, then in the statement of Hooke's law, and finally in the formulation of the unit strain energy. Because it implies linearity, smallness of effect is a sufficient, though not necessary, basis for superposition.

2.10   Units.   Symbols.   In this book we use units common in American engineering practice. Force is measured in pounds and area is usually in square inches; hence stress is expressed in pounds per square inch, abbreviated psi. To avoid large numbers, we sometimes use the kilopound, abbreviated kip; ksi stands for kilopounds per square inch.

Linear deformation, usually being very small, is expressed in inch units. Angular deformation is either in degrees or in radians; when no units are specified, the radian is to be understood. Linear strain is sometimes expressed in fractions of an inch per inch; since it is a pure number, however, it needs no units, although it is common practice to specify linear strain in percent. This holds also for shear strain, except that the radian is preferred.

The symbols agree substantially with those used by the American Standards Association. One among the few exceptions should be mentioned. The ASA alternative symbol S for stress is used here to designate the total stress, thus $S = \sqrt{\sigma^2 + \tau^2}$; hence S_x designates the X cartesian component of S, *not* the normal stress on a plane whose aspect is given by X.

2.11 Sign Conventions. Signs are a frequent source of difficulty, especially for the beginner. Part of the explanation, at least for the field of mechanics and allied subjects, is because there are two distinct sign conventions, and one difficulty stems from the failure to distinguish between the two. They are:

(1) That based exclusively on the "external" effects of forces,
(2) That based exclusively on the "internal" effects of forces.

By external effects we mean those that have to do with the state of equilibrium or nonequilibrium of a body. The acceleration of a body as an entity is an external effect of the forces impressed on the body; similarly, the forces induced at the supports of a structure, as a result of the loads on it, are external effects of those loads. In dealing with such effects, we assign the signs to *individual* forces. This means that along a given direction a force that points to one sense is called, say, positive and then any other force that points to the opposite sense is understood to be negative. Which particular sense is given the plus sign is not important. The outstanding characteristic of this first sign convention is that *forces are related to one another only and not at all to the body on which they act.*

The other difficulty arises when we try to relate the signs to the particular frame of reference chosen. Having set up the horizontal and vertical axes of a right-handed cartesian system, we then like to say that vector quantities directed to the right are positive, whereas those to the left are negative, and those directed upward are positive, whereas those downward are negative. Everything works out beautifully until we try to extend the convention to vectors inclined to the reference axes: What should we consider a vector directed, say, upward and to the right? We might say this should be positive since the angle lies in the first quadrant. But how about a vector directed upward and to the left? By now we should realize that this association with the cartesian reference frame works *only* for the cartesian components of vectors. This is illustrated in Figs. 2.6a and b. Note that the signed components occur *singly*.

We come now to the internal effects, which have to do with the changes in dimensions of the body, that is, the strains; and because strains are related to stresses, internal effects have to do also with stresses as well as with stress resultants or internal forces. In dealing with such effects, we assign the signs to *pairs* of forces rather than to individual ones. For example, if two collinear forces acting on a rod tend to elongate the rod, we may assign the positive sign to the pair; on the other hand, if their points of application are interchanged, we will have a pair that tends to shorten the rod and, since this dimensional change of contraction is opposite to that of elongation, we assign to the new pair of forces the negative sign. The outstanding characteristic of the second sign convention is that *forces are related principally to the body on which they act and only secondarily to one another*.

The final question that should naturally arise is: Can this second sign convention be tied to the frame of reference? The answer is, of course, yes it can, but, as we should now anticipate, the association will hold only for cartesian components of the vectors. What device do we use to effect the relation of force to body? We use the normal to the surface at the site of application of the force in question. This operates as follows. Let us imagine that part of the external boundary of a free body lies on a plane parallel to the y-z plane, and let us erect the normal to the plane, which, of course, will be parallel to the X axis. Then, if the *outward* (directed away from the body) normal is in the sense of increasing x, all vector components for that face (a positive-X face) shall be considered positive if they agree in sense with the positive axes, negative if they are oppositely directed. Furthermore, if the outward normal is in the sense of decreasing x, then all vector components for that face (a negative-X face) shall considered positive also if they agree in sense with the negative axes, negative if oppositely directed. This association is illustrated in Figs. 2.6c and d. Note particularly that the signed components occur *in pairs*, and that oppositely directed signed pairs tend to deform the body in opposite senses. Tensile forces are then understandably considered positive and compressive forces

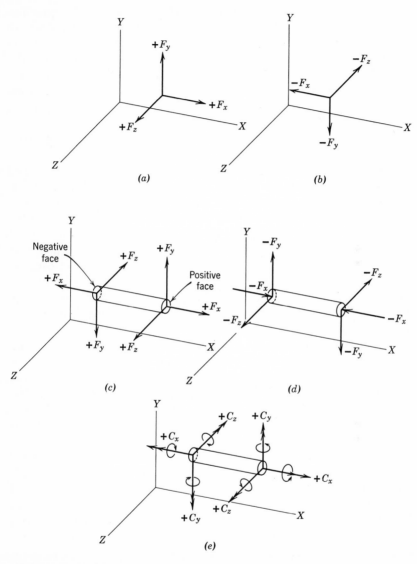

Fig. 2.6   Sign conventions for forces and moments.   Sketches a and b are for external effects, and c, d, and e are for internal effects.

negative; we have no special names for transverse components that re-
flect the difference in sign.

In this book we will use the right-handed cartesian system exclusively,
except in two instances which will be mentioned explicitly at the proper
time and place. In keeping with this, we note that the signs for localized
moment vectors follow those of force vectors; then the signs are consistent with those of the vector product, of which moment is an example.
Also, it is often necessary to distinguish between force and moment
vectors, especially when both appear on the same sketch. For this
purpose, we employ double arrowheads for the moments, single ones
for the forces. These signs and the symbolism are illustrated in Fig.
2.6e. Note that this is strictly analogous to Fig. 2.6c.

PROBLEMS

2.13. One end of the three-dimensional bent is clamped at the wall. Pass a
transverse sectioning plane at point p and retain the 3-ft part. Show on the ex-

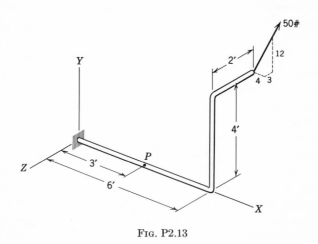

Fig. P2.13

posed face of the bent the six components of the internal force system. Ignore
the weight of the bent.

2.14. Repeat Prob. 2.13, this time retaining the forward part of the bent.

TENSION AND COMPRESSION

3.1 Simple Tension. The simplest element that is encountered in structures is the tension member. It may be a simple fastener like a bolt, or a guy wire that supports a post carrying transverse loads, or it may be a component of a pin-connected truss. In general, the tension member is a two-force member, or at least is assumed to be so, in which case its loading is described as simple tension. Exceptions are discussed elsewhere in this chapter.

Figure 3.1 shows the free-body diagram of a simple bar represented as a two-force member; this may be thought of as part of a pin-connected frame. Each force P then represents the action on this free bar of the pin that has been removed. Actually P is the resultant of a system of distributed forces. Our concern here, however, is not with this particular distribution; for our present needs, we use the point-force representation as a convenient idealization.

Let us now ask, "What is the strength of this bar as a tension member?" We immediately think of the load-carrying capacity, the usefulness, of the bar. For this example, the load-carrying capacity may be

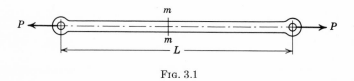

FIG. 3.1

41

defined as the maximum value attained by P before the end of useful-ness.   But what determines this end of usefulness, this "failure" as we might well call it?   To answer this question, we could do either one of two things.

One of these consists in testing a bar as nearly identical as possible to the piece in whose strength we are interested.   With suitable equipment we could make simultaneous measurements of the load P and the over-all elongation δ of the bar.   Assuming we had a complete set of data up to and including the instant the bar fractured, we could then present the relationship between load and deformation in graphical form such as Fig. 3.2, where the smooth curve represents faired values through the test points.   We would note that part of the curve is a straight line; this region of proportionality between load and deformation ends at the proportional limit, to which correspond the proportional-limit load P_{prop} and the proportional-limit elongation δ_{prop}.   In this region Hooke's law may be assumed to hold and, as explained in Chapter 2, the material may then be assumed elastic.   Hence we may say that P_{prop} or, equiv-alently, P_e (the elastic-limit load), gives one measure of the bar's strength, and also that δ_{prop} or, equivalently, δ_e, defines the end of use-fulness since permanent (inelastic) deformation would take place beyond this point.   On the other hand, if we considered the end of usefulness to mean actual destruction of the piece, then the ultimate load P_u would

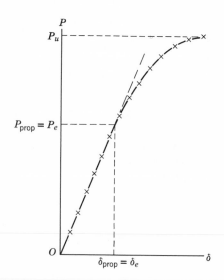

FIG. 3.2

give the strength of the bar.   Between these two values of P, any magnitude may serve as a measure of the bar's strength corresponding to some *arbitrarily* defined end of usefulness.

Although it has the advantage of exactitude for one specific case, this method suffers from the drawback of its narrow restrictiveness.   Thus from such a test we could not determine the strength of another size bar made of a different material.   Conceivably, we could test various size bars of all structurally useful materials; from these data we could select the one particular set most nearly applicable to any case at hand, or in the absence of such a specific set we could interpolate between the two nearest sets.   Fortunately, others have been doing precisely this testing for us.   A mass of information on mechanical properties of materials has come out of various testing laboratories, and, as new materials are developed, we may expect to be brought up to date by continuing tests.

The other thing to do then is to devise a theory from which some formulas may be derived that will permit smooth and continuous interpolation as well as, we trustfully hope, extrapolation from existing data. We will now illustrate the engineering approach to the theoretical handling of the above problem.

We begin by assuming the material of the bar to be a homogeneous and isotropic continuum.   This is to be understood henceforth for all materials dealt with in our discussion.   It is assumed further that the bar is straight and has a uniform cross section throughout its length, except at the ends where it is attached to other parts of the structure proper.   For obvious reasons, this is not only a convenience but also a practical necessity.   Considering our idealized model, we now assume that as the bar is loaded all transverse sections in the region of uniform cross section remain plane and parallel to one another in the deformed state.   This means that for any given load if we measured the change in the distance between any two parallel transverse sections a specified distance apart in the unloaded bar, we would come up with a constant magnitude regardless of the location of these two planes in the uniform part of the bar.   In effect, we are assuming that the linear strain along the axis of the bar, at all points throughout the uniform part, is a constant.   This also means, of course, that the originally straight bar is assumed to remain straight during deformation.   Choosing the X axis along the length of the bar, we now symbolize our assumption mathematically thus

$$\epsilon_x = \text{constant}. \qquad (a)$$

Furthermore, it appears reasonable to suppose that the cross sections of the bar do not distort and do not undergo rotations in their planes during deformation; hence we assume also that

$$\gamma_{xy} = \gamma_{yz} = \gamma_{zx} = 0. \tag{b}$$

Bringing in Hooke's law (Eqs. 2.8a), we see that the solution, at least for the region of proportionality, can be simplified to the extreme if the additional assumption is made that no normal stresses exist in transverse directions. This last one says in effect that if we consider the bar to consist of a bundle of tiny longitudinal "fibers," there is no lateral pressure between adjacent fibers. We write this out as follows:

$$\sigma_y = \sigma_z = 0. \tag{c}$$

The first of Eqs. 2.8e now gives us

$$\sigma_x = E\epsilon_x, \tag{3.1}$$

which shows that for a constant modulus E so long as the strain is constant the stress must also be constant.

Fig. 3.3

To evaluate the unknown σ_x, we now consider a free-body diagram of a portion of the bar, obtained by passing a transverse cutting plane m-m somewhere across the uniform region (Fig. 3.1) and isolating the part to either side of m-m. Figure 3.3 shows such a free body, where the internal forces, now become external, are represented as being uniformly distributed with an intensity σ_x. Body forces are assumed insignificant. From equilibrium we may write, using A for the cross-sectional area of the bar,

$$\Sigma F_x = \sigma_x A - P = 0,$$

whence
$$\sigma_x = \frac{P}{A}. \tag{3.2}$$

Since σ_x is constant in magnitude, it follows that the resultant force $\sigma_x A$ must pass through the centroid of the cross-sectional area, and since this resultant must be collinear with the external load P, it follows that the two end forces P must have a common line of action that passes through the centroid of every transverse section of the bar. This will insure the member remaining straight as it deforms and is a necessary condition for the applicability of Eq. 3.2.

From Eq. 3.1 we now find, by virtue of Eq. 3.2, that

$$\epsilon_x = \frac{\sigma_x}{E} = \frac{P}{AE}. \qquad (d)$$

Bringing in Eq. 2.5a, $\partial u/\partial x = \epsilon_x$, we obtain

$$u = \frac{P}{AE}x + C_1, \qquad (e)$$

where C_1 is some undetermined constant. Note that in keeping with the assumption that transverse planes remain planes and transverse, u is taken to be independent of both y and z. We now find the deforma-

FIG. 3.4

tion of a short length Δx in the uniform portion of the bar to be $\Delta\delta_x = u(x + \Delta x) - u(x)$, which, by Eq. e, becomes

$$\Delta\delta_x = \frac{P(\Delta x)}{AE}, \qquad (f)$$

or, in differential form,

$$d\delta_x = \frac{P}{AE}dx. \qquad (g)$$

(Alternatively, by Eq. d, $d\delta_x = \epsilon_x\,dx = (P/AE)\,dx$.) Hence the elongation of a length l, Fig. 3.4, is given by the familiar expression

$$\delta_x = \frac{Pl}{AE}. \qquad (3.3)$$

The other strain components may now be evaluated from the other equations of Hooke's law. Thus from the second and third of Eqs.

2.8e, we find

$$\epsilon_y = \epsilon_z = -\nu \frac{\sigma_x}{E}. \tag{h}$$

The corresponding displacements v and w may then be solved for if the additional simplifying assumptions are made that v is a function of y only and w a function of z only; these are consistent with earlier assumptions that the bar cross sections do not distort and do not rotate in their planes. From Eqs. 2.5a and b, $\partial v/\partial y = \epsilon_y$ and $\partial w/\partial z = \epsilon_z$, we find by Eq. 3.2 that

$$v = -\nu \frac{P}{AE} y + C_2, \tag{i}$$

and

$$w = -\nu \frac{P}{AE} z + C_3, \tag{j}$$

where C_2 and C_3 are undetermined constants. As before, we finally obtain

$$d\delta_y = -\nu \frac{P}{AE} dy \tag{k}$$

and

$$d\delta_z = -\nu \frac{P}{AE} dz, \tag{l}$$

from which the changes in the transverse dimensions of the bar may be calculated.

The correctness of the foregoing analysis may be established by applying on the results the tests of equilibrium and compatibility. It is seen that for the uniform part of the bar Eqs. 2.3 for interior points and Eqs. 2.4 for boundary points are automatically satisfied; hence equilibrium is preserved. Furthermore, Eqs. 2.7 are also identically satisfied: all terms become zero; hence geometric compatibility is not violated. Therefore the complete solution (for the uniform part of the bar) is

$$\sigma_x = \frac{P}{A}, \qquad \sigma_y = \sigma_z = \tau_{xy} = \tau_{yz} = \tau_{zx} = 0;$$

$$u = \frac{P}{AE} x + C_1, \qquad v = -\nu \frac{P}{AE} y + C_2, \qquad w = -\nu \frac{P}{AE} z + C_3.$$

We have gone into considerable detail in this analysis primarily to drive home the point that even in the simplest situations (there certainly can be none simpler than uniaxial stress), simplifying assumptions are both desirable and convenient. In the solution of more complex problems the steps are basically as just outlined, the principal difference being in the use of more sophisticated functions.

Returning to our original problem, that of determining the strength of the simple member, let us now see how the foregoing results can be used when coupled with experimental data. To this end let us first acquire some familiarity with strength properties of materials.

3.2 Strength Properties of Materials. Materials are tested in tension, in compression, in twist, in bending, or in combinations of these loadings. Machines in which two or more of these tests can be performed are called universal testing machines. By reason of its simplicity, the tension test is the most commonly and easily performed. A major portion of strength theory rests on assumptions gleaned from the tension test.

To test a material means to test a specimen made of that material. Variations in the form of the specimens and in the manner of testing them may, in general, be expected to exert some influence on the results. Therefore it is desirable to have standardized specimen dimensions and testing procedures. Such standardization is recommended by specialized organizations, of which an example is the American Society for Testing Materials.

For an accurate tension test the specimen is a round cylinder with shouldered or threaded ends (Figs. 3.5a and b). A length of the thinnest uniform portion of the specimen is marked off; this is called the *gage length* for the reason that a special measuring device called a *strain gage*, when attached to the specimen, spans this length. The gage measures the movement of one end of this length relative to the other end; this is the deformation δ.

The specimen with the strain gage attached is secured to the testing machine by special holders that insure the central application of the tension forces. This is necessary in order to prevent any tendency of the specimen to bend while being pulled. The usual testing machine is actually a straining or deforming rather than a loading device. For very slow rates of deformation, the load in the specimen is induced by the ability of the material (its elasticity) to resist being stretched; in

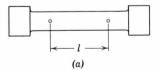

(a)

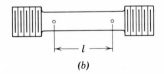

(b)

Fɪɢ. 3.5

tending to pull itself back to its unstrained state, the specimen reacts on the testing machine and it is this reaction which is registered in an indicating unit as the load P. (See Plate I.)

With the load P and the original cross-sectional area A of the specimen known, the stress may be computed, and with the corresponding elongation δ and the original gage length l determined, the accompanying strain may be calculated. When these corresponding values of stress and strain are plotted on a pair of rectangular axes, the stress conventionally as the ordinate and the strain as the abscissa, and a smooth curve is drawn through the test points, a *stress-strain diagram* is obtained.

Such a diagram is a characteristic curve of a material. Different materials have different stress-strain diagrams. Figure 3.6 shows two stress-strain diagrams, curve A for a ductile material and curve B for a brittle material. A ductile material is one that is capable of sustaining extensive permanent deformation under high levels of stress before fracture takes place. A brittle material, on the other hand, exhibits

PLATE I. Photograph at left shows a typical modern universal testing machine with tension specimen in place. Photograph at right shows a mechanical extensometer clamped onto a specimen ready for testing. (By courtesy of Riehle Testing Machines.)

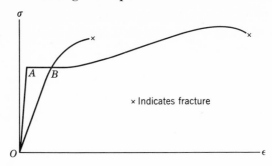

FIG. 3.6   Tension stress-strain diagrams.

little or no permanent deformation at fracture.   Mild steel is a very ductile material and curve A might well represent its stress-strain diagram.   Some magnesium alloys are very brittle; curve B might represent a tension stress-strain diagram of one such alloy.

The diagram gives us much of the information needed for the basis of the theory.   From the slope of the straight-line part we derive the modulus of elasticity as follows.   If the initial load (tare) on the specimen and the initial reading of the strain gage had been adjusted to make the diagram pass through the origin, then in calculating the slope of the initial portion, we take just one point as high up on the straight line as possible, divide the stress value by the corresponding strain value (Fig. 3.7), and obtain

$$E = \frac{\sigma}{\epsilon}. \qquad (a)$$

Otherwise we take two points on this line, as far apart as possible, and form the ratio of the stress increment to the corresponding strain increment, thus:

$$E = \frac{\Delta\sigma}{\Delta\epsilon}. \qquad (b)$$

In the curved portion of the diagram, the modulus as given by the limiting form of Eq. b represents the instantaneous rate of change of stress with respect to strain; it is then called the *tangent modulus* of elasticity at a certain level of stress:

$$E_T = \frac{d\sigma}{d\epsilon}. \qquad (c)$$

Assuming that we could precisely determine the end point a (Fig. 3.7) of the straight-line part of the diagram, we would then obtain values of

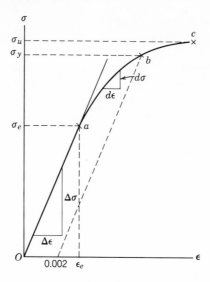

Fig. 3.7

the proportional-limit stress σ_e and the proportional-limit strain ϵ_e. The proportional-limit stress is one measure of the strength of the material; we call it the *elastic strength*.

We digress briefly to remark about the elastic limit. This point, which is at least as high as the proportional limit on the stress-strain diagram, cannot be located by merely examining the curve. To find this limit it would be necessary for one to load and then unload the specimen many times, each time increasing the load over its previous value and then determining, on release of the load, whether or not any permanent deformation remained. Only after such process can the elastic limit be located as a point on the diagram. In all our discussion we assume that the proportional limit is the same as the elastic limit.

Another strength property is defined by the yield strength (usually higher than the elastic strength), obtained as follows. Through a point on the strain axis corresponding to a strain of, say, 0.002, a straight line is drawn parallel to the straight part of the curve (Fig. 3.7). The point b at which this straight line intersects the curve gives a value of stress σ_y, considered as the yield strength at this set. This is called a *proof stress* or an *offset yield strength*, and may be quoted, for example, as 40,000 psi at 0.2% set. The assumption involved here is that if the test specimen were loaded beyond the proportional limit and then unloaded, the recovery curve would be a straight line parallel to the original

straight part of the diagram. There would thus remain a set, corresponding to the intercept on the strain axis of this unloading line. This is approximately satisfied in actual tests.* Such an arbitrary definition of
the strength of a material is employed on account of the difficulty in
locating the exact proportional limit on the diagram.

The *ultimate strength* of the material is defined by the ultimate stress
σ_u, corresponding to the greatest tension load before fracture, illustrated
by point c in Fig. 3.7. This stress may or may not be equal to the stress
at fracture. For brittle materials these values are identical, whereas for
ductile materials the fracture stress is usually less than the ultimate as
suggested by Fig. 3.6.†

Other criteria of usefulness may be obtained from the stress-strain
diagram. For instance, the amount of mechanical energy that a unit
volume of the material can absorb without permanently deforming is a
measure of its *resilience*. The area under the stress-strain diagram up to
the proportional limit, expressed in inch-pounds per cubic inch (which
is equivalent to psi), defines the material's *modulus of resilience* U_e; that
is,

$$U_e = \frac{\sigma_e \epsilon_e}{2} = \frac{\sigma_e^2}{2E}. \qquad (d)$$

(Compare this with Eq. *a* of Article 2.6.) For applications such as
springs, high resilience in the material is desirable. Equation *d* indicates that the factors which make for high resilience are high elastic
strength and low values of stiffness.

3.3 Simple Compression. What has been said of tension concerning stress and strain applies equally as well to compression, provided

* Most any metallic piece that exhibits a proportional limit, when loaded beyond
this limit, will upon unloading follow Hooke's law with approximately the same
modulus E as initially; when reloaded in the same sense, the material will display
virtually the same E, and the stress-strain curve will rejoin the original at the point
of first unloading as if there had been no interruption. This apparent raising of the
proportional limit is one aspect of the *Bauschinger effect*.

† In simple tension or compression, *true stress* is the load divided by the instantaneous cross-sectional area, and *true strain* is the accumulated deformation intensity
up to the instant, that is, $\epsilon_n = \int_{L_0}^{L} \frac{dL}{L} = \ln\left(\frac{L}{L_0}\right) = \ln(1 + \epsilon)$. The *natural* or
logarithmic strain ϵ_n, as given by this *Eulerian* definition, differs but slightly from the
engineering or *nominal* strain ϵ for small ϵ. When true stress is plotted against true
strain, the diagram obtained will begin to differ from the nominal one only past the
proportional limit. For tension the curved part of the true diagram will lie above the
nominal one, whereas for compression the opposite will be true. Therefore, in the
true stress-strain diagram, the fracture stress in tension is always the same as the
ultimate stress.

the possibility of lateral bending is precluded. Thus, if the compression member is short, like a post or pedestal, and the action line of the resultant compressive load passes through the centroid of the cross-sectional area, assumed to be uniform throughout the length of the member, then the compressive stress is P/A and the compressive strain is δ/l.

Most of the strength properties are similarly defined, the notable exception being the ultimate strength. Especially in ductile materials, it is not possible to obtain the ultimate and the fracture strengths because of the continuing increase in cross-sectional area with increasing compression load. Even in brittle materials, the manner of failure in compression cannot be considered simply the inverse of that in tension.

Experimental results indicate that, for most of the important structural materials like steel and the alloys of the light metals, the modulus of elasticity in compression is substantially equal to that in tension. The same may be said of the elastic and the offset yield strengths. Cast iron and concrete, both much stronger in compression than in tension, are two well-known exceptions.

PROBLEMS

3.1. A cast magnesium alloy block, 2 in. by 2 in. by 4 in., is compressed longitudinally. If the elastic-limit stress is 14,000 psi and the modulus of elasticity is 6.5×10^6 psi, what maximum load may be applied and what would be the maximum contraction?

3.2. An aluminum bar, 2.000 thick, 2.500 in. wide, and 20.000 in. long, is subjected to a uniformly distributed longitudinal compression load of 20,000 lb. Using $E = 9.9 \times 10^6$ psi and Poisson's ratio $\nu = 0.34$, calculate the dimensions of the bar while it is under load. How much does its volume change?

3.3. A copper tube with an outside diameter of 2.000 in. and a wall thickness of 0.500 in. is compressed by a 13,000-lb load. What are the transverse dimensions of the tube while under load?

3.4. In Prob. 3.2, if the thickness is maintained at its initial value by rigid clamps, what will be the change in the length of the bar? (*Hint:* Either use the equations of Hooke's law for plane stress or solve in two steps by superposition: σ_x first, followed by σ_y such that final $\epsilon_y = 0$.)

3.5. The following data define two points on the straight-line part of a tension load-deformation diagram:

Load (lb)	510	11,290
Deformation (in.)	0.0002	0.0039

The steel specimen had a standard 0.505 in. diameter and the gage length was 2 in. Calculate the modulus of elasticity.

3.6. A standard 0.505 in. specimen from an aluminum alloy extrusion was tested in tension, with the following computed results:

Stress (psi)	Strain	Stress	Strain
10,000	0.00097	65,000	0.00643
20,000	.00193	67,500	.00688
30,000	.00289	70,000	.00770
40,000	.00385	71,000	.00850
50,000	.00480	72,000	.01025
55,000	.00527	72,500	.01150
60,000	.00580	73,000	.01275

Neatly construct the stress-strain diagram and from it determine: (a) the modulus of elasticity, (b) the approximate proportional-limit stress, (c) the proof stress at 0.2% offset, and (d) the modulus of resilience.

3.7. In Prob. 3.6, what load corresponded to the proportional limit? What was the specimen's diameter at the proportional limit? Assume $\nu = 0.32$.

3.8. A cold-rolled steel rod, 2 in. in diameter, is expected to transmit a load that varies from 6000 lb compression to 12,000 lb tension. If $E = 29 \times 10^6$ psi, what will be the change in length of a nominal 2-ft portion of the rod between extremes in the range of loading? Assume that the rod remains straight during compression.

3.9. A surveyor's steel tape is $\frac{1}{4}$ in. wide and $\frac{1}{50}$ in. thick. When laid flat on the ground, at a temperature of 68°F, a tension of 12 lb must be maintained while readings are being taken. If the pull applied is only 7 lb, what is the error in 200 ft of tape? Assume $E = 30 \times 10^6$ psi and use the nominal length in the calculation.

3.4   The Strength of an Axially Loaded Member. We are now in a position to answer the question: What is the strength of a tension or a compression member? Recognizing stress as a convenient index, and keeping in mind the experimental relation between stress and strain as depicted in the stress-strain diagram, we define the strength of a simple two-force member as

$$P = \sigma A, \qquad (3.2')$$

where for σ we may use the elastic strength σ_e, the offset yield strength σ_y, or the ultimate strength σ_u, of the material. If we want to make sure that the member will function entirely within the elastic range, then we use σ_e. On the other hand, if a small amount of set will not be objectionable, then we use σ_y. Finally, if the greatest possible load-carrying capacity of the member is desired, then we define its ultimate strength as $\sigma_u A$, it being understood that this definition applies only to tension members.

As regards the identification of failure with the end of usefulness, let it suffice for the present to state that as far as the two-force member *as a separate entity* is concerned the end of usefulness coincides with either the beginning of excessive uncontrolled deformation or the occurrence of actual fracture. *If this member is but one of several components,* however, *then its failure need not necessarily spell failure also for the whole.* This is discussed more fully in Chapter 14.

By way of illustrating the remarks we made in the Introduction, we observe that the two equations, $\sigma = P/A$ and $\delta = Pl/AE$, are for purposes of analysis. They enable us to determine the induced force intensity and the induced deformation (or deformation intensity) when the load, dimensions, and material properties are known. The equations, $P = \sigma A$ and $P = \delta AE/l$, give measures of strength or usefulness. They enable us to find the load-carrying capacity of a given two-force member of known dimensions and material properties when certain limits are imposed on the stresses or the strains that it may sustain. Finally, the equations, $A = P/\sigma$ and $A = Pl/E\delta$, are for purposes of design. With their use we can calculate the needed cross-sectional area or the size of the member that will enable it to carry a given load without exceeding certain allowable stresses or strains. To bring out the basic differences in viewpoint represented by these equations, we array them thus:

$$\left. \begin{array}{c} \sigma = \dfrac{P}{A} \\[2ex] \delta = \dfrac{Pl}{AE} \end{array} \right\} \text{Analysis} \qquad \left. \begin{array}{c} P = \sigma A \\[2ex] P = \dfrac{\delta AE}{l} \end{array} \right\} \text{Strength} \qquad \left. \begin{array}{c} A = \dfrac{P}{\sigma} \\[2ex] A = \dfrac{Pl}{\delta E} \end{array} \right\} \text{Design.}$$

The purpose of arranging the equations in this manner is neither to suggest nor encourage solving problems by mechanically plugging numerical values in the appropriate relation. It is rather to emphasize the important fact that, whereas in some situations the stress, say, may be the independent variable and the load the dependent one, in others the roles of these two variables may well be reversed, with the load becoming the independent variable and the stress the dependent one.

PROBLEMS

3.10. A control rod, $\frac{1}{2}$ in. in diameter and 10 ft long, is made of a steel for which $E = 31 \times 10^6$ psi. If the proportional-limit strain is 0.0029, what maximum load may the rod transmit without suffering permanent set? What maximum elastic elongation is possible?

3.11. A steel pipe with an outside diameter of 2.25 in. is used to support a compressive load of 10,000 lb. If the average compressive stress is 5000 psi, what is the internal diameter of the pipe?

3.12. A concrete ($E = 3 \times 10^6$ psi) pier is 20 ft high and has a square cross section 20 in. on edge. If the top may not settle more than 0.025 in., what maximum (uniformly distributed) compressive load may the pier sustain?

3.5 Factor of Safety. In the functioning of structures, there is always involved some uncertainty regarding the magnitudes and the distribution of the loads that may have to be sustained. For instance, a building may be subjected to unexpectedly large forces during an earthquake. It is obviously impossible with present knowledge to predict accurately the maximum intensities of any future earthquakes, if indeed there are going to be any at all. Moreover, there is every likelihood that not all the assumptions on which the theory is based can be satisfied. In terms of the two-force member, this means that the end loads may not be exactly central, the cross section may not be uniform, the material is never absolutely homogeneous—all of which tend to restrict the validity of the derived equations. And then there is the ever present danger that failure of the whole structure or some part of it may result in damage to property and even loss of life. In view of all these considerations, we limit the maximum loads on the structure to a fraction of the actual load-carrying capacity and leave part of this usefulness in reserve for any contingency. In practice this means that the structure is designed to be much stronger than there is need for it to be.

This is done for a simple two-force member as follows. If P represents the strength of this member, we divide P by some number N larger than unity and obtain a *working strength* or a *usable capacity*, thus:

$$P_w = \frac{P}{N} \qquad\qquad (3.4a)$$

or
$$P = NP_w. \qquad\qquad (3.4b)$$

The number N may be interpreted in either of two ways. First, it is the number by which the load-carrying capacity of an existing member is divided in order to obtain the allowable load that may be applied on it; second, it is the number by which the actual load to be carried by a member is multiplied in order to obtain the load-carrying capacity which it is then designed to possess. In the first sense, N may be called a *factor of safety*, and in the second an *overload factor*. Whatever name it goes by, N is in essence a factor of uncertainty, of ignorance. As the number of items about which there is uncertainty becomes less and as more information is known more accurately, so this factor may be chosen successively smaller until, in the ideal limiting case when everything is known without any uncertainty, it becomes equal to unity.

Closely allied with N is the notion, *margin of safety*, which is defined by

$$\text{M.S.} = N - 1. \qquad (a)$$

It represents the fraction or multiple of the working load which may be impressed on the member as an overload before failure threatens.

Dividing both sides of the equation $P = \sigma A$ by N, where for σ we use, say, the yield strength σ_y, we obtain

$$\frac{P}{N} = \frac{\sigma_y}{N} A,$$

or $$P_w = \sigma_w A, \qquad (3.5)$$

in which σ_w is called a *working*, a *usable*, or a *design stress*. For a ductile material the working stress is ordinarily based on the yield strength as above, whereas for a brittle material it is based on the ultimate strength.

At this juncture one may well ask, Who decides the magnitude of N? The answer is that there is no one person who can decide this. Groups of persons who have had extensive experience in design and actual construction recommend different values of N for different applicatons, which in their collective judgment are most reasonable, safe, and in keeping with the latest knowledge. Such groups are called specification-making bodies. One might recommend working stresses; this is typical of civil engineering usage. Another might use factors of safety; this is often encountered in machine design practice. A third body might suggest overload factors; aeronautical engineers frequently think in terms of such factors.

Illustrative Example 1.   In the truss of Fig. 3.8a, it is desired to investigate the diagonal member BE. If the axial stress is not to exceed 10,000 psi, what is the best cross-sectional size to use for this member? With the truss loaded as shown, how much would the member deform axially? Use $E = 30 \times 10^6$ psi and ignore the weights of all members.

ANALYSIS.   The entire structure is considered as the first free body as shown in Fig. 3.8a, where the unknown reactions are indicated by dashed line arrows. The force system is completely solvable. Thus

$$\Sigma M_A = 0 = 18R_D - 12(12,000)$$

gives $\qquad R_D = 8000$ lb;

and $\qquad \Sigma F_V = 0 = V_A + 8000 - 12,000$

gives $\qquad V_A = 4000$ lb;

finally, $\qquad \Sigma F_H = 0 = H_A$

shows that $\qquad H_A = 0$.

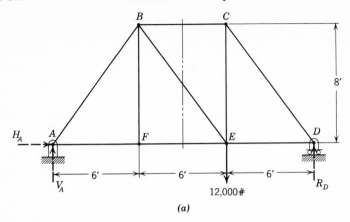

(a)

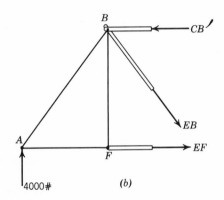

(b)

Fɪɢ. 3.8

The members BC, BE, and FE are then cut and part of the truss is considered as the next free body. Figure 3.8b shows the left half of the truss, with the senses of the unknown forces assumed. Note that each of these three members is considered a two-force member. The unknown force EB is solvable directly from the equation

$$\Sigma F_V = 0 = 4000 - \tfrac{4}{5}(EB),$$

whence $EB = 5000 \text{ lb},$

which is clearly a tension load on the member.

The idea of the best size for the member should now be interpreted to mean that size which would allow *maximum material utilization*, rather than that size which would result in the greatest possible strength. Leaning for our value judgment on the basic design equation, $A = P/\sigma$, we note that by using for σ the maximum allowable value of 10,000 psi we obtain the smallest possible value of A, thus:

$$A = \frac{5000}{10,000} = 0.500 \text{ in.}^2 \qquad\qquad Ans.$$

Hence in this case the best size also means the smallest size, which ultimately means the most economical one. This concept is in harmony with the understanding of the basic function of design which even the least technical neophyte should possess, namely, *optimization*. We remark that, from the standpoint of strength, the bar of optimum size would also be the weakest. Optimization dictates that *no part should be designed for more strength than can be effectively utilized.*

The axial deformation of the member BE, in this case an elongation, is found from the deformation equation, $\delta = PL/AE$. Making the proper substitutions, we obtain

$$\delta = \frac{5000(120)}{0.5(30)10^6} = 0.040 \text{ in.} \qquad\qquad Ans.$$

Alternatively, the strain ϵ may first be found from $\epsilon = \sigma/E$, and this value may then be multiplied by the length L to give δ as above. Observe that the use of the total length L in lieu of the length l of some uniform portion of the bar constitutes an *extrapolation* of the basic formula. The above result would differ but a negligible amount from the actual value.

PROBLEMS

3.13. For a tape $\frac{1}{4}$ in. wide and $\frac{1}{50}$ in. thick, an allowable tensile stress of 20,000 psi is specified. What is the usable tensile strength of the tape? May a tensile force of 95 lb be applied?

3.14. A hollow cast-iron cylinder with a wall thickness of $\frac{1}{2}$ in. is to bear a compressive load of 100,000 lb. Determine the necessary outside diameter based on an ultimate compressive strength of 100,000 psi for the material and a safety factor of 10.

3.15. Wire B, 0.15 in. in diameter, is of a steel whose $E = 30 \times 10^6$ psi and $\sigma_y = 36,000$ psi. Wire C, 0.10 in. in diameter, is of an aluminum alloy whose $E = 10.5 \times 10^6$ psi and $\sigma_y = 40,000$ psi. If $x = 4$ in., what maximum P may be applied on the weightless rigid bar D, based on an overload factor of 2? If

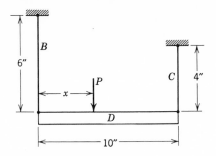

F_IG_. P3.15

F_IG_. P3.15

bar D is horizontal without any load on it, what will be its inclination under this maximum allowable P?

3.16. In the preceding problem, what is the maximum allowable P consistent with a horizontal D? What should x be?

3.17. In Prob. 3.15, what should x be for optimum conditions? Evaluate P and determine the loaded position of D.

3.18. Horizontal members B and C may be considered rigid and of negligible weight. Pins 1 and 2 are smooth. Wires D and F are vertical. The allowable tensile stress for wire D is 150,000 psi, whereas that for wire F is 100,000 psi. What maximum value may P have?

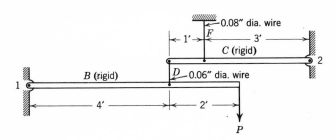

F_IG_. P3.18

3.19. In the preceding problem, what should be the optimum diameter of the overstrong wire?

3.20. In Fig. P3.18, wire D is 10 in. long and wire F is 20 in. long. The materials have the same elasticity modulus of 30×10^6 psi. If the rigid bars are horizontal before P is applied, what is the angle between them when P is 200 lb?

3.21. In the truss of Fig. 3.8a, the allowable compressive stress in member CD is 2000 psi. What is the best size (cross-sectional area) to use for this member?

3.22. In the truss of Fig. 3.8a, member FE has a cross-sectional area of 1.4 in.^{2} If the allowable stress in it is 7500 psi, what downward load applied at F may be imposed on the truss, in addition to that shown, without this stress in member FE being exceeded?

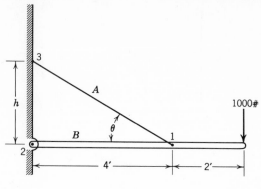

Fig. P3.23

3.23. The two-force member A supports the rigid multiforce member B in a horizontal position, through the smooth pin 1 whose location along B is fixed. The other end of A is anchored to the vertical wall by pin 3, whose location h above pin 2 is adjustable. Considering only the effects of the 1000-lb load shown, ignoring the earth pull on the members of the structure, calculate the smallest volume (optimum) that member A can have, if the allowable tensile stress in it is 10,000 psi.

3.24. Do the same for member A in this structure.

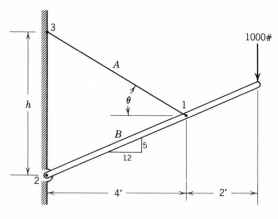

Fig. P3.24

3.25. Wires B and C have the same dimensions and properties as in Prob. 3.15. If $\theta = 60$ deg., what is the maximum allowable P? Use a safety factor of 2 based on the yielding of either or both wires. Locate the final position of the small ring 1. (*Hint:* Solve the two triangles in Fig. P3.25, which is based on the assumption of small deformations.)

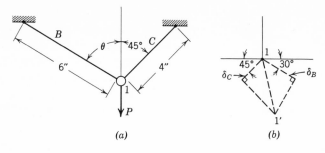

Fig. P3.25

3.26. In the preceding problem, if the inclination of wire C is fixed, what should be the angle θ for optimum conditions? Calculate the maximum allowable P then.

3.6   Tension or Compression Bars That Are Not Two-Force Members.   When axial forces on a straight member are localized at more than two points, we have a multiforce member. This is illustrated in the following.

Illustrative Example 2.   Figure 3.9a represents a hanging bar subjected to three axial loads assumed localized as indicated. (The manner

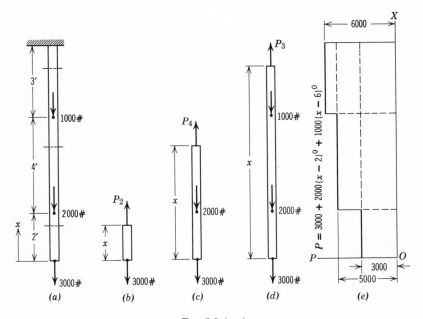

Fig. 3.9 (a–e)

in which these loads are applied is not of special concern here, although it would help the student to appreciate the notion of localized forces if he imagined the 1000-lb and 2000-lb loads to be the resultants of forces distributed uniformly on rings or collars that protrude from the bar at the indicated sections.) The minimum uniform cross-sectional area of the bar is required, based on a working stress of 12,000 psi on transverse sections. Investigate the bar for nominal axial deformation. Use $E = 10.6 \times 10^6$ psi, and ignore the earth pull on the bar.

ANALYSIS. In order not to detract from the main ideas, we assume that the local nonuniformity of stresses and strains across transverse planes in the vicinity of the concentrated loads may be ignored. Passing a transverse plane anywhere across the 2-ft length and considering the lower portion of the bar as a free body, we obtain Fig. 3.9b. The axial tension force P_2 follows from the equilibrium equation

$$\Sigma F_V = 0 = P_2 - 3000,$$

which gives $P_2 = 3000$ lb.

Similarly, passing a transverse plane anywhere across the 4-ft length and isolating the lower part of the bar, we get Fig. 3.9c, from which

$$\Sigma F_V = 0 = P_4 - 3000 - 2000$$

and $P_4 = 5000$ lb.

Finally, passing a transverse plane anywhere across the 3-ft length and isolating the lower part of the bar, we have Fig. 3.9d, whence

$$\Sigma F_V = 0 = P_3 - 3000 - 2000 - 1000$$

and $P_3 = 6000$ lb.

This variation in the axial force transmitted across any transverse section is depicted graphically in Fig. 3.9e, which shows that the greatest demand for axial strength is in the 3-ft portion, where the maximum axial force of 6000 lb has to be sustained. Therefore the minimum size must be based on this maximum force, thus:

$$A = \frac{P_{\max}}{\sigma_w} = \frac{6000}{12,000} = 0.5 \text{ in.}^2 \qquad Ans.$$

The analysis of nominal axial deformation can be pursued according to either of two methods.

Method 1. We may consider the 9-ft bar to be equivalent to three shorter bars, each acting as a two-force member. These are shown in Fig. 3.9f. If all that is desired is the total deformation of the original bar,

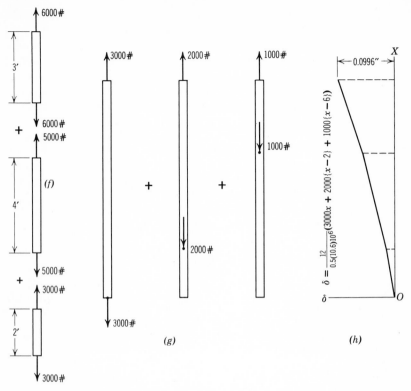

FIG. 3.9 (f–h)

it is a simple matter to calculate the individual deformations of the three bars in tandem and then add them. Using $\delta = PL/AE$, we have

$$\delta_{\text{total}} = \delta_2 + \delta_4 + \delta_3$$
$$= \frac{3000(2)12}{0.5(10.6)10^6} + \frac{5000(4)12}{0.5(10.6)10^6} + \frac{6000(3)12}{0.5(10.6)10^6}$$
$$= 0.0136 + 0.0452 + 0.0408$$
$$= 0.0996 \text{ in.} \quad \text{(elongation)}$$

On the other hand, if the deformation of any length x is desired, where x is measured from the lower end, then three separate expressions must be obtained, one for each range of values that x may take on. Thus, for the range $0 < x < 2$, we find

$$\delta = \frac{3000(x)12}{0.5(10.6)10^6} = 0.00679x. \qquad (a)$$

For the range $2 < x < 6$, we have

$$\delta = \frac{3000(2)12}{0.5(10.6)10^6} + \frac{5000(x-2)12}{0.5(10.6)10^6}$$

$$= -0.00906 + 0.01132x. \qquad (b)$$

And for the range $6 < x < 9$, we obtain

$$\delta = \frac{3000(2)12}{0.5(10.6)10^6} + \frac{5000(4)12}{0.5(10.6)10^6} + \frac{6000(x-6)12}{0.5(10.6)10^6}$$

$$= -0.0226 + 0.01358x. \qquad (c)$$

This variation in deformation as a function of position along the bar is shown in Fig. 3.9h by a plot consisting of three straight-line segments. The diagram shows that the maximum deformation occurs at $x = 9$ ft, as to be expected. Equation c gives this value:

$$\delta_{\max} = -0.0226 + 0.01358(9) = 0.0996 \text{ in.}$$

Observe that if the three separate free bodies of Fig. 3.9f are joined end to end, the result will be the free-body diagram of Fig. 3.9a. The three individual two-force members correspond to the three areas of the axial-force-variation diagram delineated by the horizontal broken lines in Fig. 3.9e. Method 1 then does make use of superposition.

Method 2. This method considers the effect of each load on the entire bar and then combines them to get the total effect. Note that Fig. 3.9e may also be decomposed into the three areas mapped out by the vertical broken lines; these three areas then correspond to the three free bodies in Fig. 3.9g. In this respect, Method 2 is more easily recognizable as superposition.

Again, if only the total deformation of the original bar is desired, one merely evaluates the deformation of each bar in Fig. 3.9g and then adds these values algebraically, thus:

$$\delta_{\text{total}} = \delta_a + \delta_b + \delta_c$$

$$= \frac{3000(9)12}{0.5(10.6)10^6} + \frac{2000(7)12}{0.5(10.6)10^6} + \frac{1000(3)12}{0.5(10.6)10^6}$$

$$= 0.0611 + 0.0317 + 0.0679 = 0.0996 \text{ in.}$$

The deformation of any length x is derived as follows. For the range $0 < x < 2$,

$$\delta = \frac{3000(x)12}{0.5(10.6)10^6} = 0.00679x. \qquad (a)$$

For the range $2 < x < 6$,

$$\delta = \frac{3000(x)12}{0.5(10.6)10^6} + \frac{2000(x-2)12}{0.5(10.6)10^6}$$

$$= -0.00906 + 0.01132x. \qquad (b)$$

And for the range $6 < x < 9$,

$$\delta = \frac{3000(x)12}{0.5(10.6)10^6} + \frac{2000(x-2)12}{0.5(10.6)10^6} + \frac{1000(x-6)12}{0.5(10.6)10^6}$$

$$= 0.0226 + 0.01358x. \qquad (c)$$

In simplified form, these three equations are, of course, identical to the ones previously derived.

Method 2 is especially interesting and important and should therefore be carefully understood. We observe that the first term in the right-hand side of Eq. a is the same as the first term in the right-hand side of each of Eqs. b and c before simplification, and that the two terms in Eq. b are the same as the first two terms in Eq. c. This suggests that, if we employ a special symbol, the three equations may be written as one, thus:

$$\delta = \frac{12}{0.5(10.6)10^6} (3000x + 2000\{x-2\} + 1000\{x-6\}). \qquad (d)$$

The braces signify that the enclosed quantity is to be ignored when negative. For example, when $0 < x < 2$, only the first term inside the parentheses is retained; this gives Eq. a. When $2 < x < 6$, only the first two terms are retained, and Eq. b follows. Finally, when $6 < x < 9$, all three terms are retained, and the result is nothing more than Eq. c.

Moreover, if δ in Eq. d is differentiated with respect to x, there is obtained

$$\frac{d\delta}{dx} = \frac{12}{0.5(10.6)10^6} (3000 + 2000\{x-2\}^0 + 1000\{x-6\}^0). \qquad (e)$$

Comparing this with $d\delta/dL = P/AE$, we find that the expression inside the parentheses is precisely the axial force transmitted at any x, which certainly is equal to the summation of all external forces to one side of x. A braced term of the form $\{x-a\}^0$, which must be taken equal to unity for all $x > a$ but zero otherwise, signifies that the force magnitude to which it is attached as a multiplier is to be included in the summation only after x exceeds a. We shall have more to say about this device in connection with beams, where it finds its widest application.

From the preceding observation, we may now write the expression for the local axial force transmitted as a function of the position coordinate x, as follows:

$$P = \Sigma(\text{forces to one side of section})$$

$$= 3000 + 2000\{x - 2\}^0 + 1000\{x - 6\}^0, \qquad 0 < x < 9. \qquad (f)$$

It is therefore proper to refer to Fig. 3.9e as the graph of Eq. f and to Fig. 3.9h as that of Eq. d.

Let us imagine that the number of axial loads on the bar is increased without limit, that the loads are all equal, and that their sites of action are successive points along the axis of the bar. Then the axial tension load will vary continuously rather than in stepwise fashion throughout the length of the bar. This is the situation when a uniform straight bar is suspended from one end and is subjected only to the earth pull and the reaction at the support.

Illustrative Example 3. Figure 3.10a represents a uniform bar suspended vertically from one end, the earth pull on it being the only load considered. The bar's cross-sectional area is A, its length is L, its specific weight (weight per unit volume) is γ, and its material has an elasticity modulus E. It is required to analyze the bar for axial stresses and deformation.

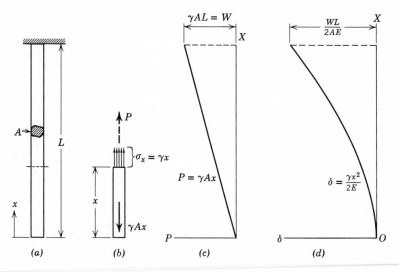

Fɪɢ. 3.10

ANALYSIS. The free-body diagram of a portion of length x, measured from the lower end of the bar, is shown in Fig. 3.10b. The forces acting on this free body are the resultant earth pull of magnitude $\gamma A x$ and the resultant P of a system of uniformly distributed parallel forces of intensity σ per unit area. Equilibrium requires that

$$\Sigma F_V = 0 = P - \gamma A x,$$

whence $\qquad\qquad\qquad P = \gamma A x, \qquad 0 < x < L. \qquad\qquad\qquad (a)$

Note that Eq. a can be written directly as an extension of Eq. f in the preceding example, which defines the internal axial force as the sum of all external forces to one side of the section in question. The Eq. a shows that the maximum axial tension force occurs at the upper end where $x = L$, its value being $P_{\max} = \gamma A L = W$, the total weight of the bar. Figure 3.10c depicts the force variation. Making use of $P = \sigma A$, we obtain

$$\sigma A = \gamma A x,$$

whence $\qquad\qquad\qquad\qquad \sigma = \gamma x. \qquad\qquad\qquad\qquad\qquad (b)$

The maximum tensile stress occurs at the upper end, or $\sigma_{\max} = \gamma L$.

Bringing in Hooke's law for uniaxial stress, Eq. 2.8e, we obtain

$$\epsilon_x = \frac{\gamma x}{E}. \qquad\qquad\qquad (c)$$

Then $\partial u / \partial x = \epsilon_x$ gives

$$u = \frac{\gamma x^2}{2E} + C, \qquad\qquad\qquad (d)$$

it being assumed as before that u is dependent only on x. Since the origin for x is at the free end of the bar, Eq. d without the constant C gives the elongation of a length x, thus:

$$\delta = \frac{\gamma x^2}{2E}. \qquad\qquad\qquad (e)$$

Figure 3.10d shows the graph of Eq. e, from which the total elongation of the bar is seen to be

$$\delta_{\text{total}} = \frac{\gamma L^2}{2E} = \frac{WL}{2AE}. \qquad\qquad\qquad (f)$$

It is interesting to note that the total elongation of a uniform bar hanging vertically from one end and subject to no other load but its weight is precisely one-half the elongation it would suffer if pulled by two forces each of magnitude equal to the total weight.

PROBLEMS

3.27. In *Project Mohole*, the steel pipe line that transmitted rotary power from the deep-sea drilling barge to the drill bit in the ocean floor was 12,000 ft long. If the buoyant force of the water is ignored and the pipe assumed uniform in cross-sectional area and freely suspended vertically from the barge, calculate (a) the maximum tensile stress in the pipe, and (b) the elongation of the pipe line. Use specific weight $\gamma = 0.284$ lb/in.^{3} and $E = 30 \times 10^6$ psi.

3.28. The pipe line in the preceding problem was in three uniform sections as follows: the top 4000 ft, $A = 4$ in.^{2}; the middle 4000 ft, $A = 2$ in.^{2}; and the bottom 4000 ft, $A = 1$ in.^{2} The sea water may be assumed to weigh a constant 64 lb/ft.^{3} Determine the maximum stress in each section of the suspended pipe, taking into account the buoyant force of the sea water.

3.29. In one of the deepest oil wells, the drill bit was momentarily stuck 25,000 ft beneath the earth's surface. While it was being pulled unstuck, a maximum tensile stress of 100,000 psi developed in the pipe. Assume that the pipe had a constant cross-sectional area (actually the pipe, which was in sections, was far from uniform throughout). How much did the top of the pipe move from the no-load position? The casing effectively prevented the pipe line from bending; hence the pipe may be assumed straight while it rested on the drill bit, with no load at the top. Ignore the friction between pipe and casing. $E = 30 \times 10^6$ psi and $\gamma = 0.284$ lb/in.^{3}

3.30. As the first 25-ft length of the casing for an oil well was being hammered into the ground, a compressive force of 200,000 lb was momentarily exerted on the top of the pipe through a rigid flat plate. This was just enough to push the casing into final position. If the outside diameter of the casing was 25 in. and its wall thickness was 0.25 in., and if the frictional resistance of the soil may be assumed uniformly distributed on the outside surface of the pipe, how much did the casing contract longitudinally? Ignore the weight of the casing and use $E = 30 \times 10^6$ psi.

3.31. The aluminum bar ($E = 10 \times 10^6$ psi), 90 in. long and having a uniform cross-sectional area of 2 in.^{2}, is subjected to the localized loads shown. (a) By the method of sections, find from equilibrium conditions the local force transmitted between adjacent loads; show the results in a force-variation diagram, observing the sign convention of Article 2.11. (b) Calculate the maximum tensile stress and the maximum compressive stress. Where do these occur? (c) Relative to the left end, which transverse section deflects the most, and how

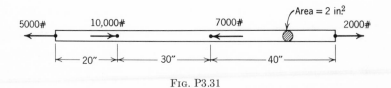

FIG. P3.31

much is this deflection? (*d*) Relative to the left end, which sections do not deflect? (*e*) What is the over-all axial deformation of the bar? Specify whether it is an elongation or a contraction. (*f*) Beneath the force-variation diagram, graph the relative deformation as a function of position along the bar, taking extensions as positive.

3.32. For the bar in Prob. 3.31, write an equation that gives the value of the local internal axial force as a function of position. Then, using the differential form of Eq. 3.3, derive the equation of the axial deformation at any section relative to the left end. From this last equation, evaluate the maximum relative deflection and the over-all deformation, and locate the sections that do not move relative to the left end.

3.33. The two steel cylinders are joined together as a unit and suspended as shown. (*a*) Sketch a graph depicting the stress on a transverse section as a function of position along the common axis. Give significant values. (*b*) Sketch a graph depicting the elongation of any length measured from the bottom. Give the maximum elongation. $E = 30 \times 10^6$ psi and $\gamma = 0.284$ lb/in.^{3}

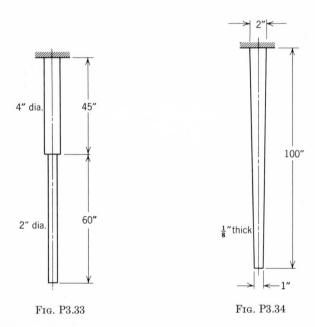

Fig. P3.33   Fig. P3.34

3.34. The uniformly tapered $\frac{1}{8}$-in. thick steel plate is suspended vertically from its wide end. Determine the elongation, assuming the formulas derived for prismatic tension members are applicable. Use the constants of the preceding problem.

3.35. The plate of Fig. P3.34 has a tensile load of 1000 lb applied at its lower end. Calculate the elongation due to the load only.

3.36. A thin uniform rod, of length L, cross-sectional area A, and specific weight γ, is spun on a smooth horizontal plane with a constant angular velocity ω about a vertical axis through one end. Show that the tensile stress at any distance x from the free end is $\sigma = (\gamma \omega^2/g)(Lx - x^2/2)$ and that the elongation of the length x is $\delta = (\gamma \omega^2/gE)(Lx^2/2 - x^3/6)$. Graph these functions and indicate the maximum values. (*Hint:* The difference between the tensile stresses on opposite faces of a differential length of rod must provide the resultant force that accelerates the differential mass at the rate of $r\omega^2$ toward the axis of rotation, where $r = L - x$.)

3.37. The composite bimetallic compression member is loaded through rigid end plates as shown. One convenient assumption we can make in analyzing the member's behavior is that transverse planes remain plane. (*a*) Why may we not assume uniaxial stress for each component if there is material continuity at the interface? (*b*) If there is no actual connection at the interface so that the individual components are free to expand or contract, and if there is no initial lack of fit in the assembly (in this case, if the two cylinders are of the same initial length), show that the elastic compressive strength of the unit is given by either of the magnitudes

$$P = \sigma_1(A_1 + A_2 n_{21}) \quad \text{or} \quad P = \sigma_2(A_2 + n_{12}A_1), \quad (3.6)$$

whichever is smaller. Here the σ's stand for the elastic-limit stresses of the two materials, the A's their cross-sectional areas, and $n_{21} = E_2/E_1$ and $n_{12} = E_1/E_2$. The quantity inside the parentheses may then be considered a "transformed" or equivalent area, and the modulus ratio n a "weighting" factor.

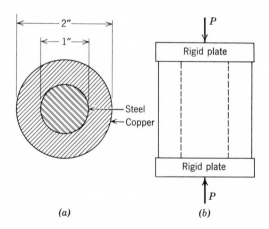

(*a*)   (*b*)

Fig. P3.37 and P3.38

3.38. Substitute in Eq. 3.6 the data given on the sketch and the following elastic properties: for copper, $E = 18 \times 10^6$ psi and $\sigma_w = 6000$ psi; for steel, $E = 30 \times 10^6$ psi and $\sigma_w = 18{,}000$ psi. What is the usable compressive strength of the unit?

3.39. What is the usable compressive strength of a member whose cross section is shown in the sketch? Where should the action line of P pierce the composite area?

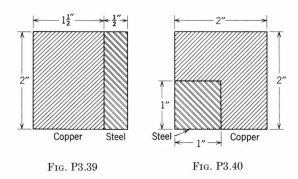

Fɪɢ. P3.39   Fɪɢ. P3.40

3.40. Repeat the preceding for this cross section.

3.41. It should be clear from an inspection of Eq. 3.6 that the two P's will, in general, not be equal. Hence, in general, only one of the materials can deliver full strength. Show that by purposely introducing initial misalignment (making one of the pieces slightly longer), one can achieve optimum material utilization. Develop an expression for this difference in initial lengths in terms of the nominal length L, the elastic constants, and the allowable stresses. In symbolic form, what is this optimum strength for a two-material composite member?

4

TORSION

4.1 Simple Shear. In Chapter 3 we discussed simple structural elements whose form is such that, in the transmission of loads, the stresses that are *obviously* involved are tensile or compressive; hence they were referred to as tension or compression members. It was implied, of course, that we had in mind only one particular family of planes, namely, transverse planes. There are other elements whose forms are such that, in performing their specific functions, they are obviously in a state of shear; accordingly, they are described as shear members. Shear pins and keys are common examples, as are the bolts that connect couplings in rotating machinery.

Figure 4.1a represents portions of two eye-bars connected by a shear pin, assumed to be a smooth cylinder. The bars each carry an axial tension force P. Figure 4.1b shows the free-body diagram of part of one bar together with part of the pin imagined cut out by two planes transverse to the pin. Equilibrium and symmetry require that the resultant shear force F on each face of the cut pin be equal to $P/2$. The shear stresses, whose resultant is F, vary from point to point across the face of the pin. Later in beam theory we will discuss this variation in more detail. For the present a crude approximation is made, namely, that the shear stresses are uniformly distributed across the face of the pin, as represented schematically in Fig. 4.1c. Dividing F by the cross-sectional area of the pin, we obtain

$$\tau_{\text{ave}} = \frac{F}{A}. \tag{4.1}$$

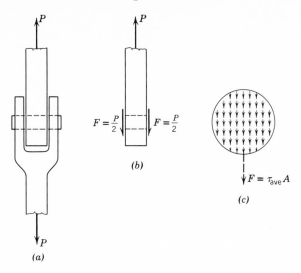

Fig. 4.1

From experiments that could be carried out in a universal testing machine, values of τ_{ave} analogous to the proportional-limit stress, the offset yield strength, or the ultimate strength in tension may be obtained. These could then be used as convenient indices when analyzing the pin for strength in shear or when designing it for the proper size to carry a given shear load.

An application of this concept of average shear stress is illustrated in the example of a key which secures a pulley or a wheel to a shaft. In Fig. 4.2a is shown a crank arm keyed to a shaft. Suppose it is desired to calculate the necessary size (the width b in this case) of key that can withstand the turning moment of the force P, it being assumed that a certain allowable τ_{ave} is given and that the length of the key is taken equal to the thickness of the crank arm.

First, it is necessary to determine the shear load that the key has to resist. Figure 4.2b shows the free-body diagram of the crank alone, where F_{KC} represents the resultant action of the key on the crank and R_{SC} the resultant action of the shaft on the crank. Taking moments about O, we have

$$\Sigma M_O = 0 = F_{KC}\left(\frac{d}{2}\right) - Pa,$$

from which $$F_{KC} = \frac{2Pa}{d}.$$

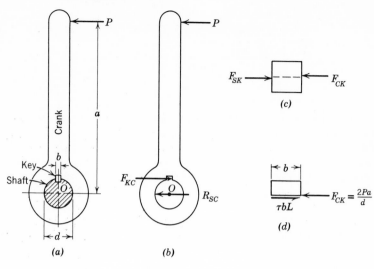

FIG. 4.2

Figure 4.2c shows the free-body diagram of the key alone, in which F_{CK} is the resultant action of the crank on the key ($|F_{CK}| = |F_{KC}| = 2Pa/d$, by the law of action and reaction), and F_{SK} is the resultant action of the shaft on the key. To preserve equilibrium, F_{SK} must equal F_{CK} in magnitude.

One-half of the key is shown isolated in Fig. 4.2d. The upper half of the key tends to slide relative to the lower half, the resultant shear load being equal to $2Pa/d$. Thus, if L is the length of the key and τ_{ave} is the allowable average shear stress, we find from

$$\Sigma F = 0 = \tau_{\text{ave}}(bL) - \frac{2Pa}{d}$$

that

$$b = \frac{2Pa}{L\, d\tau_{\text{ave}}}.$$

Knowing all the quantities involved in the right-hand side of this equation, we can find the required dimension b.

PROBLEMS

4.1. What tensile strength may the glued joint shown be expected to have, if the glue is known to develop an ultimate shear strength of 700 psi?

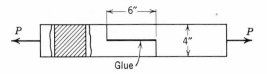

FIG. P4.1

4.2. A 4 in. by 4 in. piece of hickory wood is joined to a similar size piece of maple in the connection shown. If the ultimate strength in shear of the hickory is 2100 psi and that of the maple 1800 psi, how much tension force may the joint transmit, based on a safety factor of 3? Under this working load, what will be the average longitudinal shear stresses in the two wood pieces at the connection?

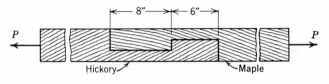

FIG. P4.2

4.3. A force of 66,000 lb is needed to punch a 1-in. diameter hole through a steel plate $\frac{1}{2}$ in. thick. What is the average ultimate shearing strength of the material?

4.4. A pulley with a 1-in. thick hub is secured to a 1-in. shaft by means of a $\frac{1}{4}$ in. by $\frac{1}{4}$ in. key, whose length equals the hub thickness. What maximum

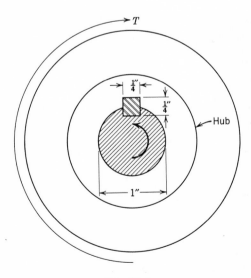

FIG. P4.4

torque may be transmitted from pulley to shaft if an allowable shear stress of 5000 psi is specified?

4.5. Rotating shafts in perfect alignment are often coupled together by a simple flange coupling, half of which is shown. The connecting bolts, arranged in a circle (of which there may be more than one), are assumed to transmit pure

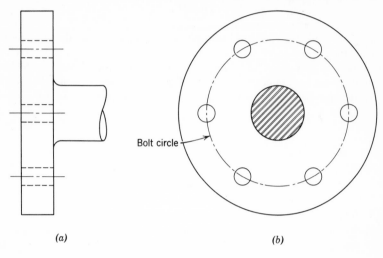

(a)   (b)

Fig. P4.5

shear action between flanges. If six bolts, each $\frac{3}{4}$ in. in diameter, are used in an 8-in. diameter bolt circle, calculate the maximum torque that may be transmitted between shafts through the coupling for a working average shear stress of 10,000 psi in the bolts.

4.2 Solid Round Shafts. The shaft is a member that is loaded in twist and is found where mechanical power has to be transmitted as in propeller-driven craft, locomotives, and automobiles. It is used to operate control devices such as the ailerons, flaps, and stabilizers of an airplane; or it may serve as a spring, as in the torsion bars of an automobile. Although members that carry torsion loads need not always be round, the shaft as such is understood to be of uniform circular cross section.

The primary objective here is to develop expressions for the strength of a shaft in terms of its dimensions, the material properties, and allowable values of stress or strain. In the derivation of these expressions, the following assumptions are made:

(1) That the shaft is a right circular cylinder.

(2) That its material is homogeneous and isotropic and obeys Hooke's law.

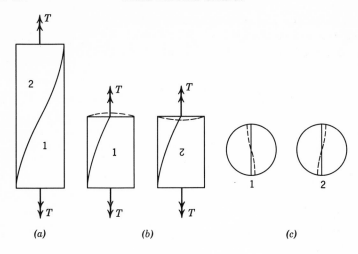

Fɪɢ. 4.3

(3) That the twisting moments lie in transverse planes.

(4) That transverse planes remain transverse planes during twist.

(5) That diameters remain straight, the circular cross sections remaining circular during deformation.

Figure 4.3a represents part of a shaft. As in the discussion of the tension bar, it is assumed that the ends of this length shaft are not taken too near the site of application of the actual twisting loads. For equilibrium, the twisting moments at the ends, represented by double-headed arrows, must be equal in magnitude and opposite in sense.

Some writers like to demonstrate that assumptions 4 and 5 can be proved. One interesting approach,* based on the powerful argument of symmetry, is as follows. Figure 4.3a shows a geometrically symmetrical shaft that is symmetrically loaded. Since the shaft is a solid of revolution (that is, it is rotationally symmetrical), the surface of any transverse cross section must assume the shape of a surface of revolution in the deformed state. Moreover, since the two halves of the shaft are identical, they must deform identically as well as symmetrically. This means that if one of them were inverted and placed alongside the other, no difference between them in the deformed state should be detectable (Figs. 4.3b and c). The only simple manner of deformation which would lead to this identity and symmetry is that in which transverse planes re-

* J. P. Den Hartog, *Strength of Materials*, pp. 17–18, McGraw-Hill Book Company, New York, 1949.

mained transverse planes, circular cross sections remained circular, and diameters remained straight.

Assumption 5 is equivalent to saying that

$$\gamma_{yz} = 0, \qquad (a)$$

where the Y and Z axes are parallel to transverse planes and the X axis is in the direction of the cylinder's longitudinal axis. Equation a insures that perpendicular lines on any transverse plane remain perpendicular while the shaft deforms, or that transverse sections do not distort. Assumptions 4 and 5 together lead to the expressions

$$\gamma_{zx} = Cy \qquad \text{and} \qquad \gamma_{xy} = -Cz, \qquad (b)$$

which mean that transverse sections rotate bodily in their planes.

To understand Eqs. b better, let us imagine the shaft to consist of a great number of concentric cylindrical shells of infinitesimally small wall thickness. One such shell is shown in Fig. 4.4a, in which the sense of twist is indicated. A small square at the piercing point of the Y axis deforms into a small rhombus, as shown in sketch b; the shear strain is γ_{zx}, and is positive for the assumed sense of twist. A similar square at the piercing point of the Z axis deforms as shown in sketch c; the shear strain is $-\gamma_{xy}$ (look up the sign convention discussed in Article 2.3). The magnitude of the shear strain depends on the radius of the shell: the larger the radius, the larger the strain; or, $\gamma_{zx} \propto y$ and $-\gamma_{xy} \propto z$. Since the orientation of the Y and Z axes in the cylinder is purely arbitrary,

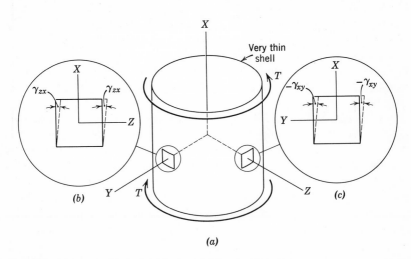

(a)

Fig. 4.4

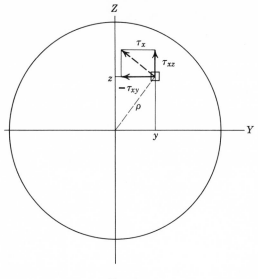

Fɪɢ. 4.5

the same proportionality constant must be involved in these variations; hence Eqs. *b*.

Bringing in Hooke's law (Eqs. 2.8*a*), we write

$$\tau_{zx} = C'y \qquad \text{and} \qquad -\tau_{xy} = C'z, \tag{c}$$

where the new constant C' now involves the shear elasticity modulus G. Figure 4.5 shows these stress components at a point whose coordinates are y and z. By similar triangles, it follows that the resultant shear stress τ_x is proportional and perpendicular to ρ, the radial distance of the point from the center, which is also the radius of the imaginary shell. Therefore this is the pattern of stress distribution: τ_x varies linearly with ρ and is tangent to the circle concentric with the periphery of the cylinder. This is represented pictorially by Fig. 4.6 and mathematically by

$$\frac{\tau}{\rho} = \frac{\tau_{max}}{r} = \text{constant}, \tag{d}$$

where the subscript of the generic τ has been dropped for simplicity.

The significant quantiy τ_{max} is now determined from statics. Consider Fig. 4.6 to be an end view of the free-body diagram. Owing to rotational symmetry, the resultant of the forces $\Delta F = \tau(\Delta A)$ cannot be a force; hence the condition of translational equilibrium is satisfied.

Rotational equilibrium requires that

$$\Sigma M_x = 0 = \Sigma \rho(\Delta F) - T,$$

or that $$0 = \Sigma \rho \tau (\Delta A) - T. \tag{e}$$

By Eq. d, $\tau = \tau_{\max}\rho/r$, which, when substituted in Eq. e, gives us

$$0 = \sum \frac{\tau_{\max}}{r} \rho^2(\Delta A) - T. \tag{f}$$

Passing on to the limit, replacing the finite summation symbol by the integral sign, and simplifying, we obtain

$$\frac{\tau_{\max}}{r} \int \rho^2 \, dA = T,$$

from which we finally get

$$\tau_{\max} = \frac{Tr}{I_p}, \tag{4.2}$$

where $I_p = \int \rho^2 \, dA$ is the polar second moment of area of the shaft cross section relative to its center. By virtue of Eq. d, the shear stress at any distance from the center, other than the radius of the shaft, is

$$\tau = \frac{T\rho}{I_p}. \tag{g}$$

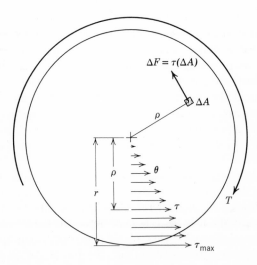

$$\Delta F = \tau(\Delta A)$$

Fɪɢ. 4.6

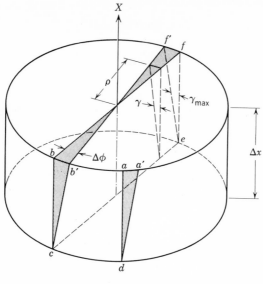

F IG. 4.7

From Eq. 4.2 the formula may be written

$$T = \frac{\tau_{\max} I_p}{r}, \tag{4.2'}$$

which shows how the elastic torque-carrying capacity of a shaft may be reckoned in terms of its dimensions and the strength properties of its material. If some meaningful value is used for $\tau_{\max}$, such as an allowable stress, for example, then T in Eq. 4.2' represents the maximum twisting moment which may be transmitted by the shaft cross section; it is therefore proper to call this quantity T the *strength of a shaft cross section*.

It is also desirable to have an expression for the deformation of the shaft. To derive this, we must first relate the shear strain to the relative rotational displacement of two neighboring transverse sections. Figure 4.7 represents a differential length Δx of shaft. The rotational displacement of the upper relative to the lower face results in the warping of diametral planes like *bcef* into *b'cef'*. The small angle $\Delta\phi$, between the initial position of the diameter *bf* and its deformed position *b'f'*, is related to the maximum shear strain $\gamma_{\max}$ at the outermost points through the common arc $\widehat{ff'}$. Remembering that the angles involved are assumed very small, we may write

$$\hat{f}' = r(\Delta\phi) = (\Delta x)\gamma_{max}, \qquad (h)$$

whence
$$\Delta\phi = \frac{\gamma_{max}}{r}\,\Delta x. \qquad (i)$$

We now invoke Hooke's law in the equation $\gamma_{max} = \tau_{max}/G$ and substitute for τ_{max} its value from Eq. 4.2. Doing this, we obtain

$$\Delta\phi = \frac{\tau_{max}}{rG}\,\Delta x = \frac{T}{I_pG}\,\Delta x,$$

which in the limit becomes

$$d\phi = \frac{T}{I_pG}\,dx. \qquad (j)$$

It is seen that the angle of twist per unit length, $d\phi/dx$, is a constant T/I_pG throughout any uniform portion of a shaft. This means that straight-line elements on the surface of the cylinder, such as line cb in Fig. 4.7, transform into helices. This can be visually demonstrated with a rubber model.

If l is a length of shaft of uniform cross section, between whose ends no external loads are applied, then by Eq. j we have

$$\phi = \frac{Tl}{I_pG}. \qquad (4.3)$$

The corresponding equation of strength,

$$T = I_pG\,\frac{\phi}{l}, \qquad (4.3')$$

expresses the torque capacity as a function of some allowable angle of twist per unit length, ϕ/l, the shaft cross-sectional dimensions, through I_p, and the material constant G. The term I_pG/l is known as the torsional rigidity; it represents the spring constant of the torsion member.

In the preceding analysis no mention was made of the normal stresses. If it is further *assumed* that transverse planes as well as coaxial cylindrical surfaces are free of normal forces, that is, if

$$\sigma_x = \sigma_y = \sigma_z = 0, \qquad (k)$$

then, so long as the proportional limit is not overstepped, the foregoing solution is the correct one because the equations of both equilibrium and compatibility are satisfied.

Illustrative Example 1. What minimum size solid shaft will transmit a twisting moment of 200,000 in.-lb without exceeding an allowable transverse shear stress of 10,000 psi? What would be the twist deformation due to this load, in a length of 20 diameters, if $G = 12 \times 10^6$ psi?

SOLUTION. We know from the calculus that I_p for a circular area relative to its center is $\pi d^4/32$. Substituting this in Eq. 4.2, and using for $\tau_{\max}$ the allowable value of 10,000 psi (in order to achieve maximum material utilization) and for T the given value of 200,000 in.-lb, we have after rearranging terms

$$\frac{I_p}{r} = \frac{\pi d^4/32}{d/2} = \frac{200,000}{10,000} = 20,$$

whence $\qquad\qquad d = \sqrt[3]{[20(16)]/\pi} = 4.67$ in. $\qquad\qquad$ *Ans.*

Making the proper substitutions in Eq. 4.3, using for the length, $l = 20d$, we now find

$$\phi = \frac{Tl}{I_p G} = \frac{Tl\tau_{\max}}{TrG} = \frac{20d\tau_{\max}}{(d/2)G}$$

$$= \frac{20(10,000)2}{12(10)^6} = \frac{1}{30}\text{ radian,}$$

which is equivalent to $(1/30)(180/\pi) = 1.91$ deg. $\qquad\qquad$ *Ans.*

It is instructive to compare the equations for the shaft with the analogous equations of Chapter 3. For convenience they are shown in Table 4.1.

TABLE 4.1

	Tension Member		Shaft	
Analysis	$\sigma = \dfrac{P}{A}$	(3.2)	$\tau_{\max} = \dfrac{Tr}{I_p}$	(4.2)
	$\delta = \dfrac{Pl}{AE}$	(3.3)	$\phi = \dfrac{Tl}{I_p G}$	(4.3)
Strength	$P = \sigma A$	(3.2′)	$T = \dfrac{\tau_{\max} I_p}{r}$	(4.2′)
	$P = \dfrac{\delta AE}{l}$	(3.3′)	$T = \dfrac{\phi I_p G}{l}$	(4.3′)
Design	$A = \dfrac{P}{\sigma}$	(3.2″)	$\dfrac{I_p}{r} = \dfrac{T}{\tau_{\max}}$	(4.2″)
	$A = \dfrac{Pl}{\delta E}$	(3.3″)	$I_p = \dfrac{Tl}{\phi G}$	(4.3″)

The important conclusion which stands out in this comparison is that, whereas the strength of a tension member does not depend on the form of its cross section, the strength of a shaft does; this dependence is reflected in the term I_p/r, which may therefore be called a *form factor*. This observation leads to the question of whether or not optimization of material utilization can be achieved by changing the form of the shaft cross section.

PROBLEMS

4.6. What fraction of the total twisting strength of a solid round shaft is contributed by that portion of it in the form of the outermost shell whose thickness is one-tenth the diameter?

4.7. What percentage of its original twisting strength is lost when a solid shaft is turned down to 0.8 its original diameter? Compare this answer with that of Prob. 4.6. Why the difference? If it is a tension member about which the questions of this and the preceding problem are asked, will the two answers be the same?

4.8. A solid shaft is 8 in. in diameter and is of a steel for which $G = 11.6 \times 10^6$ psi and $\tau_w = 8000$ psi. Calculate the maximum twisting moment that it may transmit. What will be the angle of twist in degrees in a length of 20 diameters?

4.9. A steel rod, $\frac{1}{2}$ in. in diameter and 10 ft long, is used as a shaft in a control mechanism. If the working torque needed to actuate the control is 100 ft-lb, how much will the driven end rotate before the far end starts to move? This is called the "wind-up" of the shaft. Use the preceding elastic constant.

4.10. What is the length of an aluminum alloy ($G = 4 \times 10^6$ psi) shaft of 2-in. diameter if the angle of twist is 10 deg when the maximum shearing stress is 8000 psi?

4.11. A solid shaft must not twist more than 0.10 deg/ft and the maximum shearing stress in it must not exceed 5000 psi. If $G = 6 \times 10^6$ psi, what should its diameter be so that these two allowables are developed simultaneously? What would be the usable twisting strength of such a shaft?

4.12. Assume that the formulas derived for straight round shafts hold for the gently tapered torsion member shown. (*a*) Derive an expression for the angle through which one end will twist relative to the other, in terms of D, d, L, T, and G. (*b*) Substitute $G = 4 \times 10^6$ psi and the data given on the sketch, and report the result in degrees.

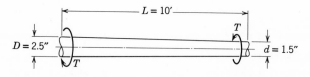

FIG. P4.12

4.13. The 15-ft shaft is subjected to the localized external torque loads shown. In terms of a constant G and a uniform I_p, derive expressions giving the twist deformation of any section in each of the three regions relative to the left end. Sketch a graph showing this variation in the relative angular displacement and give key values, including the over-all angle of twist.

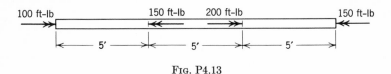

100 ft-lb   150 ft-lb   200 ft-lb   150 ft-lb

|←———— 5′ ————→|←———— 5′ ————→|←———— 5′ ————→|

FIG. P4.13

4.14. The 10-ft shaft bears the load distributed as shown. The 5-ft region is subject to a uniformly distributed external torque load of 10 ft-lb/ft, opposite in

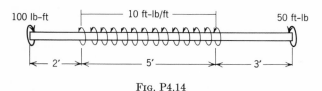

100 lb-ft   ├———— 10 ft-lb/ft ————┤   50 ft-lb

|← 2′ →|←———— 5′ ————→|←—— 3′ ——→|

FIG. P4.14

sense to the 100 ft-lb. In terms of a constant G and a uniform I_p, derive expressions as called for in the preceding problem. Sketch a similar graph, giving key values.

4.3   Hollow Round Shafts. Since our discussion is confined for the present to shafts of circular cross section, we see that the only way the cross-sectional form can be altered and still have the preceding theory hold is by removing some of the material in the form of a coaxial circular cylinder: for such an interior boundary, the foregoing stress distribution does not violate the boundary conditions. This means hollowing out the shaft. Let us now see how such a change alters material utilization.

From Eq. *g* and Fig. 4.6 it follows that, for small values of ρ, τ is small. The resulting ΔF has then but a small turning moment; therefore the material nearest the geometric axis contributes only little to the total torsional strength of the shaft. Accordingly, removal of this material will decrease the shaft strength only slightly. But how does this improve the situation, if the strength of the shaft is reduced? The explanation is, since I_p varies as the fourth power of the diameter, whereas the cross-sectional area A varies only as the second power, it follows that removing any material with small ρ will decrease the area much more than the second moment. Hence there will be improvement in that the torsional strength per unit of cross-sectional area will increase, resulting in better utilization of the material.   Following are the quantitative relations.

For two shafts of the same external diameter,

$$\frac{(T/A)_{\text{hollow}}}{(T/A)_{\text{solid}}} = 1 + \left(\frac{d_i}{d_o}\right)^2, \tag{4.4}$$

in which d_i is the internal diameter and d_o the outside diameter of the hollow shaft.   It is clear that the ratio is always greater than unity.

For two shafts of the same cross-sectional area,

$$\frac{(T/A)_{\text{hollow}}}{(T/A)_{\text{solid}}} = \frac{T_{\text{hollow}}}{T_{\text{solid}}} = \frac{1 + (d_i/d_o)^2}{\sqrt{1 - (d_i/d_o)^2}}, \tag{4.5}$$

which ratio again is always greater than unity.   Equation 4.5 accounts for the statement, often loosely made, that a hollow shaft is stronger than a solid shaft.   This is true if the two shafts are of the same material and have the *same* cross-sectional area; it is not necessarily true otherwise.

It is not to be supposed that hollowing out a shaft entails no sacrifice other than the economic one (it is an expensive operation).   Removal of any material from the shaft reduces its stiffness or rigidity, so that under a given twisting load a hollow shaft will deform more than a solid one of the same diameter.   If this decrease in rigidity is not serious in the particular application, then it is not a disadvantage.

PROBLEMS

4.15. Derive Eqs. 4.4 and 4.5.

4.16. Calculate the maximum twisting moment that a hollow shaft, with an outside diameter of 6 in. and an inside diameter of 3 in., may transmit without the allowable shearing stress of 10,000 psi being exceeded.

4.17. Compared to a solid shaft with a 1-in. diameter, how much stronger percentagewise is a hollow one of the same material having an outside diameter of 2 in. and an equal cross-sectional area?

4.18. A solid steel shaft is to be replaced by a hollow one of the same outside diameter and of an alloy having twice the elastic shearing strength of the material in the solid shaft.   What should be the ratio of the outside to the inside diameter?   What would be the percentage weight saving if the specific weights are the same?

4.19. A hollow shaft with an inside diameter of 4 in. transmits a torque of 20,000 in.-lb.   If the minimum shear stress is 5000 psi, what is the maximum?

4.20. Design a hollow shaft subject to a working torque of 100,000 in.-lb. The outside diameter is to be 4 in. The material has a shear yield strength of 60,000 psi and an overload factor of 3 is to be used.

4.21. Repeat the preceding problem for a ratio of the outside to the inside diameter of 2.

4.22. A hollow shaft of steel ($\gamma = 0.284$ lb/in.^{3}) may not weigh more than 3.0 lb/ft. Design it for a working twisting strength of 10,000 in.-lb based on an allowable shear stress of 10,000 psi.

4.23. A hollow shaft with a 2-in. inside diameter must carry a torque of 40,000 in.-lb without exceeding a shearing stress of 8000 psi. What is the least outside diameter that it may have?

4.24. A 12-ft long magnesium alloy hollow shaft, whose inside diameter is 4 in., winds up 5.5 deg as the maximum shearing stress attains a value of 5000 psi. What twisting moment does it transmit? $G = 2.4 \times 10^6$ psi.

4.25. A composite shaft consisting of two (or more) concentric cylinders of different materials may be assumed to behave in such a manner that diameters remain straight. Show that, when there is no initial strain in the assembly, the twisting strength of such a bimetallic composite shaft is given by one of the expressions

$$T = \frac{2\tau_1}{d_1}(I_{p1} + I_{p2}n_{21}) \quad \text{or} \quad T = \frac{2\tau_2}{d_2}(I_{p2} + I_{p1}n_{12}), \quad (4.6)$$

whichever is smaller. Here the τ's represent the allowable shear stresses in the two materials, the d's the outer diameters of the individual cylinders, the I_p's the polar second moments of their cross-sectional areas, and the n's the ratios of the elasticity moduli: $n_{21} = G_2/G_1$ and $n_{12} = G_1/G_2$. The quantity inside the parentheses may be considered the equivalent I_p of the "transformed" area, the transformation being effected by the "weighting factor" n.

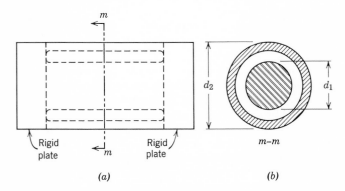

FIG. P4.25 and P4.26

4.26. It should be clear from Eq. 4.6 that the two T's are, in general, not equal. This means that only one material can be exploited to its full elastic potential, if there is perfect initial fit. Show how, by prestraining or purposely introducing initial misfit, optimization can be achieved. In terms of the preceding elastic constants and dimensions, derive an expression for the necessary unit angle of twist that *one* component must have imposed on it, which, when "locked in" (by joining the two on their lateral surfaces, if they fit snugly one inside the other, or by connecting their ends to rigid plates), will allow optimum material utilization during subsequent loading in the *same* sense as the prestraining.

4.27. A composite shaft has the cross section shown. The following are given: for aluminum, $G = 4 \times 10^6$ psi, $\tau_e = 15,000$ psi; for steel, $G = 11.6 \times 10^6$ psi, $\tau_e = 20,000$ psi. Determine by Eq. 4.6 the elastic twisting strength of the shaft, when there is no prestraining. With this load on the shaft, what is the maximum shearing stress in the understressed component?

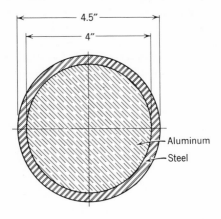

FIG. P4.27

4.28. For the shaft of the preceding problem, represent the twisting moment to be transmitted as a clockwise couple on the exposed face shown in the sketch. Which component should be prestrained clockwise, and how much (angle of twist per unit length), in order to make possible optimum material utilization? Would it be just as valid to prestrain the other component in the opposite (counterclockwise) sense instead? Calculate the optimum twisting strength of the composite shaft.

4.29. In Fig. P4.25, the inner core is of steel and is 3 in. in diameter, whereas the outer shell is of brass with an outside diameter of 5 in. and a wall thickness of $\frac{1}{2}$ in. For brass, $G = 5 \times 10^6$ psi and $\tau_e = 20,000$ psi; for steel, $G = 12 \times 10^6$ psi and $\tau_e = 30,000$ psi. What maximum elastic torque may the composite shaft transmit without prestrain? How much with prestrain?

4.4 Strength Properties in Torsion. It is extremely difficult if not impossible to test a material in pure shear of uniform intensity and hence to obtain a stress-strain diagram in shear. Although the material in a twisted shaft is in a state of pure shear, measurements made on the surface are influenced by the strengthening effect of the material inside. To approximate the condition of pure shear of uniform intensity, extremely thin-walled cylinders are tested as hollow shafts. In such cases, strain measurements on the surface can no longer be satisfactorily made with mechanical gages, and resort must be made to the use of electric strain gages. From the shear stress-strain diagram may be obtained strength indices similar to those in tension, with the exception of ultimate strength. Fracture without crippling of the wall cannot be made to take place in a thin-walled hollow shaft without internal support.

Instead of the stress-strain diagram the load-deformation curve, which is much simpler to obtain, can be used to define strength properties. Values of the twisting moment are laid off on the axis of ordinates and the angle of twist (or the angle of twist per unit length), in either radians or degrees, on the axis of abscissae. The angle of twist is measured by the relative rotational displacement of the two arms of a *twist meter* clamped onto the shaft at the ends of the gage length l.

Figure 4.8 represents one such load-deformation diagram. From the straight-line portion the value of G can be obtained, by Eq. 4.3, thus:

$$G = \frac{Tl}{\phi I_p} = \left(\frac{\Delta T}{\Delta \phi}\right) \frac{l}{I_p}.$$

An approximate value of the proportional-limit stress may be gotten with the aid of Eq. 4.2, if for T is substituted the proportional-limit

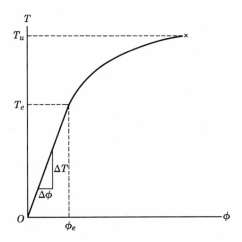

Fig. 4.8

torque. The offset yield strength cannot be determined for the reason that the formula, $\tau_{max} = Tr/I_p$, no longer holds beyond the proportional limit. The offset strain can easily enough be laid off on the horizontal axis at a value given by Eq. i of Article 4.2, thus. $\gamma_{max} = r(\Delta\phi/\Delta x) = r\phi/l$.

Nevertheless, if the equation, $\tau_{max} = Tr/I_p$, were assumed to hold beyond the proportional limit, then the value of τ_{max} corresponding to the torque T_y defined by the offset strain would afford some convenient index to the shear yield strength of the material. We may call this index the *modulus of yield in torsion*. Similarly, the fictitious stress, obtained from the same Eq. 4.3, corresponding to the ultimate torque T_u is a convenient index to the ultimate shear strength of the material; we call it the *modulus of rupture in torsion*. These indices are defined by the equations

$$\text{Modulus of yield in torsion} = \frac{T_y r}{I_p}. \tag{a}$$

$$\text{Modulus of rupture in torsion} = \frac{T_u r}{I_p}. \tag{b}$$

The resilience of the shaft is measured by the area under the straight-line part of the load-deformation curve, thus:

$$U = \frac{T_e \phi_e}{2}. \tag{c}$$

Substituting the values of T_e and ϕ_e in terms of τ_e from Eqs. 4.2 and 4.3, we get from the preceding

$$U = \frac{\tau_e I_p}{2r}\left(\frac{\tau_e l}{Gr}\right) = \frac{\tau_e^2 I_p l}{2Gr^2}. \tag{d}$$

Dividing both sides of Eq. d by the volume of the shaft, we obtain the resilience per unit volume of the *member* (not to be confused with the resilience of the *material*):

$$\frac{dU}{dV} = \frac{\tau_e^2 I_p}{2Gr^2 A}. \tag{4.7}$$

For a solid shaft this becomes

$$\left(\frac{dU}{dV}\right)_{\text{solid}} = \frac{\tau_e^2(\pi d^4/32)}{2G(d^2/4)(\pi d^2/4)} = \frac{\tau_e^2}{4G}; \tag{4.7a}$$

and for a hollow shaft

$$\left(\frac{dU}{dV}\right)_{\text{hollow}} = \frac{\tau_e^2 \pi (d_o^4 - d_i^4)/32}{2G(d_o^2/4)\pi(d_o^2 - d_i^2)/4}$$

$$= \frac{\tau_e^2}{4G}\left[1 + \left(\frac{d_i}{d_o}\right)^2\right]. \qquad (4.7b)$$

It is seen that the hollow shaft has a greater resilience per unit volume than the solid shaft, the ratio of the two quantities being $1 + (d_i/d_o)^2$, which is the same result shown by Eq. 4.4. Observe that, if the shear stresses were uniformly distributed (possible only when $d_i = d_o$ for the hollow shaft, which means a shaft of zero wall thickness), the resilience per unit volume of the member would coincide with the modulus of resilience of the material, $U_e = \tau_e^2/2G$.

The ratio of the resilience per unit volume of the member to the modulus of resilience of the material gives an idea of how efficiently the material is utilized. Let us call this ratio the *factor of utilization, α*. For a solid shaft,

$$\alpha_{\text{solid}} = \frac{\tau_e^2}{4G}\left(\frac{2G}{\tau_e^2}\right) = \frac{1}{2}, \qquad (e)$$

whereas for a hollow shaft,

$$\alpha_{\text{hollow}} = \frac{1}{2}\left[1 + \left(\frac{d_i}{d_o}\right)^2\right]. \qquad (f)$$

It should be clear from the preceding that the ideal value of unity for α, which can be achieved in simple tension, can never be attained in shafts.

PROBLEMS

4.30. The following readings were recorded from the torsion test of a $\frac{5}{16}$-in. hot-rolled mild steel rod:

T (in.-lb)	θ (deg)	T	θ
18.2	2	144	16
35.5	4	163	18
53.6	6	172	20
71	8	180	25
89.5	10	181	30
113.8	12	182	35
125	14	182	40

The gage length was 22 in. Neatly sketch a load-deformation diagram, drawing a straight line to "average out" the values represented by the first several points. (a) From the slope of this line calculate the shear modulus of elasticity. (b) Make an estimate of the proportional limit and from the corresponding torque establish the proportional-limit stress τ_e.

4.31. These data define two points on the straight-line part of a load-deformation diagram from the torsion test of a brass shaft:

T (in.-lb)	100	750
θ (deg)	2	9

The specimen had a diameter of $\frac{9}{16}$ in. and the gage length was 26 in. Determine the shear modulus of elasticity.

4.32. In the shaft of Prob. 4.16, what is the resilience per unit volume? How much is the factor of utilization? $G = 12 \times 10^6$ psi.

4.5   Rotating Shafts. For shafts that transmit power, it is common practice to specify the horsepower and the speed of rotation involved. A convenient formula relating torque in inch-pounds to horsepower and speed of the shaft in revolutions per minute is derived as follows:

Work done by a constant T through an angle $\theta = T\theta$ in.-lb.

Work done by T in one revolution $= 2\pi T$ in.-lb.

Work done by T in one minute $= 2\pi n T$ in.-lb/min.

$$= \frac{2\pi n T}{12} \text{ ft-lb/min.}$$

Therefore   horsepower, hp $= \dfrac{2\pi n T}{12(33,000)}$,

whence $$T = \frac{63,000 \text{ hp}}{n}. \tag{4.8}$$

This shows that for a given horsepower the slower the shaft the larger the torque that can be transmitted. The preceding formula, used in conjunction with, say, Eq. 4.2, leads to the conclusion that for a given power to be transmitted the higher the speed of rotation the smaller the size shaft needed based on a fixed allowable shear stress.

A shaft may have power supplied to it at one location and power taken off from it at several other locations along its length. When this happens, the torque distribution becomes nonuniform. One practical example discussed next involves a stepwise variation in the torque being transmitted.

Illustrative Example 2.   A shaft driven through a pulley by an electric motor is to be provided with two other pulleys for power take-off. Suppose that 50 hp at 200 rpm is delivered to the shaft at the one pulley and that 30 hp and 20 hp are taken off from it at the other two pulleys. It is required to find the minimum uniform diameter of solid shaft that may be used if the maximum shear stress is not to exceed 10,000 psi.

SOLUTION.   By Eq. 4.8, the torques corresponding to the three horse-power values are

$$T_1 = \frac{63,000(50)}{200} = 15,750 \text{ in.-lb,}$$

$$T_2 = \frac{63,000(30)}{200} = 9450 \text{ in.-lb,}$$

and
$$T_3 = \frac{63,000(20)}{200} = 6300 \text{ in.-lb.}$$

At first glance it would appear that the 15,750 in.-lb torque should be the controlling value. This would be the case if the 50 hp were supplied to the shaft at one *end* pulley and the other two pulleys were located to the same side of the driven pulley. As any good shop man who is worth his salt should know however, this is not the best arrangement. Power should be supplied to the center pulley and taken off from the two ends. If power were supplied to an end pulley, then the two portions of the shaft between pulleys would strain in the same sense and these strains would be cumulative. On the other hand, if the power were supplied to the middle pulley, then the two portions of the shaft to either side of this pulley would strain in opposite senses and only the greater of the strain values would lead to the controlling criterion. Figures 4.9 and 4.10 illustrate this. Figure 4.9*a* shows the first arrangement, and

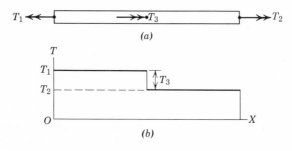

Fig. 4.9

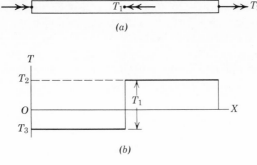

FIG. 4.10

Fig. 4.9*b* depicts the corresponding torque variation. The second, better arrangement is shown in Fig. 4.10*a* and its corresponding torque variation in Fig. 4.10*b*. It should be clear from these figures that the *smallest* of the *maximum* demands for twisting strength occurs in the second arrangement; hence the controlling torque is 9450 in.-lb.

Substituting 9450 for T and 10,000 for τ_{max} in Eq. 4.2″, we have

$$\frac{I_p}{r} = \frac{\pi d^4/32}{d/2} = \frac{9450}{10,000},$$

from which we find

$$d = \sqrt[3]{[16(9450)]/\pi(10,000)} = 1.69 \text{ in.} \qquad Ans.$$

If the angle of twist per unit length for each portion of this uniform size shaft is desired, it may be obtained with the use of Eq. 4.3. Thus, assuming $G = 12 \times 10^6$ psi, we find for that length which carries 6300 in.-lb torque,

$$\frac{\phi}{l} = \frac{T_3}{I_p G} = \frac{6300}{[\pi(1.69)^4/32]12(10)^6} = 6.56 \times 10^{-4} \text{ rad/in.}$$

or $\qquad \dfrac{\phi}{l} = \dfrac{6.56(180)}{10^4 \pi} = 0.0376 \text{ deg/in.}$

For the length that carries 9450 in.-lb torque, it follows by proportion that

$$\frac{\phi}{l} = \frac{9450}{6300}(0.0376) = 0.0564 \text{ deg/in.}$$

Like T_2 and T_3, these unit angular deformations are opposite in sense, so that the actual movement of one end of the shaft relative to the other end is the numerical difference between the two values.

In view of the extremely small magnitudes of the angle of twist per unit length in actual shafts, it is customary to reckon these in degrees per 20 diameters of length. So expressed, these values become

$$0.0376(20)1.69 = 1.27 \text{ deg}/20 \text{ diameters}$$

and $0.0564(20)1.69 = 1.905 \text{ deg}/20 \text{ diameters}.$

Illustrative Example 3.   Figure 4.11a represents an aluminum-alloy shaft, 2 in. in diameter, subjected to the external torque loads indicated. It is desired to analyze the shaft for stresses and deformation. Use $G = 4 \times 10^6$ psi.

ANALYSIS.   The twisting moment transmitted across any transverse section is the algebraic sum of the twisting loads to either side of

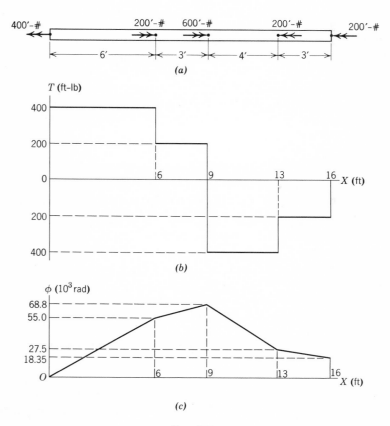

Fig. 4.11

the section. This can easily be verified if a transverse cutting plane is imagined passed anywhere across the shaft and a free-body diagram drawn of that part to either side of the plane. If x denotes the distance of a transverse section from the left end, then the local twisting moment transmitted is given by the expression

$$T = 400 - 200\{x - 6\}^0 - 600\{x - 9\}^0 + 200\{x - 13\}^0, \qquad (a)$$

for the range $0 < x < 16$; the braced terms are to be discarded when negative (see Example 2 of Chapter 3). Equation a, when plotted, results in Fig. 4.11b, which shows that the maximum twisting moment transmitted is 400 ft-lb, throughout the 6-ft and 4-ft portions. Hence the maximum shear stresses occur at the periphery of the shaft in these regions, and they are of magnitude

$$\tau_{max} = \frac{Tr}{I_p} = \frac{400(12)1}{\pi(2)^4/32} = 3056 \text{ psi}.$$

The shear stresses at the periphery of the shaft in the 3-ft regions are found by proportion to be half as large, or 1528 psi.

The angle of twist for a length x of shaft, which is the angle through which any transverse section displaces relative to the left end, is found by summing the angles of twist of all the differential lenghts dx included in this region. Any such small length, taken between the externally applied loads, deforms an amount

$$d\phi = \frac{T}{I_p G} dx,$$

where the twisting moment T as given by Eq. a is considered uniform throughout dx. Therefore the angle of twist up to a distance x is

$$\phi = \int_0^x \frac{T}{I_p G} dx$$

$$= \frac{1}{I_p G} \left[\int_0^x 400 \, dx - \int_6^x 200 \, dx - \int_9^x 600 \, dx + \int_{13}^x 200 \, dx \right]$$

$$= \frac{1}{I_p G} [400x - 200\{x - 6\} - 600\{x - 9\} + 200\{x - 13\}]. \qquad (b)$$

The graph of Eq. b is shown in Fig. 4.11c, from which it can be seen that all sections rotate in the same sense relative to the left end and that the section which rotates the most is at $x = 9$. Equation b gives this rotation when the value 9 is substituted for x, thus:

$$\phi_{max} = \frac{144(32)}{4(10)^6\pi(2)^4}[400(9) - 200(3)]$$

$$= \frac{0.216}{\pi} = 0.0688 \text{ rad or } 3.94 \text{ deg,}$$

where the factor 144 accounts for the conversion of the torque from foot-pounds to inch-pounds and the length from feet to inches. The right end of the shaft rotates relative to the left end a total amount of

$$\phi_{total} = \frac{72}{\pi(10)^6}[400(16) - 200(10) - 600(7) + 200(3)]$$

$$= \frac{0.0576}{\pi} = 0.01833 \text{ rad or } 1.05 \text{ deg.}$$

PROBLEMS

4.33. What horsepower may be safely transmitted at 75 rpm by a hollow shaft with an outside diameter of 4 in. and an inside diameter of 2 in., if the allowable shear stress is 10,000 psi?

4.34. An automobile torque tube must transmit 100 hp at 2000 rpm. If the working shear stress is 12,000 psi and if the outside diameter is 2.75 in., what should the wall thickness be?

4.35. A marine propeller shaft transmits 5000 hp at 150 rpm. The allowable shearing stress is 6000 psi and the allowable angle of twist is 1 deg in a length of 10 ft. If $G = 11.6 \times 10^6$ psi, what should be the diameter of the solid shaft? Which criterion controls? Can optimum material utilization be achieved with a hollow shaft? If so, what should be its dimensions? How much lighter would the hollow shaft be compared to the solid one?

4.36. A solid round shaft with a 4-in. diameter and a 10-ft length turns at 150 rpm. Four feet from the left end 70 hp is supplied to the shaft by a motor; of this, 40 hp is taken off at the left end and the remaining 30 hp leaves off at the right end. Calculate the maximum shearing stress in the shaft and the relative twist deformation between the two extremes. $G = 12 \times 10^6$ psi.

4.37. The solid shaft transmits power at 150 rpm as indicated on the sketch. (a) Plot a diagram showing the variation of the twisting moment as a function of position, taking the origin for x at the left pulley A. The external torque loads may be assumed at the midplanes of the pulleys, considered very thin. (b) If the allowable shear stress is 8000 psi, what should be the smallest uniform diameter for the shaft? On this basis, and assuming a constant G, plot a graph showing the twist rotation of any section relative to the left end; give key values in terms of G, including the maximum and the over-all twist deformation.

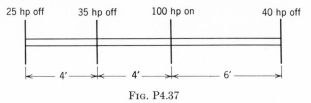

FIG. P4.37

4.38. For optimum material utilization, a shaft which transmits piecewise uniform twisting moments should not have a uniform diameter throughout its entire length. What should be the diameters of a stepped shaft for Prob. 4.37 in order that the allowable shear stress is developed in all regions? For such a shaft, plot a graph showing the twist rotation of any section relative to the left end and give key values in terms of G, assumed constant.

4.39. In an oil well, the pipe line which constitutes the shafting that transmits power to the drill bit is in three lengths, each 4000 ft long and of uniform size. The bottom third has an outside diameter of 2 in., the middle third of 3 in., and the upper third of 4 in. All tubing has the same wall thickness of $\frac{1}{2}$ in. If the shaft is designed to function at a maximum shear stress of 5000 psi, exclusive of any direct axial effects, what uniform twisting moment does this correspond to? On the basis of the highly idealized assumption that no power is lost between shaft and casing, what horsepower is delivered to the pipe at the drilling rig when the shaft is turning at 500 rpm? Calculate the wind-up of the stepped shaft. $G = 11.6 \times 10^6$ psi.

4.40. A dentist's drill is driven by a flexible cable turning at 3000 rpm. The cable may be treated as a straight solid round shaft, $\frac{1}{8}$ in. in diameter. The power supplied to the shaft by a small motor with its associated gearing is $\frac{1}{25}$ hp, of which only 50% is available at the drill bit, the balance being dissipated in friction between the cable and its casing. Assume that the frictional moment is uniformly distributed throughout the 5-ft length of the shaft. Determine (a) the maximum shear stress in the shaft and (b) the wind-up or relative twist between the cable ends. $G = 12.0 \times 10^6$ psi. (*Hint:* The twisting moment transmitted at any section equals the sum of all the external torque loads to one side of the section.)

4.6   Solid Shafts of Noncircular Cross Sections. Shafts with noncircular cross sections may no longer be assumed to behave such that their transverse sections remain plane. A rigorous analysis indicates that such sections warp during twist.[*] The theoretical relations among the maximum shear stress, the twisting moment, the cross-sectional dimensions, the angle of twist per unit length, and the shear modulus of elasticity have been worked out for a number of cases. The following formulas are due primarily to Saint-Venant.[†]

[*] J. P. Den Hartog, *Advanced Strength of Materials*, pp. 1–3, McGraw-Hill Book Company, New York, 1952.

[†] S. Timoshenko and J. N. Goodier, *Theory of Elasticity*, pp. 263–267, 277–278, McGraw-Hill Book Company, New York, 1951.

RECTANGULAR CROSS SECTION.   Let a be the short side and b the long side.   Then

$$\tau_{\max} = \frac{T}{k_1 a^2 b},\tag{4.9}$$

this maximum stress occurring at the centers of the long sides, points on the periphery *nearest* to the geometric axis of the bar;

and
$$\frac{\phi}{l} = \frac{T}{k_2 G a^3 b}.\tag{4.10}$$

The numerical factors k_2 and k_1 depend on the ratio b/a as shown by the graphs in Fig. 4.12.   For very thin rectangular sections, both k_1 and k_2 may be taken equal to $\frac{1}{3}$.

ELLIPTICAL CROSS SECTION.   Let a represent the semimajor axis and b the semiminor axis.   Then

$$\tau_{\max} = \frac{2T}{\pi a b^2},\tag{4.11}$$

this maximum stress occurring at the ends of the minor axis, again points on the periphery that are nearest to the goemetric axis of the shaft.   The angle of twist per unit length is

$$\frac{\phi}{l} = \frac{T(a^2 + b^2)}{\pi a^3 b^3 G}.\tag{4.12}$$

Note that when $a = b$, Eqs. 4.11 and 4.12 reduce to the corresponding expressions for a solid round shaft.

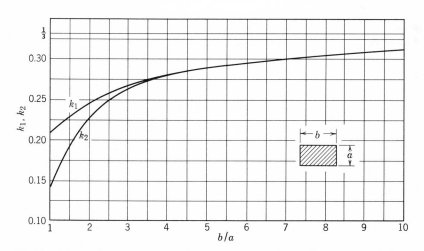

FIG. 4.12   Variation of the numerical factors k_1 and k_2 in formulas 4.9 and 4.10.

EQUILATERAL TRIANGULAR CROSS SECTION. If a is the length of the sides, then

$$\tau_{\max} = \frac{20T}{a^3},\tag{4.13}$$

which maximum stress occurs at the centers of the edges, points on the periphery nearest to the geometric axis of the shaft.

Also
$$\frac{\phi}{l} = \frac{80T}{\sqrt{3}a^4G}.\tag{4.14}$$

PROBLEMS

4.41. For the same allowable shear stress, what size rectangular cross section has a twisting strength equal to that of a 1-in. circular cross section, if $b/a = 2$? Compare their rigidities.

4.42. Repeat Prob. 4.41 for an elliptical section whose major axis is twice the length of its minor axis.

4.43. Repeat Prob. 4.41 for an equilateral triangular section.

4.44. Within the limits of linear elasticity, the energy stored in a loaded member may be assumed equal to the external work done by the gradually applied load. Utilizing this idea, express the energy stored per unit length of shaft in terms of the maximum shear stress, and hence evaluate the factor of utilization for each of the following cross sections: (a) square, (b) rectangle for which $b/a = 2$, (c) ellipse for which $a/b = 2$, and (d) equilateral triangle.

4.45. Open thin sections in torsion may be treated as rectangular sections of large b/a ratios. If the thickness a is uniform, then for the dimension b one uses the rectified or developed width. The approximation is further made that the numerical factors k_1 and k_2 (Eqs. 4.10 and 4.9) are both equal to $\frac{1}{3}$. Based on an allowable shear stress of 2000 psi and a G of 4×10^6 psi, calculate the torsional strength and the torsional rigidity for each of the cross sections shown.

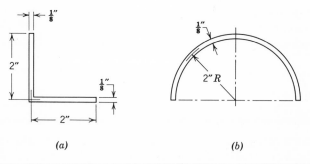

(a)   (b)

Fig. P4.45

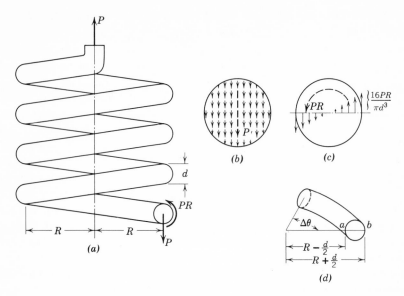

FIG. 4.13

4.7   Closely Coiled Helical Spring. A helical spring is formed by wrapping a long piece of wire or rod continuously around a cylindrical arbor, the successive turns or coils being spaced uniformly. The center line of the wire when released will lie in the form of a helix on the surface of a cylinder whose diameter equals that of the arbor increased by that of the wire, plus any springback. When the coils are spaced very closely, we have a closely coiled spring. The loading, consisting of two opposite axial forces, tends either to elongate or to contract the spring. The designations *tension spring* and *compression spring* suggest the intended loading.

Useful formulas for helical springs are derived on the basis of an extrapolation of the basic equations developed for the torsion of right circular cylinders. This extrapolation is carried out as follows.

Consider the tension spring represented in Fig. 4.13a. Its mean coil diameter is $D = 2R$ and the wire diameter is d. Imagine a longitudinal diametral plane passed, cutting one of the coils, and isolate part of the spring as a free body. For equilibrium to be maintained, the action of the removed portion must consist of (1) a resultant shear force P to prevent translation and (2) a resultant twisting moment PR to prevent rotation. (Note that the shear force P is assumed to have an action line through the centroid of the wire cross-sectional area.) We now propose to evaluate the stresses and strains due to P and due to PR, individually, and then to superpose the results.

First, we remark on the necessity of assuming that the spring is closely coiled. For a very small helix angle, the area of the wire exposed by the longitudinal sectioning plane is practically equal to the right cross-sectional area. Hence, the twisting moment PR may be considered to lie in a plane transverse to the wire axis.

If we now make (1) the crude assumption that the shear force P on the exposed face of the wire may be replaced by the statically equivalent system of uniformly distributed shear stresses, whose magnitude is $\tau_{ave} = P/A = 4P/\pi d^2$ (Fig. 4.13b), and (2) the not so crude assumption that the twisting moment PR may be replaced by the statically equivalent system of stresses distributed as in a round shaft, whose maximum value is $\tau_{max} = Tr/I_p = 16PR/\pi d^3$ (Fig. 4.13c), then we do not violate equilibrium. Furthermore, if we superpose one system of stresses on the other, adding stress components at certain key points just like ordinary vectors (these stresses act on the same plane), we obtain *one* pattern of stress distribution. In view of the fact that, as explained in Chapter 2, equilibrium is merely a necessary, not a sufficient, condition for the correctness of stress systems, we must look on our result as nothing more than a first approximation. Let us see what this is like.

Carrying out the superposition for points on the wire cross section lying on that wire diameter which is perpendicular to the spring axis, we find that at the inner points the stresses are additive, whereas at the outer points they are subtractive. Hence we conclude that the maximum shear stresses occur at the innermost points of the helicoidal surface. Their magnitude is

$$\tau_{max} = \frac{Tr}{I_p} + \frac{P}{A} = \frac{16PR}{\pi d^3} + \frac{4P}{\pi d^2}$$

$$= \frac{16PR}{\pi d^3}\left(1 + \frac{d}{2D}\right). \tag{4.15}$$

The "correction factor" $(1 + d/2D)$ in this equation decreases as the ratio of the coil diameter D to the wire diameter d increases; this signifies that the influence of the direct shearing action of P becomes less, the total effect approaching the twisting action of PR.

There is another reason why the shear stresses at points on the inside of the coils are greater than at those on the outside. If the twisting moment PR is assumed to leave the diameters of the wire cross section straight, as in the solid round shaft, it is seen that all points on the periphery of the wire do shift tangentially the same amount. Observe, however, that for those points such as a in Fig. 4.13d the length, $(R - d/2)\Delta\theta$, over which this shear deformation is distributed, is shorter than the length, $(R + d/2)\Delta\theta$, for points such as b. Taking this into account, as well as the fact that the shear stresses whose resultant is P are not uniformly distributed, Wahl derived the more accurate formula * for the maximum shear stress in a helical spring:

$$\tau_{\max} = \frac{16PR}{\pi d^3}\left(\frac{4m - 1}{4m - 4} + \frac{0.615}{m}\right), \tag{4.16}$$

where $m = D/d$. The quantity inside the parentheses is called the *Wahl correction factor*. Formula 4.16 is widely used in mechanical spring design.

Let us now turn our attention to the deflection. This is the result of two relative displacements: (1) of adjacent wire cross sections as they twist and (2) of adjacent wire cross sections as they slide. Thus a short length of wire, $R(\Delta\theta)$, contributes the following increments to the total deflection, measured along the axis of the spring:

(1) Due to twist,

$$\Delta\delta_1 = R(\Delta\phi) = R\frac{T(\Delta l)}{I_p G} = R\left[\frac{PR(R\,\Delta\theta)}{(\pi d^4/32)G}\right]. \tag{a}$$

This is the axial movement of the point of application of the load P due to the rotation of the arm R through the small angle $\Delta\phi$.

(2) Due to sliding,

$$\Delta\delta_2 = (R\,\Delta\theta)\gamma = (R\,\Delta\theta)\frac{\tau_{\text{ave}}}{G} = (R\,\Delta\theta)\frac{4P}{\pi d^2 G}, \tag{b}$$

where a uniform shear stress distribution due to P is assumed. Adding the two quantities, we obtain

$$\Delta\delta = \Delta\delta_1 + \Delta\delta_2$$
$$= \frac{32PR^3(\Delta\theta)}{\pi d^4 G} + \frac{4PR(\Delta\theta)}{\pi d^2 G}. \tag{c}$$

For the whole spring with N active coils, the angle $\Delta\theta$ accumulates to $2\pi N$. Therefore the total deflection accumulates to

$$\delta = \frac{32PR^3(2\pi N)}{\pi d^4 G} + \frac{4PR(2\pi N)}{\pi d^2 G}$$
$$= \frac{64PR^3 N}{d^4 G}\left[1 + \frac{1}{2}\left(\frac{d}{D}\right)^2\right]. \tag{d}$$

---

* A. M. Wahl, *Mechanical Springs*, pp. 32–37, Penton Publishing Company, Cleveland, 1944.

The second term inside the brackets represents the proportional part of the total deflection contributed by the direct shearing action of P. It should be clear that even for comparatively small values of D/d this contribution is small compared to that due to the twisting moment PR. Accordingly, the second term is ignored and expression d simplifies to

$$\delta = \frac{64PR^3N}{d^4G}. \tag{4.17}$$

Illustrative Example 4. A closely coiled helical spring, with a 2-in. mean coil diameter, consists of 10 active turns of $\frac{3}{8}$-in. diameter wire. If the maximum shear stress is not to exceed 40,000 psi and $G = 12 \times 10^6$ psi, calculate the maximum allowable axial load and the corresponding axial deflection, (1) using no correction factor, and (2) using the Wahl correction factor.

SOLUTION. (1) The mean coil radius is $R = D/2 = 1$ in. Hence the twisting moment $PR = P$ in.-lb. By Eq. 4.2′,

$$T = \frac{\tau_{\max}I_p}{r} = \frac{\tau_{\max}\pi d^3}{16}.$$

Therefore $P = T = \dfrac{40,000\pi(\frac{27}{512})}{16} = 414$ lb.   *Ans.*

By Eq. 4.17, $\delta = \dfrac{64(414)(1)^3 10}{(\frac{3}{8})^4(12)10^6} = 1.115$ in.   *Ans.*

(2) Since $m = D/d = \frac{16}{3}$, the Wahl correction factor becomes

$$\frac{64 - 3}{64 - 12} + \frac{1.845}{16} = 1.288.$$

Therefore $P = \dfrac{414}{1.288} = 321$ lb   *Ans.*

and $\delta = \dfrac{1.115}{1.288} = 0.866$ in.   *Ans.*

RESILIENCE OF THE HELICAL SPRING. Within the limits of Hooke's law, the deflection of the spring may be written in the form, $\delta = P/K$, or $P = K\delta$. The proportionality factor K, called the *spring constant* or *spring modulus*, is defined as numerically equal to the load that will produce a unit deflection. By Eq. 4.17, $K = d^4G/64R^3N$. As P is gradually applied, the spring stores energy in the amount of

$$U = \frac{P\delta}{2} = \frac{P^2}{2K} = \frac{K\delta^2}{2}. \qquad (e)$$

Dividing U by the volume of the spring material, one obtains the resilience per unit volume

$$\frac{dU}{dV} = \frac{P\delta}{2AL} = \frac{2P\delta}{\pi^2 d^2 DN}. \qquad (f)$$

Substituting the data of the previous example, and using the corrected values of P and δ, we find

$$\frac{dU}{dV} = \frac{2(321)0.866}{\pi^2(\frac{9}{64})2(10)} = 20.05 \text{ in.-lb/in.}^3$$

The shear modulus of resilience of the *material*, based on a stress of 40,000 psi and a G of 12×10^6 psi, is

$$U_e = \frac{\tau^2}{2G} = \frac{(40,000)^2}{2(12)10^6} = 66.7 \text{ in.-lb/in.}^3$$

Hence the factor of utilization for this spring is

$$\alpha = \frac{20.05}{66.7} = 0.30 \text{ or } 30\%.$$

PROBLEMS

4.46. A closely coiled helical spring transmits a tension force of 400 lb. The mean coil diameter is 5 in., the wire diameter is $\frac{5}{8}$ in., and the number of turns is 15. (a) Determine the maximum shear stress, using Wahl's correction factor. (b) If $G = 11.6 \times 10^6$ psi, what is the spring's modulus? (c) Calculate the resilience per unit volume. What is the factor of utilization for this spring?

4.47. A phosphor bronze spring consists of 12 turns of $\frac{3}{8}$-in. wire on a mean coil diameter of 4 in. If the shear stress is not to exceed 40,000 psi, what load may it support? What is the spring rate? This is merely another name for the spring constant. $G = 6.25 \times 10^6$ psi.

4.48. A closely coiled helical spring is to resist a maximum of 1500 lb in compression. Its free (unloaded) length is 7 in. and its modulus must be 750 lb/in. A high-strength steel $(G = 12 \times 10^6$ psi) may be used with an elastic shearing limit of 120,000 psi. The mean coil diameter is 4 in. How large should the wire diameter be and how many turns must the spring have? Use a safety factor of 2. (*Hint:* Find d from Eq. 4.16 without the correction factor first, and then improve on this value by iteration. With d known, N can easily be found.)

4.49. A helical spring, made of $\frac{3}{4}$-in. wire with a mean coil diameter of 6 in. and having 15 active coils, is connected "in series" to another helical spring, consisting of 20 turns of 1-in. wire on a mean coil diameter of 8 in. What maximum common tension load may be transmitted by the springs if the shearing stress is not to exceed 50,000 psi? If G for both is 12×10^6 psi, what is the equivalent spring constant for the unit?

4.50. The two springs just described are nested, the smaller one being placed concentrically inside the larger. Assume that they are of the same free length. In resisting an axial load, they are then "in parallel." How much load may the assembly support and what is its equivalent spring constant? In order that both springs could deliver full strength, which one should have its free length slightly shortened (by a change in the pitch angle of the helix, for example) and by how much?

4.8   Thin-Walled Tubes in Torsion.   The thin-walled tube as a structural element is of frequent occurrence in aircraft and seacraft. The use of the thin-walled tube, not only to transmit to the rest of the craft the lift forces of the surrounding fluid but also to maintain the shape and rigidity of the structure, is characteristic of *stressed skin* or *monocoque* construction. Examples are the fuselage and the wings of an airplane. Such components are designed to withstand twisting combined with bending. We analyze here only the twisting action.

Figure 4.14a represents part of a thin-walled tube subjected to a twisting moment T. It is assumed (1) that throughout the length l the cross-sectional form and area of the tube are approximately constant, (2) that there are no sharp corners and no abrupt changes in wall thickness, and (3) that the twisting moment lies in a transverse plane. Imagine cut out from the wall a small rectangular block of dimensions Δp (along the mean perimeter) and Δx (along the length of the tube). The thickness t need not be the same across the four edges. The free-body diagram of this small block is shown in Fig. 4.14b, in which the q's are the *resultant forces per unit length* along the four edges of the block. In aircraft structural practice, q is called *shear flow;* it is expressed in terms of force per unit length.

From the equilibrium equation,

$$\Sigma F_p = 0 = q_1(\Delta p) - q_3(\Delta p),$$

it follows that $q_1 = q_3$. From the equation,

$$\Sigma F_x = 0 = q_2(\Delta x) - q_4(\Delta x),$$

it follows that $q_2 = q_4$. Finally, from the equation,

$$\Sigma M = 0 = q_1(\Delta p)\Delta x - q_2(\Delta x)\Delta p,$$

we find that $q_1 = q_2$.   Therefore

$$q_1 = q_2 = q_3 = q_4 = q, \qquad (a)$$

which means that the shear flow is constant along the mean circumference of the shell, regardless of any slight variation in wall thickness. Dividing the shear flow by the local thickness, one gets the local *average* shear stress, thus

$$\tau_{\text{ave}} = \frac{q}{t}. \qquad (b)$$

This result shows that the average shear stress depends only on the wall thickness and not at all on the radial distance.

The constancy of the shear flow leads to an interesting and useful relation between q and the twisting moment T.   In Fig. 4.14c is rep-

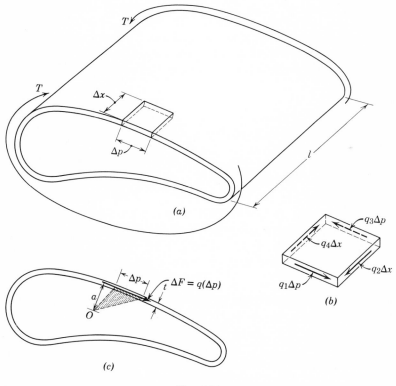

FIG. 4.14

resented the resultant tangential force ΔF contributed by the shear flow over the small length Δp, that is, $\Delta F = q(\Delta p)$. The point 0 represents any longitudinal axis, not necessarily the centroidal axis. Denoting by a the perpendicular distance from 0 to the action line of ΔF, we find the moment of ΔF about the axis through 0 to be $a(\Delta F)$, which, in terms of the shear flow, is

$$\Delta M = a(\Delta F) = a[q(\Delta p)] = [a(\Delta p)]q.$$

Since the quantity $a(\Delta p)$ gives twice the area of the little oblique triangle with base Δp and altitude a, we may write

$$\Delta M = q(2\Delta A),$$

from which it follows that

$$M = \Sigma\, \Delta M = 2q\Sigma\, \Delta A = 2qA,$$

where A is the area enclosed by the mean perimeter P. The only possible resultant of the closed-loop q-system is a pure moment M, and clearly this M must be the same as T. Hence

$$T = 2Aq = 2A\tau t. \tag{4.18}$$

The relation between the torque T and the angle of twist per unit length ϕ/l may be obtained by equating the work done by T to the strain energy stored in the tube. Assuming T is applied gradually, we find the external work done to be $T\phi/2$. Since the shear stress is practically constant (for small t), the energy stored in each unit volume of material may be taken equal to the modulus of resilience in shear, $\tau\gamma/2 = \tau^2/2G$; then the energy stored in a longitudinal strip of length l, width Δp, and thickness t becomes

$$\Delta U = \frac{\tau_\mathrm{ave}^2}{2G}\,[lt(\Delta p)]. \tag{c}$$

Substituting for τ_ave its value from Eq. 4.18, we obtain

$$\Delta U = \frac{T^2}{4A^2 t^2}\left[\frac{lt(\Delta p)}{2G}\right] = \frac{T^2 l}{8A^2 G}\left(\frac{\Delta p}{t}\right). \tag{d}$$

Therefore the total energy stored in the tube is

$$U = \int dU = \frac{T^2 l}{8A^2 G}\int_P \frac{dp}{t}, \tag{e}$$

where the integration is to be carried out over the mean perimeter P.

Equating the work done to the energy stored, we obtain

$$\frac{T\phi}{2} = \frac{T^2 l}{8A^2 G} \int_P \frac{dp}{t},$$

from which we finally arrive at the sought for relation *

$$\frac{\phi}{l} = \frac{T}{4A^2 G} \int_P \frac{dp}{t}. \tag{4.19}$$

In the special situation when the wall thickness is constant, this becomes

$$\frac{\phi}{l} = \frac{TP}{4A^2 Gt}. \tag{4.19a}$$

Illustrative Example 5.   The thin-walled tube shown in section (Fig. 4.15) is to transmit a twisting moment in the plane of the figure.   The wall thickness is $\frac{1}{8}$ in.   To avoid crippling of the wall, the average shear stress must not exceed 1200 psi.   Determine the usable torsional strength of the tube.   Assuming this torque load applied on the tube, calculate the angle of twist per unit length. $G = 4 \times 10^6$ psi.

SOLUTION.   The area enclosed by the mean perimeter is

$$A = \frac{\pi}{4} (9.875)^2 + 10(9.875) = 175.3 \text{ in.}^2$$

The allowable shear flow is $q = 1200(\frac{1}{8}) = 150$ lb/in.   From Eq. 4.18, we find the allowable twisting moment to be

$$T = 2(175.3)150 = 52{,}600 \text{ in.-lb.} \qquad \textit{Ans.}$$

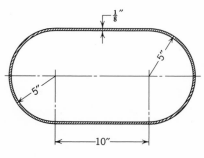

Fɪɢ. 4.15

---

* Equations 4.18 and 4.19 were derived by R. Bredt in 1896. See Timoshenko and Goodier, *op. cit.* on p. 98, p. 299.

The mean perimeter is

$$P = 2(10) + \pi(9.875) = 51 \text{ in.}$$

Using Eq. 4.19a, we finally obtain

$$\frac{\phi}{l} = \frac{52,600(51)}{4(175.3)^2(4)10^6(\frac{1}{8})}$$

$$= 43.6 \times 10^{-6} \text{ rad/in.} \qquad\qquad Ans.$$

PROBLEMS

4.51. Approximately what is the least ratio of inside to outside diameter of a hollow shaft in order that the Bredt formula (Eq. 4.18) will not be in error by more than 10%?

4.52. Compare the torsional rigidities of two shafts with the cross sections shown. The shafts are of the same material and the cross sections have the same wall thickness t and equal areas enclosed by the mean perimeters.

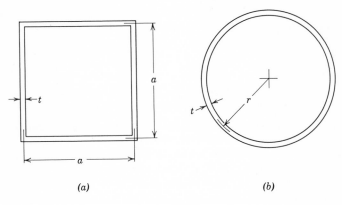

(a)   *(b)*

FIG. P4.52

4.53. The fuselage of an airplane may be treated approximately as an ellipse with a mean major diameter of 10 ft and a mean minor diameter of 8 ft. The shell thickness is $\frac{1}{2}$ in. Based on an allowable shearing stress of 2000 psi, what torsional strength does the fuselage have? If $G = 4 \times 10^6$ psi, what maximum twist deformation in a length of 15 ft may be expected? The approximate circumference of an ellipse is $2\pi\sqrt{(a^2 + b^2)/2}$, where a and b are the semiaxes.

5

BENDING: SHEAR FORCE AND MOMENT

5.1 Introduction. Members loaded transversely by forces which tend to bend them are called beams; they are the most common structural components the engineer deals with. Beams are to be found in almost all structures. The floor on which we walk may be thought of as being many parallel beams lying side by side. Wooden planking is a well-known example. The floor rests for support on other, secondary, beams, which in turn rest on main beams that transmit the effects of applied loads finally to the columns and the foundation. Certain types of bridges have among their component parts many beams; indeed, the entire bridge may be considered to act as one composite beam. The axles of a locomotive and of all the cars it pulls are beams. The wings of an airplane, and even the fuselage, may behave as beams.

We do not have to go far in order to find other examples of beams. Our arms certainly act as beams when we raise loads by flexing them. When we walk, our feet act as beams. The pencil with which we write is a beam on which we may not bear down too heavily lest the point breaks. The tree as it sways in the wind acts as a cantilever beam.

Beams are not only the most common structural members but are also the most important of the elements. Their study traditionally constitutes the "meat" in strength theory.

5.2 Types of Beams. Beams may be classified according to material composition and unstrained form. Thus a *simple* beam is one that is

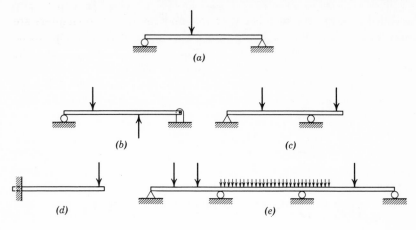

Fig. 5.1

made of only one material, is straight in the unstrained state, and is of uniform cross section. It is quite distinct from, say, a *compound* beam that may be composed of two or more materials (for example, a reinforced concrete beam), or from a *uniformly stressed* beam that may have a varying cross section, or from a *curved* beam such as a hook or an arch.

Beams may also be classified after their manner of support. A *simply supported* beam, such as that represented in Fig. 5.1a, rests on supports that permit rotation freely. It is implied that the support is capable of reacting in one sense only, as suggested by the "knife edge." If it is desired to imply the possibility of either sense for the reaction, a hinge (Fig. 5.1b) may be depicted. A simply supported beam that extends beyond a support is called a beam with an *overhang*, Fig. 5.1c. A beam that is supported at one end only is called a *cantilever* beam, Fig. 5.1d; the supported end, shown embedded in a wall, is referred to as a *built-in end*. A cantilever beam is all overhang.

Finally, beams may be classified according to whether or not the reactions at the supports may be determined without recourse to principles other than those of equilibrium. A *statically determinate* beam is one which involves reactive forces that can be uniquely solved for from the equilibrium equations alone. If equations other than those of equilibrium are needed to effect a solution for these reactive forces, then the beam involved is a *statically indeterminate* one. A beam that rests on several simple supports, called a *continuous* beam, is statically indeterminate, Fig. 5.1e.

Although any member that carries transverse loads may, in general, be called a beam, the member that this and the next two chapters are concerned with is defined by certain rather stringent limitations to be discussed later. For the present, it is sufficient to assume (1) that the beam is originally straight and horizontally supported, (2) that it is longer than it is thick (in order that the word "transverse" will have specific meaning), and (3) that the loads and reactions involved constitute a parallel coplanar force system.

5.3 Shear Force and Moment. Consider the cantilever beam carrying a concentrated load shown in Fig. 5.2a. Let us imagine a transverse cutting plane passed a distance x from the left end and draw the free-body diagram of this length beam, Fig. 5.2b. For equilibrium to obtain, it is necessary that the contact forces, exerted on the part being considered by the part imagined removed, be reducible to (1) a resultant transverse tangential force V_{RL} and (2) a resultant moment M_{RL}. The force V_{RL}, called the *resisting shear force*, represents that action of the right portion on the left which tends to prevent relative sliding between them. The moment M_{RL}, called the *resisting moment*, represents that action of the right portion on the left which tends to prevent relative rotation between them.

Assuming the earth pull on the beam to be so small compared to the applied load P that it may be ignored, we find from

$$\Sigma F_V = 0 = P - V_{RL}$$

that $V_{RL} = P,$ (a)

and from $\Sigma M_O = 0 = Px + M_{RL}$

that $M_{RL} = -Px.$ (b)

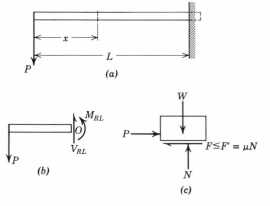

(a)

(b)

W

$P \longrightarrow$

$F \leq F' = \mu N$

N

(c)

Fig. 5.2

The right-hand members of Eqs. *a* and *b* denote what are called, respectively, the *shearing force* and the *bending moment*, also called the *external shear force* and the *external moment*, to distinguish them from the resisting shear force and the resisting moment. These latter should then be called the internal shear force and the internal moment, denoted by the left-hand terms in the preceding equations.

Although the term resisting shear is used interchangeably, almost synonymously, with the term shearing force, and resisting moment with bending moment, it is highly desirable to appreciate fully the distinction between the "external" and the "internal" systems. The shearing force and bending moment constitute an *active* system, whereas the resisting shear force and resisting moment are a *RE-active*, passive, or induced system. In Fig. 5.2, P, being an active force, is capable of making the left end of the beam deflect downward or rotate counterclockwise. On the other hand, V_{RL}, being a passive force, can at best only *tend* to prevent the left end of the beam from moving downward; it certainly cannot raise that part relative to the rest of the beam. Likewise, M_{RL} can only tend to prevent counterclockwise rotation of the left end; it cannot rotate this end clockwise relative to the rest of the beam.

An analogy that is helpful in developing the "feel" for this important distinction is given by the example of a block resting on a horizontal surface. Figure 5.2c shows the free-body diagram of such a block under the action of an active force P. In order to preserve equilibrium, the tangential friction force F must equal P in magnitude. The force P, being active, is capable of producing motion of the block, relative to the surface, in the sense of P which is to the right. On the other hand, the force F, being passive, can only tend to prevent the block from moving to the right and cannot cause it to move to the left relative to the surface. As the force P is increased by the external agency that acts on the block, F increases to maintain equilibrium, that is, up to the value of the limiting-friction force, $F' = \mu N$, where μ is the coefficient of static friction and N is the normal force between the two bodies. Any further increase in P beyond that which causes F to equal F' would result in the block accelerating to the right. Similarly, in Fig. 5.2b, as P increases, both V_{RL} and M_{RL} increase also, preserving equilibrium; they may, however, increase only up to certain values that depend on the material properties and possibly also on the form of the beam cross section. Any further increase in P beyond that which causes these limiting values in V_{RL} and M_{RL} may well result in either fracture or excessive deformation.

Thus, just as the limiting-friction force F' depends on the characteristic constant known as the coefficient of friction, so do the limiting values of V and M depend on characteristic indices or stresses. Our basic objective is to develop the expressions for V and M in terms of these stresses. Before doing so, however, let us first determine the variation of the shear force and the moment throughout the length of the beam. Knowing these, we can then calculate the maximum numerical values of V and M in any given situation. It is in these maximum values that we are primarily interested.

PROBLEMS

5.1. After determining the support reactions, evaluate the shearing force and the bending moment that are transmitted across any transverse section within each of the following ranges for x (measured from the left end): $0 < x < 5$, $5 < x < 10$, and $10 < x < 15$. In each case, use the method of sections and apply the conditions of equilibrium on the left free body. Assume all unknown internal force components to be positive according to the sign convention discussed in Article 2.11.

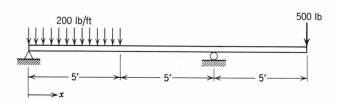

FIG. P5.1

5.2. Repeat Prob. 5.1, with a 2000-ft-lb clockwise moment load added at $x = 5$ ft.

5.3. Determine V and M for any x within the following ranges: $0 < x < 6$, $6 < x < 10$, and $10 < x < 15$.

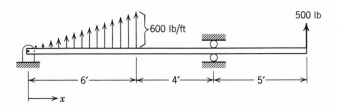

FIG. P5.3

5.4. Repeat the preceding for this beam.

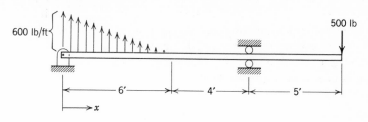

5.4 Shearing-Force and Bending-Moment Equations.   Equation a of the preceding article is called a *shearing-force equation*, and Eq. b a *bending-moment equation*.   They are valid for all values of x between zero and L.   In that example, the shearing force is constant, whereas the bending moment is variable, attaining its maximum value PL when $x = L$.

Let us consider next the simply supported beam in Fig. 5.3a, whose free-body diagram is shown in sketch b.   The reactions R_A and R_B are found from equilibrium, thus:

$$\Sigma M_B = 0 = -R_A L + P_1(L - a) + P_2(L - b)$$

gives

$$R_A = \frac{1}{L}[P_1(L - a) + P_2(L - b)],$$

and $\Sigma F_V = 0 = R_B + \dfrac{1}{L}[P_1(L - a) + P_2(L - b)] - P_1 - P_2$

yields

$$R_B = \frac{1}{L}(P_1 a + P_2 b).$$

Imagine a cutting plane passed tranversely across the beam a distance x from the left end, in the region $0 < x < a$.   The free-body diagrams of the two portions are shown in Fig. 5.3c, in which the senses of V and M are assumed positive according to the convention explained in Article 2.10.   Note particularly that, since V and M are internal effects of the loads P_1 and P_2, the sign convention that governs them is the second one: the pair V_{RL} and V_{LR}, as well as the pair M_{RL} and M_{LR}, is shown with a positive sense.   For the left free body, we find from the equilibrium equations,

$$\Sigma F_V = 0 = R_A + V_{RL}$$

and

$$\Sigma M = 0 = -R_A x + M_{RL},$$

that $$V_{RL} = -R_A \qquad (a)$$

and $$M_{RL} = R_A x. \qquad (b)$$

From the equilibrium equations for the right free body,

$$\Sigma F_V = 0 = -V_{LR} - P_1 - P_2 + R_B$$

and $\Sigma M = 0 = -M_{LR} - P_1(a - x) - P_2(b - x) + R_B(L - x),$

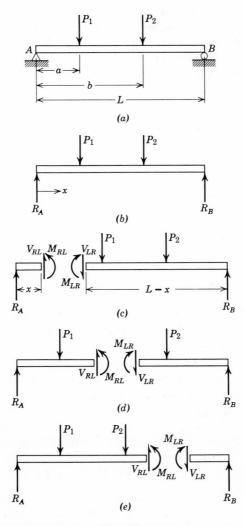

Fig. 5.3

we obtain $V_{LR} = -P_1 - P_2 + R_B$ (c)

and $M_{LR} = -P_1(a - x) - P_2(b - x) + R_B(L - x).$ (d)

Equating a to c and b to d, we obtain, after transposing all terms to one side of the equality sign,

$$0 = R_A - P_1 - P_2 + R_B$$

and $0 = -R_A x - P_1(a - x) - P_2(b - x) + R_B(L - x).$

These are nothing more than the equations of equilibrium for the entire beam, Fig. 5.3b, the moment center being taken anywhere in the region $0 < x < a$. Observe that every time an equilibrium equation is written the first sign convention governs.

Repeating the process for the range $a < x < b$, Fig. 5.3d, we obtain

$$V_{RL} = -R_A + P_1,$$ (e)

$$M_{RL} = R_A x - P_1(x - a),$$ (f)

$$V_{LR} = -P_2 + R_B,$$ (g)

and $M_{LR} = -P_2(b - x) + R_B(L - x).$ (h)

Finally, for the region $b < x < L$, Fig. 5.3e, we obtain the following:

$$V_{RL} = -R + P_1 + P_2,$$ (i)

$$M_{RL} = R_A x - P_1(x - a) - P_2(x - b),$$ (j)

$$V_{LR} = R_B,$$ (k)

and $M_{LR} = R_B(L - x).$ (l)

These results indicate that in determining the shearing force V and the bending moment M it makes no difference whatsoever which group of forces one considers on *either* side of the transverse section in question. When numerical problems are involved and the values of V and M at some one particular section are desired, choosing that side with the smaller number of forces could save both time and effort. Which side to work with is then properly left to one's judgment. On the other hand, for purposes of discussion, it is best, because it is least confusing, to confine our attention to a specific side of the section being considered; for convenience let this be the left side of the generic section. We now formalize for future work the process described above into the following rules of operation:

RULE 1. *The shearing force at any section of a horizontal beam is obtained by adding algebraically all transverse forces that lie to the left of the section, downward forces being given the plus sign and upward forces the minus sign.*

RULE 2. *The bending moment at any section of a horizontal beam is obtained by adding algebraically the moments of all forces that lie to the left of the section, relative to a moment center at the section in question, clockwise moments being given the plus sign and counterclockwise moments the minus sign.*

In applying these rules, one must interpret the final signs of V and M in the light of the second sign convention explained in Article 2.10.

Let us now return to our example, Fig. 5.3, and collect the equations for V and M as follows:

$$V = -R_A \qquad\qquad\qquad\left.\begin{array}{l} \\ \end{array}\right\}0 < x < a \qquad (a)$$

$$M = R_A x \qquad\qquad\qquad\qquad\qquad\qquad\qquad (b)$$

$$V = -R_A + P_1 \qquad\qquad\left.\begin{array}{l} \\ \end{array}\right\}a < x < b \qquad (e)$$

$$M = R_A x - P_1(x - a) \qquad\qquad\qquad\qquad\qquad (f)$$

$$V = -R_A + P_1 + P_2 \qquad\left.\begin{array}{l} \\ \end{array}\right\}b < x < L, \qquad (i)$$

$$M = R_A x - P_1(x - a) - P_2(x - b) \qquad\qquad\qquad (j)$$

where, it is hoped, the dropping of the subscripts causes no confusion. We may do this because V_{LR} and V_{RL}, as a pair, and M_{LR} and M_{RL}, as a pair, always bear the same sign.

Special attention is called to the following significant fact. The term $-R_A$ is common to Eqs. *a*, *e*, and *i*; and $-R_A + P_1$ is common to Eqs. *e* and *i*. Therefore Eq. *i* may be considered to "contain" both Eqs. *a* and *e*. Similarly, the term $R_A x$ is common to Eqs. *b*, *f*, and *j*, and $R_A x - P_1(x - a)$ occurs in both Eqs. *f* and *j*. Therefore Eq. *j* may be considered to contain both Eqs. *b* and *f*. In view of all this, we may now look upon the last two equations *i* and *j* as generic equations, that is, they give the values of V and M at *any* section so long as it is understood that the effect of P_1 is to be taken into account only when x exceeds a and that of P_2 only when x exceeds b. Hence, in order to cover the entire range of x from one end of the beam to the other, we need write only two equations, one for V and the other for M, using the convenient device of the braced term, thus

$$V = -R_A + P_1\{x - a\}^0 + P_2\{x - b\}^0 \left.\begin{array}{l} \\ \end{array}\right\}0 < x < L, \qquad (m)$$

and $\qquad M = R_A x - P_1\{x - a\} - P_2\{x - b\} \qquad\qquad\qquad (n)$

where each braced term is to be considered only when it is positive, discarded when negative. This device is explained more fully later in this chapter.

PROBLEMS

The following exercises have been designed to help the student master Rules 1 and 2. They must therefore be solved by direct application of these rules. Do check your results, however, by establishing that the corresponding free bodies, isolated by sectioning planes, are indeed in equilibrium when the solved for actions are shown on them.

5.5. For the beam whose free-body diagram is shown, write the shearing-force and bending-moment equations for each of the following four ranges of x: $0 < x < 3$, $3 < x < 9$, $9 < x < 12$, and $12 < x < 15$.

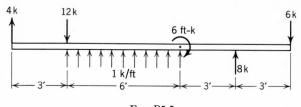

FIG. P5.5

5.6. In Fig. P5.1, if $V = +500$ lb at $x = 7$ ft, what is M there? Show V and M acting on a positive-X face.

5.7. In Fig. P5.1, if $M = +400$ ft-lb at $x = 4$ ft, what is V there? Show V and M acting on a positive-X face.

5.8. In Fig. P5.3, the left reaction is 830 lb downward. Where is V zero? What is M there? Show M acting on a positive-X face.

5.9. In Fig. P5.1, if the left reaction is 500 lb, upward, where is M zero other than at the two extremes of the beam? What is V there? Show V acting on a positive-X face.

5.10. At a certain transverse section of this beam, there are transmitted $V = -100$ lb and $M = +400$ ft-lb. Where is this section? What is the roller reaction?

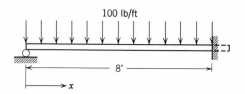

FIG. P5.10

5.11. This beam, partly shown, is subject to a uniformly distributed load of intensity p lb/ft. At $x = 3$ ft, $V = +200$ lb and $M = -150$ ft-lb. At $x = 5$ ft, $V = +100$ lb. What is M at $x = 5$? Where is V zero? Where is M zero?

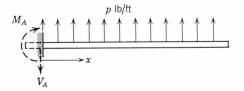

Fig. P5.11

5.12. Evaluate the left reaction. (*Hint:* A hinge cannot transmit any moment.)

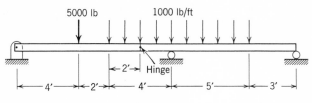

Fig. P5.12

5.5 The Concept of Beam Loading. In our discussion up to this point, we have assumed that concentrated forces do exist. We realize, of course, that no physical body, acting as the agent of the mechanical action known as force, can actually exert this action on the load-bearing structural member through the medium of contact over an area that has no dimension. We have used the point force merely as a convenient idealization. In the actual physical case, the nearest we ever get to obtaining point force action is through a roller or knife edge which, owing to the high contact pressure intensity, quickly flattens out, thereby presenting for the transmission of the load a finite area of contact.

It is proper to consider a point force to be the limiting case of a distributed force system, as the area of transmission shrinks and the distribution intensity increases without limit. Hence, we will be dealing with more realistic loads consisting of forces distributed with uniform or with varying intensities. Since our discussion of beams is confined for the present to relatively thin bars so that the force systems involved may be considered coplanar, the distribution will usually be over a length rather than over an area. Intensities will then be reckoned in force units per unit length.

If the point force is an abstraction, there is yet another kind of load that has, in a manner of speaking, an even higher degree of abstractness. This is the notion of the concentrated moment. A localized moment load, lying in the longitudinal plane of the beam, is imagined exerted on the beam by a giant screwdriver through a slot in the face of the beam.

As the slot shrinks, the moment becomes localized to a point. Since a moment may always be represented by a statically equivalent couple, a point moment presents the double abstraction of two parallel and oppositely directed forces of infinite magnitude having lines of action a zero distance apart.   In practice, moment loads are transmitted to beams by cross members which are themselves subjected to twist.

5.6   Differential Relations between Bending Moment, Shear Force, Load Intensity, and Position.

Figure 5.4 represents the free-body diagram of a very small length Δx cut out from a beam. The following act on this body:

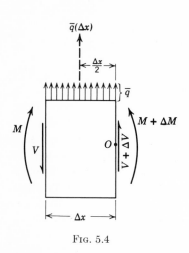

$\bar{q}(\Delta x)$

$\dfrac{\Delta x}{2}$

$\bar{q}$

M

$M + \Delta M$

V

O

$V + \Delta V$

FIG. 5.4

(1) A system of continuously distributed forces, which may include the earth pull on the beam itself, of average intensity $\bar{q}$ force units per unit length. The resultant $\bar{q}(\Delta x)$ is shown acting halfway between the end faces of the little block; this is correct in the limit.

(2) A shear force V on the left face.

(3) A moment M on the left face.

(4) A shear force $V + \Delta V$ on the right face.

(5) A moment $M + \Delta M$ on the right face.

All quantities are assumed positive and are so represented. Applying to the free body the first of two equilibrium equations, we have

$$\Sigma F_V = 0 = -V + \bar{q}(\Delta x) + (V + \Delta V),$$

from which $\Delta V = -\bar{q}(\Delta x).$

Therefore $\dfrac{\Delta V}{\Delta x} = -\bar{q}.$

As Δx is taken smaller, the ratio $\Delta V/\Delta x$ becomes the first derivative of V with respect to the position coordinate x, and the average load intensity $\bar{q}$ becomes the local load intensity q. Hence we have our first relationship

$$\frac{dV}{dx} = -q. \tag{5.1}$$

Taking moments about a point on the right face, such as O, we have the second equilibrium equation

$$\Sigma M_O = 0 = -M + V(\Delta x) - \frac{\bar{q}(\Delta x)^2}{2} + (M + \Delta M),$$

whence

$$\Delta M = -V(\Delta x) + \frac{\bar{q}(\Delta x)^2}{2}.$$

Dividing through by Δx and letting Δx approach zero, we have in the limit

$$\frac{dM}{dx} = -V. \tag{5.2}$$

Substituting V from Eq. 5.2 in Eq. 5.1, we obtain finally

$$\frac{d^2M}{dx^2} = +q. \tag{5.3}$$

The preceding differential relations are fundamental and should be thoroughly understood. They say in a nutshell: *The rate of change of shear force relative to position equals the negative of the local load intensity, and the rate of change of bending moment relative to position equals the negative of the shear force there.* Rates of change are best depicted graphically. This useful geometric intepretation is exploited in the last article of this chapter.

The alternative forms,

$$\int dV = -\int q\, dx + C_1, \tag{5.1'}$$

$$\int dM = -\int V\, dx + C_2, \tag{5.2'}$$

and

$$\int dM = +\iint q\, dx\, dx + C_1 x + C_2, \tag{5.3'}$$

likewise have useful geometric interpretations. They are also made use of in the last article.

PROBLEMS

5.13. For the beam of Prob. 5.5, show that the shearing-force equations are indeed the same as the first derivatives with respect to x of the bending-moment equations.

5.14. Depict in a sketch the graph of a possible M-x function consistent with each of the situations shown. If more than one possibility exists, show three typical graphs.

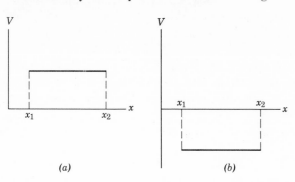

FIG. P5.14

5.15. Repeat the preceding for these shear distributions.

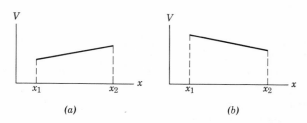

FIG. P5.15

5.16. Depict in a sketch the graph of the corresponding V-x function. Is there only one possibility?

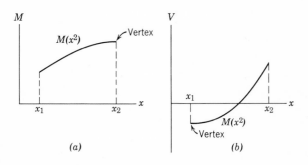

FIG. P5.16

5.17. (a) If V is stationary, how is M behaving in that neighborhood?
(b) If M is stationary, how is V behaving in that neighborhood?
(c) If M is zero, is there anything special about how V behaves in that neighborhood?

(d) If q is constant and positive (upward), how does M vary?

(e) If M is changing linearly, how is q behaving in that neighborhood?

5.7 Singularity Functions. In order that we could take full advantage of Eqs. 5.1, 5.2, and 5.3, as well as of their inverse forms, 5.1′, 5.2′, and 5.3′, throughout the entire range of the position coordinate x, it is necessary that the load intensity q exist everywhere in x. The simplest example of when this is so is a beam bearing a uniformly distributed load of intensity p throughout its entire length. In such a case the operations of obtaining V from q and M from V can be carried out in the usual manner of integrating without any difficulty, except *at* supports where point forces are assumed to exist. At such locations, as explained earlier, the load intensity becomes infinite; in other words, q becomes a singularity. If these singularities occur at the end points of the range x, such as happens for a simply supported beam without overhangs, we get around the difficulty by not including these end points among the values that the variable x may assume. But what happens when such singularities occur between end points or, equally as bad, when q is only sectionally continuous? This is the situation, for instance, in a beam which bears a combination of concentrated loads and loads distributed over discrete segments of the span and which is supported at points other than the ends. To handle such cases without the necessity of writing several sets of equations connecting the piecewise-continuous functions, we make use of a clever device, the singularity function.

The family of singularity functions * is defined by the equation

$$F_n(x) = \{x - x_0\}^n, \quad n \text{ is any integer.} \tag{5.4}$$

For all positive values of n, including zero, the quantity inside the braces is to be considered only when positive or zero and discarded when negative; thus the value of the function is simply the ordinary power of the argument when this is positive. The function differs from ordinary ones for negative values of n because then it has the peculiarity of becoming infinite at $x = x_0$ but zero everywhere else.

There is no limit to the order n so long as these properties are observed. The lowest order, however, for which the mathematical idealization is

---

* The terminolog has been adopted from E. A. Guillemin, *Introductory Circuit Theory*, pp. 196–203, John Wiley and Sons, New York, 1953, but the notation is virtually that used by W. H. Macaulay, "Note on the Deflection of Beams," *Messenger of Mathematics*, Vol. 48, pp. 129–130 (1919). The technique of handling the influence of several point forces on the bending moment in beams, without writing several equations, seems to have been used first by A. Föppl, *Festigkeitslehre*, pp. 129–132, B. G. Teubner, Leipzig, 1905.

susceptible of physical interpretation is -2. Following is an array of singularity functions of various orders.

$$F_{-2}(x) = \{x - x_0\}^{-2} \qquad = \infty, \quad \text{when } x = x_0$$
$$= 0, \quad \text{when } x \neq x_0. \tag{5.4a}$$

$$F_{-1}(x) = \{x - x_0\}^{-1} \qquad = \infty, \quad \text{when } x = x_0$$
$$= 0, \quad \text{when } x \neq x_0. \tag{5.4b}$$

$$F_0(x) = \{x - x_0\}^0 \qquad = 1, \quad \text{when } x \geq x_0$$
$$= 0, \quad \text{when } x < x_0. \tag{5.4c}$$

$$F_n(x) = \{x - x_0\}^n, \quad n > 0, = (x - x_0)^n, \quad \text{when } x \geq x_0$$
$$= 0, \quad \text{when } x < x_0. \tag{5.4d}$$

The graphs of these equations are shown in Fig. 5.5. The descriptive names are intended to conjure up some association with familiar physical situations or geometrical figures. *Doublet* is the name given to F_{-2} because of the association with the point moment or couple. *Impulse* obviously is intended to suggest an impulsive force, that is, a force of very large magnitude but of extremely short duration in time (imagine the independent variable is t rather than x).* The name *unit step* is self-explanatory, as is *unit ramp*. For higher-order singularities no conveniently descriptive names are obvious, nor are they needed. The term half-parabola does no more than describe the geometrical figure for F_2.

For purposes of differentiation and integration we define the following additional properties:

$$\frac{d}{dx} \{x - x_0\}^n = \{x - x_0\}^{n-1}, \qquad\qquad \text{for } n \leq 0 \quad (5.5a)$$
$$= n\{x - x_0\}^{n-1}, \qquad\qquad \text{for } n > 0. \quad (5.5b)$$
$$\int_0^x \{\alpha - x_0\}^n \, d\alpha = \{x - x_0\}^{n+1}, \qquad\qquad \text{for } n \leq 0 \quad (5.6a)$$
$$= \frac{1}{n+1} \{x - x_0\}^{n+1}, \qquad \text{for } n > 0. \quad (5.6b)$$

* We have taken liberties in the definitions of the impulse and the doublet at which mathematicians, so used to the elegance of "epsilon methods," would look askance. More rigorously defined, the unit-impulse function is $\mathcal{I}(x - x_{0,\epsilon}) = \frac{1}{\epsilon} [\mathcal{U}(x - x_0) - \mathcal{U}(x - \overline{x_0 + \epsilon})]$, where $\mathcal{U}(x - x_0)$ is the unit-step function; then the unit-doublet function is $\mathcal{D}(x - x_{0,\epsilon}) = \frac{1}{\epsilon} [\mathcal{I}(x - \overline{x_0 - \epsilon}, \epsilon) - \mathcal{I}(x - x_{0,\epsilon})]$. Our own definitions represent the limits of these functions as ϵ approaches zero. When they are so defined, the impulse and the doublet are the *Dirac functions* of order 1 and 2 used in mathematical physics.

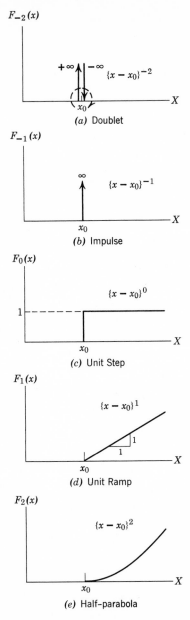

$F_{-2}(x)$

$+\infty$ $-\infty$ $\{x - x_0\}^{-2}$

x_0

(*a*) Doublet

$F_{-1}(x)$

∞ $\{x - x_0\}^{-1}$

x_0

(*b*) Impulse

$F_0(x)$

$\{x - x_0\}^0$

1

x_0

(*c*) Unit Step

$F_1(x)$

$\{x - x_0\}^1$

1

1

x_0

(*d*) Unit Ramp

$F_2(x)$

$\{x - x_0\}^2$

x_0

(*e*) Half-parabola

Fɪɢ. 5.5 Graphs of singularity functions.

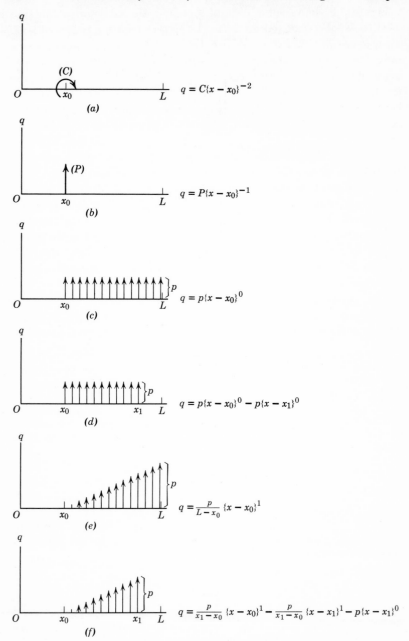

$$q = C\{x - x_0\}^{-2}$$
(a)

$$q = P\{x - x_0\}^{-1}$$
(b)

$$q = p\{x - x_0\}^0$$
(c)

$$q = p\{x - x_0\}^0 - p\{x - x_1\}^0$$
(d)

$$q = \frac{p}{L - x_0}\{x - x_0\}^1$$
(e)

$$q = \frac{p}{x_1 - x_0}\{x - x_0\}^1 - \frac{p}{x_1 - x_0}\{x - x_1\}^1 - p\{x - x_1\}^0$$
(f)

Fig. 5.6

Figure 5.6 shows some examples of how the singularity function is used to express load intensities. The sign convention observed is: *Upward forces and clockwise moments bear the plus sign, whereas downward forces and counterclockwise moments bear the minus sign.* It cannot be overemphasized that this sign convention is intended only for singularities that represent loads, that is, forces or moments exerted on the member by agents *external* to it. These signs do *not* apply, for instance, to the determination of V by Rule 1, with which they would be in direct conflict.

Note that the coefficient of each singularity function is a constant. In this text we use this function with constant coefficients only. Every such coefficient is then considered the "strength" of the particular singularity, thus: the couple C in units of force times length is the strength of the doublet (sketch a); P in units of force is the strength of the impulse (sketch b); p in units of force per unit length is the strength of the step (sketch c); and so on. Furthermore, we limit distributed loads only to those whose variation can be expressed in positive integral powers of x, including zero.*

Two of the preceding examples need special mention. Figure 5.6d shows how to handle a uniform load that is sectionally distributed. This is derived from the case in sketch c by straightforward superposi-

* For more complex variations it is still a simple matter to express the load intensity as a function of position, *if this is all that is desired*, because all one needs to do is to multiply the continuous expression by the unit-step function. For example, suppose

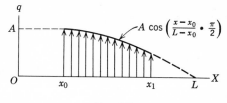

FIG. 5.7

that the load varies harmonically as shown in Fig. 5.7, but that the distribution is only over the region x_0 to x_1. Then this load intensity is

$$q = [\{x - x_0\}^0 - \{x - x_1\}^0] A \cos\left(\frac{x - x_0}{L - x_0}\frac{\pi}{2}\right).$$

Now, however, to differentiate or to integrate correctly, we must have rules other than those defined by Eqs. 5.5 and 5.6. These would lead us to the powerful methods of operational mathematics, which should properly be left to the appropriate mathematics course. For instance, see D. L. Holl, C. G. Maple, B. Vinograde, *Introduction to the Laplace Transform*, Chapter 3, Appleton-Century-Crofts, New York, 1959.

tion: to the step function of strength p starting at $x = x_0$ is added the step function of strength $-p$ starting at $x = x_1$; this results in a load of uniform intensity p distributed only over the stretch from x_0 to x_1.

The case in Fig. 5.6f is arrived at in either one of two ways. One is by superposing two ramp functions and one step function; these are shown in sketches a to d, Fig. 5.8, which are self-explanatory. Observe that the coefficient of both q_a and q_b, $p/(x_1 - x_0)$, is the slope of the load-intensity diagram; it gives the strength or magnitude of the ramp, since the unit ramp has a slope of unity (Fig. 5.5d). The other method

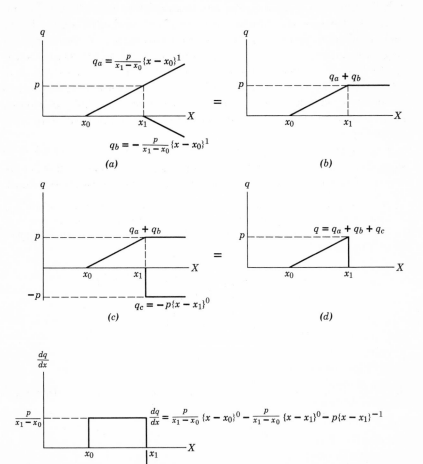

Fig. 5.8

makes use of the differentiation and integration properties of the singularity function; it is especially suited to variations in load intensity of degree one or higher in x, such as are often specified in actual engineering problems. First, the derivative curve, dq/dx as a function of x, is sketched, Fig. 5.8e. This is derived from the fact that from x_0 to x_1 the q-x curve (Fig. 5.6f) has a constant positive slope of $p/(x_1 - x_0)$ and that everywhere outside this interval its slope is zero. At x_1 the q-x curve is vertical: it drops downward in the increasing sense of x. Since the sudden decrease from p to zero suggests an infinite rate of change in q, there is shown at x_1 on the derivative curve an impulse of strength $-p$, Fig. 5.8e. The derivative dq/dx may now be written down directly as a combination of the step and the impulse functions, thus:

$$\frac{dq}{dx} = \frac{p}{x_1 - x_0} \{x - x_0\}^0 - \frac{p}{x_1 - x_0} \{x - x_1\}^0 - p\{x - x_1\}^{-1}.$$

Integrating now from zero to any generic x (in order to avoid introducing integration constants), thus:

$$\int_0^q dq = \frac{p}{x_1 - x_0} \int_0^x \{x - x_0\}^0 \, dx$$

$$- \frac{p}{x_1 - x_0} \int_0^x \{x - x_1\}^0 \, dx - p \int_0^x \{x - x_1\}^{-1} \, dx,$$

we obtain, by virtue of Eq. 5.6a, the final result

$$q = \frac{p}{x_1 - x_0} \{x - x_0\}^1 - \frac{p}{x_1 - x_0} \{x - x_1\}^1 - p\{x - x_1\}^0.$$

In situations where higher degrees of x than one are involved in the load-intensity variation, it is convenient first to sketch the successive derivative curves until the highest-order singularity is reduced to the step. This last derivative is then written out as a combination of singularities of order zero *and lower.* Then, repeated integration according to Eqs. 5.6 will finally give the desired expression for the load intensity as a function of x.

Illustrative Example 1. Figure 5.9a shows a 15-ft beam resting on a knife-edge support at $x = 0$ and on a roller support at $x = 10$; it bears a uniformly varying downward load from $x = 1$ to $x = 4$, a uniformly distributed upward load from $x = 4$ to $x = 6$, a counterclockwise point moment at $x = 8$, and a downward point force at the right end. Express the load intensity q as a function of x and then, by successive integra-

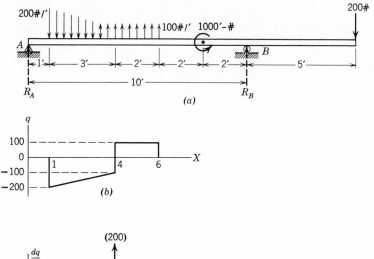

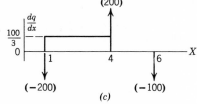

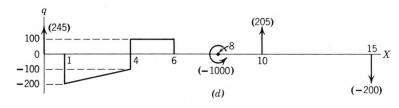

Fig. 5.9

tion, derive from the q function the expressions for V and M. In particular, evaluate V and M at $x = 5$, first from the V and M equations
and later by direct application of Rules 1 and 2.

SOLUTION.   The reactions are first calculated, thus:

$$\Sigma M_B = 0 = -10R_A + \frac{100(3)8}{2} + 100(3)7.5$$

$$- 100(2)5 + 1000 - 200(5),$$

whence $\qquad\qquad R_A = 245 \text{ lb.}$

From

$$\Sigma M_A = 0 = 10R_B - \frac{100(3)2}{2} - 100(3)2.5$$
$$+ 100(2)5 + 1000 - 200(15),$$

we find $R_B = 205$ lb.

At this point in numerical problems, it is a good idea to perform a check before proceeding further. Thus, using an equilibrium equation different from those already used, we ask

$$\Sigma F_V = 245 + 205 - \frac{200 + 100}{2}(3) + 100(2) - 200 = 0,$$

and we find that the left-hand side indeed reduces to zero.

Since the distributed loading involves a power of x higher than zero, in this case one, it is handled by itself first; this is partly by way of illustrating the preceding explanation. Figure 5.9b shows the q-x diagram in which downward forces have been plotted below and upward forces above the X axis. The derivative curve is sketched in Fig. 5.9c, where the sign convention for ordinates and slopes in right-handed systems has been observed. The derivative dq/dx may now be written down directly, thus:

$$\frac{dq}{dx} = -200\{x - 1\}^{-1} + \tfrac{100}{3}\{x - 1\}^0$$
$$- \tfrac{100}{3}\{x - 4\}^0 + 200\{x - 4\}^{-1} - 100\{x - 6\}^{-1}.$$

Integrating once, we obtain

$$q = -200\{x - 1\}^0 + \tfrac{100}{3}\{x - 1\}^1 - \tfrac{100}{3}\{x - 4\}^1$$
$$+ 200\{x - 4\}^0 - 100\{x - 6\}^0.$$

We are now ready to handle the entire beam, whose load variation is depicted in Fig. 5.9d. The expression for q is:

$$q = 245\{x - 0\}^{-1} - 200\{x - 1\}^0 + \tfrac{100}{3}\{x - 1\}^1 - \tfrac{100}{3}\{x - 4\}^1$$
$$+ 200\{x - 4\}^0 - 100\{x - 6\}^0 - 1000\{x - 8\}^{-2}$$
$$+ 205\{x - 10\}^{-1} - 200\{x - 15\}^{-1}, \qquad 0 < x < 15. \qquad (a)$$

One integration according to Eq. 5.1 gives the expression for V, thus:

$$V = -245\{x - 0\}^0 + 200\{x - 1\}^1 - \frac{100}{3(2)}\{x - 1\}^2 + \frac{100}{3(2)}\{x - 4\}^2$$
$$- 200\{x - 4\}^1 + 100\{x - 6\}^1 + 1000\{x - 8\}^{-1} - 205\{x - 10\}^0$$
$$+ 200\{x - 15\}^0, \qquad 0 < x < 15. \qquad (b)$$

A second integration according to Eq. 5.2 gives the expression for M, thus:

$$M = 245\{x - 0\}^1 - \tfrac{200}{2}\{x - 1\}^2 + \frac{100}{3(6)}\{x - 1\}^3 - \frac{100}{3(6)}\{x - 4\}^3$$

$$+ \tfrac{200}{2}\{x - 4\}^2 - \tfrac{100}{2}\{x - 6\}^2 - 1000\{x - 8\}^0 + 205\{x - 10\}^1$$

$$- 200\{x - 15\}^1, \qquad 0 < x < 15. \tag{c}$$

These are the desired equations. At $x = 5$ ft, Eq. b gives

$$V_5 = -245 + 200(4) - \tfrac{100}{6}(4)^2 + \tfrac{100}{6}(1)^2 - 200(1)$$

$$= +105 \text{ lb.} \qquad\qquad \square \lceil V = 105 \text{ lb.} \quad Ans.$$

Equation c gives

$$M_5 = 245(5) - 100(4)^2 + \tfrac{100}{18}(4)^3 - \tfrac{100}{18}(1) + \tfrac{200}{2}(1)$$

$$= +75 \text{ ft-lb.} \qquad\qquad \square \rangle M = 75 \text{ ft-lb.} \quad Ans.$$

Applying Rules 1 and 2 directly, taking into account only those forces to the left of $x = 5$, we obtain

$$V_5 = -245 + \tfrac{300}{2}(3) - 100(1) = +105 \text{ lb}, \qquad\qquad Ans.$$

and $\qquad M_5 = 245(5) - \dfrac{100(3)}{2}(3) - 100(3)2.5 + 100(1)\tfrac{1}{2}$

$$= +75 \text{ ft-lb}, \qquad\qquad Ans.$$

which are the same values as those before, as of course they should be.

One final word of explanation concerning concentrated loads must be made before we move along. When a point force acts on the beam at $x = x_0$, the value of V *right there* must remain undefined; we must be extremely careful to distinguish between the two values of V on either side of x. In denoting these we may use a variety of symbols, among them being: V at $x = x_0 - \epsilon$, or V at $x_0(-)$, or V_{A-}, or V_{Al}, for the value of V slightly to the left of x_0 (or section A); for the value of V slightly to the right of x_0 we may then use V at $x = x_0 + \epsilon$, or V at $x_0(+)$, or V_{A+}, or V_{Ar}. Similar remarks hold for M in the presence of point moment loads, and analogous symbols may be used appropriately for its values slightly to the left and slightly to the right of x_0. All this is in keeping with the discussion in Article 5.5 and with the definitions of the doublet and the impulse functions.

PROBLEMS

5.18 to **5.25.** In all these problems:

(a) Evaluate the reactions first. Use the calculus where needed.

(b) Sketch the q-x curve and as many derivative curves as necessary to reduce the highest-order singularity to a step.

(c) Write out the q-x equation, either directly or through integration.

(d) From the q-x equation, derive the V-x equation by integration.

(e) Finally derive the M-x equation.

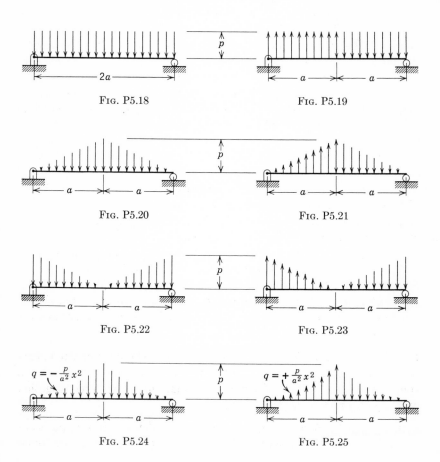

FIG. P5.18   FIG. P5.19

FIG. P5.20   FIG. P5.21

FIG. P5.22   FIG. P5.23

$q = -\frac{p}{a^2}x^2$ $q = +\frac{p}{a^2}x^2$

FIG. P5.24   FIG. P5.25

5.26. After evaluating the reactions, write the V-x equation directly; from this derive the M-x equation.

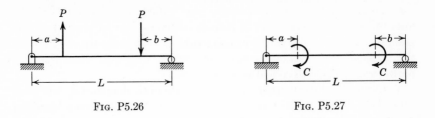

FIG. P5.26   FIG. P5.27

5.27. After evaluating the reactions, write the M-x equation directly.

5.8   Shear-Force and Bending-Moment Diagrams. The variation of the shear force V and the bending moment M as expressed in the V-x and M-x equations may be depicted graphically, resulting in useful visual aids. The principal excuse for the shear-force and bending-moment diagrams is in the fact that we are interested almost always in the largest values of V and M (sometimes also in where M changes sign), and, although the equations can give us everything we need to know concerning these two quantities, even only rough sketches of their diagrams help us quickly to narrow down the ranges of x that should be investigated. Indeed, for loadings that are no more complicated than those with uniformly varying intensity, these diagrams do actually pinpoint the location of the critical values. Another excuse, secondary for our purposes but of primary importance to those engaged in numerical work (especially stepwise machine computation), is that the shear-force and bending-moment diagrams lend themselves to graphical or semigraphical calculations, depending on whether accurate scale drawings or only approximate sketches of them are made.

In executing these diagrams it is best to proceed step by step, bringing to bear on the task Rules 1 and 2 and Eqs. 5.1 to 5.3 together with their inverse forms. This is illustrated in the following example. The procedure followed here is an alternative to actual point-by-point plotting of the V-x and M-x equations, which may be done when these are already available.

Illustrative Example 2. Figure 5.10a shows a simply supported beam with an overhang, carrying a combination of uniformly distributed and concentrated loads. The V-x and M-x diagrams are required, together with significant numerical values.

PROCEDURE. Letter symbols are used to denote various positions along the beam. The reactions, determined from equilibrium, are found to be: $R_A = 5500$ lb and $R_E = 11,100$ lb, both upward. The q-x diagram is now sketched as previously explained, upward forces being plotted above and downward forces below the X axis; this shows up as a combination of impulses and steps, Fig. 5.10b. The strength of each impulse is understood to be in pounds, whereas that of each step is in pounds per foot. The numbers in parentheses within the figure represent the areas of the component parts of the q-x diagram, thus: the area between B and C is $1000(6) = 6000$ lb, etc.

To start the V-x diagram, Fig. 5.10c, we note that to the left of A there is no shear force, but immediately to the right a shear force of -5500 lb is transmitted; this is what Rule 1 says. Alternatively, Eq.

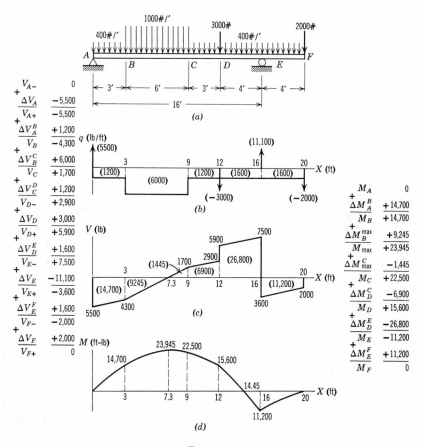

FIG. 5.10

5.1 requires that the slope of the V-x curve at A is infinite in a sense opposite to q; therefore this part of the curve must be a vertical line, downward in the increasing sense of x. Furthermore, Eq. 5.6a shows that the integral of an impulse is a step, the strength of the step being the same as that of the impulse; hence at A the V-x diagram drops downward from zero to -5500 lb.

From A to B the V-x curve must be a straight line inclined upward (positive slope) because q is constant and negative; moreover, Eq. 5.1$'$ requires that the change in V equals the negative of the area under the q-x curve: $\Delta V = -(-1200) = +1200$ lb, where areas below the X axis are considered negative. Hence V increases from -5500 at A to -4300 at B. The rest of the diagram can now be constructed without any difficulty. The various calculations are tabulated on the left side of Fig. 5.10 for convenience.

Worthy of special mention is the closure of the V-x diagram, that is, the fact that it starts with a zero value immediately to the left of A and ends up with a zero value immediately to the right of F. This closure signifies that the equilibrium equation $\Sigma F = 0$ is satisfied and hence that the reactions R_A and R_E are correct *collectively;* in the absence of any previous check, there is as yet no assurance that these are correct individually. Also deserving of special note is the point between B and C where the V-x diagram crosses the X axis. The distance of this point from B is calculated from similar triangles, thus: $d/4300 = 6/(4300 + 1700)$, from which $d = 4.3$ ft. The other location where V changes sign is obviously at the right support E.

Before starting the M-x diagram, Fig. 5.10d, it is convenient to evaluate the areas of the component parts of the V-x diagram. These values in ft-lb are indicated in parentheses within the sketch, Fig. 5.10c. The construction of the bending-moment diagram follows substantially the same lines as that of the shear-force diagram. We note that at A the bending moment is zero, by Rule 2. Between A and B, where the V-x diagram is an inclined straight line (first degree in x), the M-x diagram must be parabolic (second degree in x). From Eq. 5.2 we know that the slope of the M-x curve decreases in the increasing sense of x because V in the same region increases algebraically; hence, from A to B the M-x diagram must be concave downward, beginning with a positive slope at A of 5500 ft-lb/ft and ending with a positive slope at B of 4300 ft-lb/ft. By Eq. 5.2$'$ the change in M equals the negative of the area under the V-x curve in any given interval of x; therefore $M_B = M_A - (-14,700) = +14,700$ ft-lb. The rest of the M-x curve may be sketched in similar fashion. Tabulated on the right side of Fig. 5.10 are the various calculations needed for the construction.

The following salient points in the relationship between the V-x and M-x diagrams should be especially noted. Where the V-x curve crosses the X axis, there is a peak in the M-x curve: that between B and C is the vertex of a parabola, whereas that at E is a point. Where two ramps in the V-x diagram come together without any discontinuity, such as at B and C, the parabolic arcs of the M-x diagram come together tangentially; on the other hand, where two ramps in the V-x curve are separated by a step, such as at D and E, there is a point in the M-x curve because at that location there is a discontinuity in the first derivative of M. The closure of the M-x diagram means that the equilibrium equation, $\Sigma M = 0$ relative to a moment center at the right end of the beam, is satisfied. Hence the closures of the V-x and M-x diagrams insure the correctness of the reactions, both collectively as well as individually.

There remains now only the determination of where the M-x diagram crosses the X axis between D and E. As in the previous consideration of where the V-x curve crosses the X axis, it is presumed that the V-x and the M-x equations are not available; this being so, the most direct way of locating where M changes sign is to make use of Eq. 5.2'. For our immediate purpose this equation says: Since the change in M from point D to this unlocated point is $-15,600$ ft-lb, the *net* area under the V-x curve in the same interval must be $+15,600$ ft-lb. Denoting by d the distance of this point from D, we reduce the problem to finding that trapezoid with an altitude d under the V-x curve, from D to the right, whose area is 15,600. The height of the V ordinate between D and E is seen to be $5900 + 400d$, where 400 is the slope of the V-x curve there (from the q-x diagram). Then the area of the trapezoid is $5900d + 400d(d/2)$. We now establish the equality

$$5900d + \frac{400d^2}{2} = 15,600,$$

from which we find that $d = 2.45$, the other value of d being rejected as extraneous. This places the section of zero M at 14.45 ft from the left end.

It is clear from the diagrams that the largest shear force is 7500 lb, just to the left of E, and that the two largest bending moments of opposite signs are $+23,945$ ft-lb, at $x = 7.3$ ft, and $-11,200$ ft-lb, at $x = 16$ ft. As mentioned earlier in this chapter, these are key values in the functioning of the beam. The significance of where M changes sign will be brought out later.

PROBLEMS

In the following exercises, evaluate the reactions first where these are not known. Then sketch to approximate scale the V-x and M-x diagrams, observing the sign conventions explained earlier. Give significant values of V and M and their locations.

5.28. Beam of Fig. P5.26.
5.29. Beam of Fig. 5.9.
5.30. Beam loaded as shown.

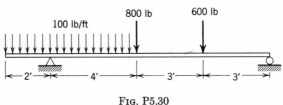

FIG. P5.30

5.31. Beam of Fig. P5.19.
5.32. Beam representing the action of a "floating" foundation.

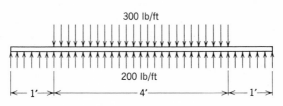

FIG. P5.32

5.33. Beam of Fig. P5.27.
5.34. Beam of Fig. P5.20.
5.35. Beam of Fig. P5.21.
5.36. Beam of Fig. P5.22.
5.37. Beam of Fig. P5.23.
5.38. Given this shear-force diagram, (a) construct the bending-moment diagram, noting that there is a point couple of magnitude C at each end of the beam; these are represented as impulses on the V-x diagram. (*Hint:* Determine C from the necessary closure of the M-x diagram.)
(b) Sketch the free-body diagram of the beam.

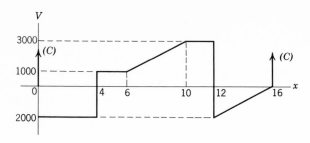

FIG. P5.38

The following exercises have been designed to help equip the student to handle stepped beams in later work. The various functions, which can be combined in any manner, represent bending moment components.

5.39. Given $M = C$; M is then divided by n_1, in the region $0 < x < a$, and by $n_2 > n_1$, in the region $a < x < L$. Derive the expression for the M/n function.

5.40. Do Prob. 5.39 for the case $n_2 < n_1$.

5.41. Given $M = Rx$; M is then divided by n_1, in the region $0 < x < a$, and by $n_2 > n_1$, in the region $a < x < L$. Derive the expression for the M/n function.

5.42. Do Prob. 5.41 for the case $n_2 < n_1$.

5.43. Given $M = C - Cx/L$; M is then divided by n_1, in the region $0 < x < a$, and by $n_2 > n_1$, in the region $a < x < L$. Derive the expression for the M/n function. Note that this can be done by superposing the case of Prob. 5.39 on that of Prob. 5.41.

5.44. Do Prob. 5.43 for the case $n_2 < n_1$.

5.45. Given $M = px^2$; M is then divided by n_1, in the region $0 < x < a$, and by $n_2 > n_1$, in the region $a < x < L$. Derive the expression for the M/n function.

5.46. Do Prob. 5.45 for the case $n_2 < n_1$.

CHAPTER

6

BENDING: BEAM STRENGTH

6.1 Load-Carrying Capacity. Although the load-carrying capacity of a beam depends on its strength, this quantity cannot very well be interpreted as a measure of such strength unless a certain manner of applying the load and supporting the beam is understood. The situation here is in marked contrast to that of the simple tension member; it is necessarily so because of the unlimited variety of ways in which beams may be loaded and supported. Accordingly, we find it necessary to introduce the concept, "strength of a beam section."

The strength of a beam is determined by the strengths of its various cross sections. By the *strength of a beam section* we mean the *capacity of that cross section to transmit the resisting shear force and the resisting moment that are exerted by one part of the beam on the adjacent part.* If a beam does not have a uniform cross section, then the strengths of its various sections will differ from one another. On the other hand, if the beam does have a uniform cross section, then the strength of any one section is the same as that of any other. In this sense only may we properly speak of the beam as being of *uniform strength.* In this chapter we will discuss beam behavior within the limitations of Hooke's law only; in Chapter 14 we will consider inelastic bending strength and its implications.

6.2 Strength in Bending. It is well for the student before proceeding further to review the discussion of the helical spring. He should observe that it is not possible for either the direct shear force P or the twisting moment PR to exist individually (Fig. 4.13a). Equilibrium requires that they both be present.

In a beam the situation is quite different. It is perfectly possible for a single transverse section to be subjected to a shear force only without a moment, or to a moment only without a shear force. For example, in the beam of Fig. 5.10, across the section 14.45 ft to the right of A there is transmitted from one part of the beam to the adjacent part a shear force of 6880 lb unaccompanied by any moment. This means that a hinge may be installed at this section without disturbing the equilibrium and stability of the beam under this particular loading. In the same beam, at the section 7.3 ft to the right of A there is transmitted a moment of 23,945 ft-lb unaccompanied by any shear force.

In fact, although it is not possible to have a *finite* length of beam carry shear force without bending moment (why not?), it is easy enough to subject a considerable length of beam to pure bending. The beam represented in Fig. 6.1a is an example. This is a symmetrically loaded beam. Figures 6.1b and c show the shear-force and bending-moment diagrams. Ignoring the earth pull on the beam, one can see that the central portion of length $L - 2a$ is subjected to a constant bending moment of magnitude Pa. It is therefore a reasonable first step for us

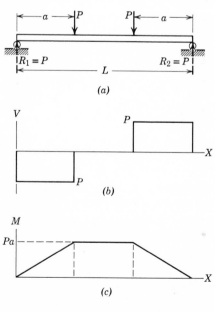

Fig. 6.1

to evaluate the stresses due to bending moment ahead of those due to shear force. For this purpose we make the following assumptions:

(1) In the unstrained state the beam is prismatic, that is, it is straight and uniform in cross section.

(2) The cross section is symmetrical and is relatively thin normal to the plane of symmetry.

(3) The loads consist of bending moments only and they lie in that plane (called the *plane of loading*) which contains the axes of symmetry of all cross sections.

(4) The material is homogeneous and isotropic and obeys Hooke's law.

(5) There are no initial stresses in the beam.

(6) Transverse planes before bending remain transverse planes during bending.

Part of a beam bent by two moments projects on the plane of loading as shown in Fig. 6.2a. A simple experiment with a flexible model, like an ordinary rubber eraser, reveals that, as the beam bends, the material in the concave side contracts, whereas that in the convex side extends. We may therefore conclude that on a transverse plane some points experience tensile strain, whereas others experience compressive strain. Furthermore, owing to the continuity of material, it is also reasonable to say that somewhere between the extreme longitudinal boundaries there are points which experience no linear strain normal to the transverse plane.

Let us set up a cartesian reference frame with the X axis normal to a transverse plane, the Y axis coinciding with the axis of symmetry of the cross section, and the Z axis at an undetermined location in the transverse plane. In view of the remarks in the preceding paragraph and specifically of assumption 6, we may now quantify the assumed manner of deformation in the symbolic form

$$\epsilon_x = C_1 y + C_2 z. \tag{a}$$

By virtue of assumptions 1 to 3, we may further narrow down the deformation mechanism by saying that all transverse planes remain perpendicular to the plane of loading, or that they rotate about parallel axes normal to the x-y plane. Equation a then simplifies to

$$\epsilon_x = C_1 y. \tag{b}$$

Bringing Hooke's law into the picture next, we find that in order to simplify the problem we need to make additional assumptions, this time regarding stresses. The following appear to be reasonable:

$$\sigma_y = \sigma_z = \tau_{xy} = \tau_{yz} = \tau_{zx} = 0. \tag{c}$$

What we are in effect assuming is that each point on this transverse plane experiences simple uniaxial stress. Thus Hooke's law transforms Eq. b into

$$\sigma_x = C_1 E y = C y. \tag{d}$$

Having involved the stress, we now make use of equilibrium to establish its relation to the bending moment. Equilibrium in translation requires that

$$\Sigma F_x = 0 = \Sigma \Delta F = \Sigma \sigma_x (\Delta A),$$

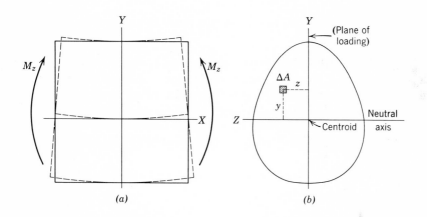

(a)   (b)

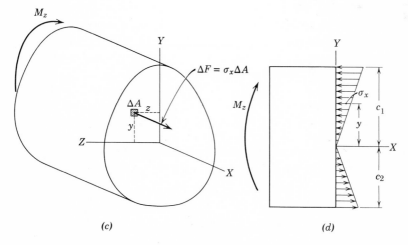

(c)   (d)

Fig. 6.2

which in the limit becomes

$$0 = \int \sigma_x \, dA = C \int y \, dA.$$

From this it follows that the first moment of area relative to the Z axis vanishes, or that

$$\bar{y}A = 0. \tag{e}$$

Since obviously the cross-sectional area A is not zero, we obtain the significant result

$$\bar{y} = 0. \tag{6.1}$$

By virtue of Eq. b, this result indicates that all points lying on the Z axis just located experience no strain and hence no stress. The locus of such "neutral" points is the *neutral axis*. Equation 6.1 then means that *in the pure bending of symmetrical beams, the neutral axis is on that line in the transverse plane which passes through the centroid of the cross-sectional area and is normal to the axis of symmetry, assumed to lie in the plane of loading.* (See Fig. 6.2b.)

Turning next to equilibrium in rotation about the Z axis, we write

$$\Sigma M_z = 0 = -M_z - \Sigma y(\Delta F),$$

which becomes $\qquad 0 = -M_z - \int y \, dF.$

Noting that $dF = \sigma_x \, dA$, as shown in the schematic free-body diagram of Fig. 6.2c, and making the substitution in the preceding equation, we get after transposition

$$M_z = -\int \sigma_x y \, dA, \tag{f}$$

which, because of Eq. d, becomes

$$M_z = -C \int y^2 \, dA = -CI_z, \tag{g}$$

where $I_z = \int y^2 \, dA$ is the second moment of area of the cross section relative to the neutral axis. Using Eq. d once again, we replace C by the ratio σ_x/y and finally obtain from Eq. g the second significant relation

$$\sigma_x = -\frac{M_z y}{I_z}. \tag{6.2}$$

This equation tells us that *for a positive bending moment M_z the normal stress on a transverse plane varies linearly with the distance y from the* *neutral axis and is tensile where y is negative, compressive where y is positive.* (See Fig. 6.2d.) In this statement we find a useful association: In plotting the bending-moment diagram, we lay off the M ordinate to that side of the reference axis analogous to the compressive side of the beam.

If c denotes the distance of the farthest point from the neutral axis, and σ the correspondingly largest value of σ_x, then substituting them in Eq. 6.2 results in the well-known handbook formula

$$\sigma = \frac{Mc}{I}, \tag{6.3}$$

from which all signs and subscripts have been dropped to achieve utmost simplicity. In using Eq. 6.3, one determines by inspection the axes involved and the sense of the "maximum" stress. If the cross section has two axes of symmetry, one of them being the neutral axis, then there is only one value to use for the distance c, and the ratio I/c is given the special symbol Z and the special name, *section modulus.*

Equation 6.3, rewritten in the form

$$M = \frac{\sigma I}{c}, \tag{6.3'}$$

gives the expression for the bending strength of a beam section referred to in the introduction, if for σ is used some meaningful value such as an allowable stress and for c the pertinent distance. In general, there are two values of c; moreover, the allowable value of tensile stress may differ from that of compressive stress. Hence a beam section can have two measures of its strength, depending on the sense of the bending moment it has to resist.

Finally, considering equilibrium in rotation about the Y axis, we write

$$\Sigma M_y = 0 = \Sigma z(\Delta F),$$

which in the limit and after proper substitutions becomes

$$0 = C \int zy \, dA. \tag{h}$$

Using the symbol I_{yz} for the integral $\int zy \, dA$, which is the mixed second moment of area relative to the Y and Z axes, we obtain from Eq. h the third important result

$$I_{yz} = 0. \tag{6.4}$$

Since Y is a principal centroidal axis, it being an axis of symmetry, Eq. 6.4 is automatically satisfied by the restrictive assumptions spelled out earlier. If, on the other hand, the cross section does not have an axis of symmetry, we conclude from Eq. 6.4 that in order for Eq. 6.2 to have any validity the plane of loading must contain a principal inertial axis of the cross section.

PROBLEMS

6.1. Explicitly state an important assumption implied in item 3 (p. 144), which makes possible the results of the foregoing analysis. (*Hint:* See Eqs. 2.3.)

6.2. Suppose we assume the system, $\sigma_x = Cy^2$, with all the other stress components being zero, is equilibrium in pure bending *possible?* How about for $\sigma_x = Dy^3$? Derive a symbolic expression for D in terms of M_z.

6.3. Prove that the second system in Prob. 6.2 cannot be *correct*. Do this by sketching the deformed shape of two adjacent chunks of beam and show that they cannot possibly fit together.

6.3 Significance of the Beam Formula, $M = \sigma I/c$. Owing to the similarity in form of this formula to $T = \tau I_p/r$, which gives the torsional strength of a shaft cross section, some of the remarks made in comparing the shaft with the simple tension member may be made again. The principal one of these is that, whereas the strength of a tension member depends only on the magnitude of the cross-sectional area and not at all on the form, the strength of a beam section most definitely does depend on the form of the area as well as on its magnitude. The ratio I/c here plays the role of the form factor. This is shown in the following.

Illustrative Example 1. Compare the strengths in bending of a square section and a circular section of the same area, assuming the same allowable stress for both.

SOLUTION. Let a be the side of the square. Then the section modulus is

$$Z_s = \left(\frac{I}{c}\right)_s = \frac{a^4/12}{a/2} = \frac{a^3}{6}.$$

If d is the diameter of the circle, then for the areas to be equal, $\pi d^2/4 = a^2$, from which $d = 2a/\sqrt{\pi}$. The section modulus for the circle is found to be

$$Z_c = \left(\frac{I}{c}\right)_c = \frac{\pi d^4/64}{d/2} = \frac{\pi 16a^4/64\pi^2}{a/\sqrt{\pi}} = \frac{a^3}{4\sqrt{\pi}}.$$

Therefore the ratio of the two strengths is

$$\frac{M_s}{M_c} = \frac{(I/c)_s}{(I/c)_c} = \frac{a^3/6}{a^3/4\sqrt{\pi}} = 1.18.$$

The notion of the form factor naturally leads to the subject of optimum beam strength. Let us consider the rectangular section shown in Fig. 6.3a. Since the material near the neutral axis (the plane of loading is assumed vertical) contributes little to the bending strength of the section (for the two reasons that the stress level is low and the lever arm of each resultant differential force is small), it may be removed without the strength of the whole decreasing substantially. Such material may not, however, be removed entirely because continuity of the section must be preserved. We therefore do the next best thing and remove only part of the material near the neutral axis, leaving a connecting web as indicated in Fig. 6.3a. Members of such cross section are called *I-beams*.

We can do even better than this. Instead of merely removing the material, let us transfer it further from the axis, as shown in Fig. 6.3b, and obtain a still more efficient form. This is called a *wide-flange section*. Such a distribution of material achieves yet another purpose—it makes the section stronger in bending with respect to a vertical neutral axis, since the second moment of area relative to this axis is also increased. Especially in a long beam, this increase in strength relative to the vertical axis is important because it also means increased stability against sidewise deflection. Deflections are discussed in the next chapter.

The I-section and the **WF**-section are two of several *structural shapes* manufactured in steel and the light metals. These two forms are the only doubly symmetrical ones. Structural handbooks contain data about commercial sizes made, their weights per unit length, design

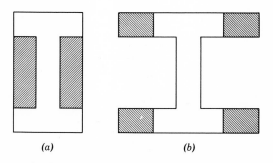

(a)   (b)

Fig. 6.3

properties such as dimensions, area, second moment of area, and section modulus relative to each of the axes of symmetry. Abridged tables taken from one such handbook are found in the Appendix.

It is instructive to compare the bending strength of a WF-section with that of a rectangular one of the same depth and cross-sectional area (hence the same weight per unit length). Let us take as an example a 24WF100 steel section (24 in. nominal depth and 100 lb/ft). Table II, p. 457, gives the following information: $h = 24.00$ in., $A = 29.43$ in.^{2}, $I/c = 248.9$ in.^{3} A rectangular section of the same height and area would have an I/c of $bh^2/6 = Ah/6 = 29.43(24.00)/6 = 117.72$ in.^{3} Hence the ratio of the bending strengths is

$$\frac{M_{WF}}{M_{rect}} = \frac{(I/c)_{WF}}{(I/c)_{rect}} = \frac{248.9}{117.7} = 2.12$$

which shows that the wide-flange section is fully twice as strong as the rectangular one for bending about an axis perpendicular to the web.

Illustrative Example 2. Figure 6.4 shows an 8WF31 section, minus all the fillets. Determine how much of the bending strength is contributed by the flanges and how much by the web, assuming a plane of loading parallel to the web.

SOLUTION. The second moment of area relative to the neutral axis is

$$I_z = \frac{8(8)^3}{12} - \frac{(8 - 0.288)(8 - 0.866)^3}{12}$$

$$= 341.4 - 233.3 = 108.1 \text{ in.}^4$$

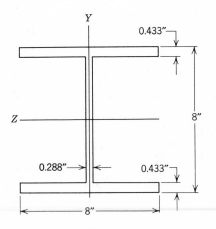

FIG. 6.4

(The fillets increase this value to 109.7 in.[4]) The strength of the section is therefore

$$M = \frac{\sigma(108.1)}{4} = 27\sigma.$$

In terms of the allowable stress σ, the bending stress at the junction of flange and web is by proportion $(4 - 0.433)\sigma/4 = 0.892\sigma$. Hence, if the web were acting alone as a rectangular beam section, its strength based on an allowable stress of 0.892σ would be, by Eq. 6.3',

$$M_{\text{web}} = \frac{(0.288)(8 - 0.866)^2(0.892\sigma)}{6} = 2.18\sigma.$$

Therefore the web contributes only $2.18/27 = 0.0808$ or 8.08% of the total elastic bending strength of the section, whereas the flanges account for the 91.92%. *Ans.*

PROBLEMS

6.4. (*a*) What is the bending strength of a rectangular section, of width b and depth h, when the neutral axis is parallel to the edge b? When the neutral axis is parallel to the edge h?

(*b*) What is the ratio of the two strengths and what useful practical conclusion can you draw from it?

6.5. Determine the strength of an elliptical beam section, with semiaxes a and b, for bending about one of its axes. Specify which axis your answer corresponds to.

6.6. For the same allowable stress in compression and tension, calculate the strength of an equilateral triangular beam section, with an edge of length a, for bending about a neutral axis parallel to an edge.

6.7. How should a log of uniform diameter d be trimmed down to leave a beam with a rectangular cross section of optimum bending strength? What is the percentage loss in weight? What is the percentage loss in bending strength? Would this be the heaviest rectangular beam that can be cut out of the log?

6.8. Repeat the preceding, assuming the log to have an elliptical cross section, with semiaxes A and B.

6.9. The cross section of a uniform bar is an equilateral triangle of edge a. What are the dimensions of the strongest rectangular beam that can be cut out of this bar?

6.10. In which position does a square beam section develop greatest bending strength, when the neutral axis is parallel to an edge or when it coincides with a diagonal? Find the ratio of the two strengths.

6.11. For each of the beam sections shown, what percentage of the total bending strength is contributed by the shaded portions? What percentage loss in strength would result in trimming off this material from each beam?

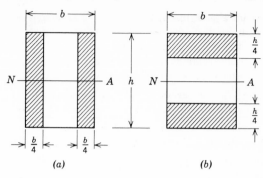

FIG. P6.11

6.12. From the tables in the Appendix, select the two lightest rolled shapes, one an I- and the other a WF-section, which are at least as strong as a 12 in. by 4 in. rectangular beam of the same material when used in the best position. What percent lighter is each one compared to the rectangular beam?

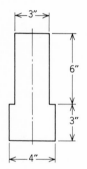

6.13. Select the lightest WF-section which is at least as strong as an 8 in. by 4 in. rectangular beam of the same material, if the beam depth is limited to 10 in. What percent lighter is the rolled shape?

6.14. For what material strength properties would a T-section be preferable to a doubly symmetrical one? Explain.

6.15. For a vertical plane of loading, what is the ratio of the greatest bending stresses of opposite signs in this beam section?

FIG. P6.15

6.16. A certain material has an allowable compressive stress that is twice the allowable tensile stress. For optimum conditions, how long should be the stem of this T-beam that is made of this material? In terms of the smaller stress value, calculate this optimum bending strength. The plane of loading is vertical.

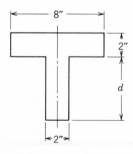

FIG. P6.16

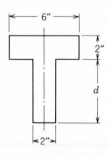

FIG. P6.17

6.17. This T-beam is to be of a material whose elastic-limit strengths in compression and tension are in the ratio of 5 to 3. What should the dimension d be in order that the strength properties of the material may be fully exploited? Calculate this optimum bending strength in terms of the larger stress.

6.18. From the Appendix tables, we note that a 20I75 and a 21 W̶62 steel beam have comparable maximum bending strengths. Using the dimensions given in the tables, make an estimate for each section of the percentage of the total bending strength accounted for by the flanges.

6.4 Strength in Shear. Knowing the strength of a beam section in bending, we now seek its strength in shear. We recall that in the helical spring, we made the crude assumption that the shear force P gives rise to uniformly distributed tangential stresses. In the present analysis it is possible to introduce considerable refinement by assuming that the relation, $\sigma_x = -M_z y / I_z$, which was derived on the express limitation of pure bending, holds also when shear force accompanies the moment. Observe that this is an extrapolation.

Consider a small length Δx cut out of a beam in a region that transmits both bending moment and shear force, but which is free of any external loads (load intensity is zero), Fig. 6.5a. The left face has acting on it a shear force V and a bending moment M, whereas the right face is subjected to a resisting shear force V and a resisting moment $M + \Delta M$. Imagine a longitudinal cutting plane passed parallel to the neutral plane at a distance y_1 above it, isolating a chunk as shown in Fig. 6.5b.

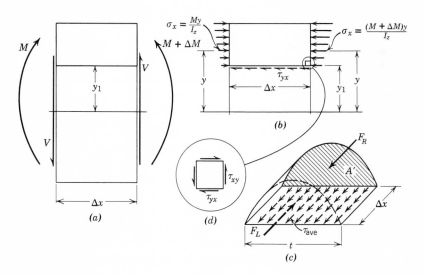

Fig. 6.5

The free-body diagram shows the varying normal stresses due to the moments on the end faces. At a distance y from the neutral plane, the differential normal force ΔF_L corresponding to a small area ΔA on the left face has the magnitude

$$\Delta F_L = \sigma(\Delta A) = \frac{My}{I}(\Delta A),$$

whereas that for the right face has the value

$$\Delta F_R = \sigma(\Delta A) = \frac{(M + \Delta M)y}{I}(\Delta A).$$

Summing up these differential forces for each face, we find for the left face the resultant normal force

$$F_L = \int_{A'} \frac{My}{I}\, dA, \qquad (a)$$

and for the right face,

$$F_R = \int_{A'} \frac{(M + \Delta M)y}{I}\, dA = \int_{A'} \frac{My}{I}\, dA + \int_{A'} \frac{(\Delta M)y}{I}\, dA, \qquad (b)$$

where each integration is to be carried out over the area A', which is that part of the entire cross section to either side of the level y_1 (in this example, above y_1).

It is evident that the resultant normal forces F_R and F_L are unequal, differing by an amount $\int_{A'} (\Delta M/I)y\, dA$; hence, if there were no other forces, the block would slide. Since the body is in equilibrium, it being part of a beam that is in equilibrium, we must assume that some force not yet accounted for prevents sliding: this must be the action of the material beneath the block exerted tangentially over a rectangular area of dimensions t by Δx, where t is the local thickness of the beam cross section at the level y_1 (see Fig. 6.5c). Let us now assume that, like the normal stresses on transverse planes, this tangential action on the longitudinal plane consists of a continuously distributed system of stresses; and owing to the obvious dependence of these tangential stresses on the bending stresses, we assume further that they do not vary across the thickness t but will, in general, vary along Δx for any given level y_1. Calling the average intensity, τ_{ave}, for the small rectangular area $t(\Delta x)$, we find the resultant tangential force to be

$$F_T = \tau_{\text{ave}} t(\Delta x). \qquad (c)$$

Equilibrium is assured by the condition

$$\Sigma F_x = 0 = F_L - F_R - F_T,$$

from which it follows that

$$-\int_{A'} \frac{(\Delta M)y}{I} \, dA - \tau_{\text{ave}} t(\Delta x) = 0.$$

In the integral on the left, the summation process is carried out over part of the cross-sectional area for which the position coordinate x is kept constant; hence the ratio $\Delta M/I$, which generally depends on x, remains constant and may be taken outside the integral sign. Doing this and solving for τ_{ave}, we obtain

$$\tau_{\text{ave}} = -\frac{\Delta M}{\Delta x} \frac{1}{It} \int_{A'} y \, dA. \qquad (d)$$

Passing on to the limit and noting that $-(dM/dx) = V$ and that $\int_{A'} y \, dA = \bar{y}A' = Q$, the first moment of the area A' relative to the neutral axis, we finally get *

$$\tau = \frac{V\bar{y}A'}{It} = \frac{VQ}{It}. \qquad (6.5)$$

Note that in the limit τ_{ave} becomes the local intensity τ, which depends on x and y but not on z (by assumption). From the manner in which Eq. 6.5 was derived, it should be clear that the shear stress it gives is the component on a longitudinal plane, or τ_{yx}, in formal subscript notation. We know, however, that $\tau_{xy} = \tau_{yx}$ (see Chapter 2); therefore Eq. 6.5 also gives the transverse shear stress, which is in the direction of the transverse shear force V, Fig. 6.5d.

Before we derive from Eq. 6.5 a meaningful expression for the shear strength of a beam section, it is important that we understand the full significance of all the terms in the equation, especially that of Q/t. For any given x, the ratio V/I is fixed; hence τ depends only on Q/t. The first moment of area Q is a function of the level y_1; it varies from zero at either extreme (where $\bar{y}$ becomes c, a numerical maximum, but A' becomes zero) to a maximum at the level of the neutral axis (where A' becomes a maximum and $\bar{y}$ is not zero). If the thickness t is constant,

---

* This analysis is based on one originated by D. J. Jourawski in 1844 for rectangular beam sections. See S. Timoshenko, *History of Strength of Materials*, pp. 141–144, McGraw-Hill Book Company, New York, 1953.

as in a rectangular section, or if t varies in such a way that it attains its least value at the neutral axis, then the ratio Q/t is necessarily a maximum at the neutral axis. When this is the situation, τ_{xy} as given by Eq. 6.5 is a maximum at the neutral axis. On the other hand, if t varies in some other fashion, then Q/t may or may not attain its maximum value at the neutral axis. If the variation of t is continuous, the location and value of $(Q/t)_{\max}$ may be established by the calculus; if t varies in stepwise fashion, then at least one level other than the neutral axis should be looked into for a possible maximum Q/t, usually that level *nearest* to the neutral axis where t is least.

With the preceding remarks, we may now derive from Eq. 6.5 the strength criterion

$$V = \frac{\tau I}{(Q/t)_{\max}}, \tag{6.5'}$$

where for τ an allowable or design value should be used.

Illustrative Example 3. Derive the expression for the shear stress τ_{xy} in a rectangular beam section that transmits a shear force V in the Y direction, and analyze its variation. From these results, investigate whether the shear strength of a rectangular section depends on its orientation relative to the plane of loading.

ANALYSIS. Figure 6.6a shows a rectangular beam section for which the plane of loading is assumed vertical. For any level y above the neutral axis, the area A' shown shaded is

$$A' = b \left(\frac{h}{2} - y \right),$$

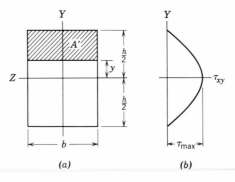

(a)   (b)

FIG. 6.6

and the location of its centroid is obvious by inspection:

$$\bar{y} = \frac{h/2 + y}{2}.$$

Hence, $Q = \bar{y}A'$ becomes

$$Q = b\left(\frac{h}{2} - y\right)\left(\frac{h/2 + y}{2}\right) = \frac{b}{2}\left(\frac{h^2}{4} - y^2\right). \qquad (e)$$

Since $t = b$, which is constant, we get

$$\frac{Q}{t} = \frac{h^2/4 - y^2}{2}. \qquad (f)$$

Substituting $bh^3/12$ for I, we finally obtain from Eq. 6.5

$$\tau = \frac{VQ}{It} = \frac{6V}{bh^3}\left(\frac{h^2}{4} - y^2\right). \qquad (g)$$

This is the equation of a parabola; its graph is shown in Fig. 6.6b. At the extreme levels, where $y = \pm h/2$, τ is zero as explained in the previous general discussion. At the neutral axis, where $y = 0$, τ has its maximum value

$$\tau_{max} = \frac{3}{2}\frac{V}{bh}. \qquad (h)$$

We note from Eq. h that the shear strength of a rectangular section may be written in the form

$$V = \frac{2bh\tau}{3}, \qquad (i)$$

by which it should be clear that the shear strength depends only on the allowable shear stress τ and the magnitude of the cross-sectional area bh, and does not depend on the orientation of the plane of loading relative to either b or h. Contrast this with the dependence of the bending strength on the relative orientation of the plane of loading.* (See Prob. 6.4.)

Illustrative Example 4.   For the idealized WF-section of Fig. 6.4, repeated in Fig. 6.7, determine the variation of the transverse shear stresses

---

* The preceding remarks are approximately correct only when b is of the same order of magnitude as h. If b is very large compared to h, then the component τ_{xz}, which was assumed nonexistent in the elementary derivation, will have a maximum value that can exceed $(\tau_{xy})_{max}$. See S. Timoshenko and J. N. Goodier, *Theory of Elasticity*, p. 328, McGraw-Hill Book Company, New York, 1951.

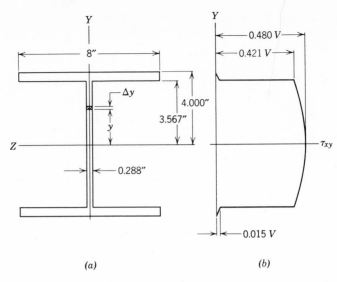

(a)   (b)

FIG. 6.7

and calculate how much of the shear strength is contributed by the web
and how much by the flanges.   Use $I = 108.1$ in.[4]

SOLUTION.   At any level y less than 3.567 in. (see Fig. 6.7a),

$$\frac{Q}{t} = \frac{8(0.433)3.784 + 0.288(3.567 - y)(3.567 + y)/2}{0.288}$$

$$= 45.5 + 0.5(12.73 - y^2) = 51.86 - 0.5y^2.$$

Hence the shear stress is

$$\tau = \frac{V(51.86 - 0.5y^2)}{108.1}, \qquad -3.567 < y < 3.567.$$

At $y = 0$, $\tau_{\max} = 0.480V$ psi.   At $y = 3.567$, the value of τ based on a
thickness of 0.288 in. is $0.421V$ psi, whereas that based on a thickness of
8 in. is $0.015V$ psi.   At $y = 4$ in., $\tau = 0$.   Figure 6.7b shows the variation
of the transverse shear stress τ_{xy} across the height of the beam section:
it is symmetrical relative to $y = 0$, parabolic between $y = 0$ and $y =
3.567$ in. as well as between $y = 3.567$ in. and $y = 4$ in., and exhibits a
singularity at $y = 3.567$ in.

To determine the contribution of the web to the shear strength, we
sum up the resultant forces ΔF corresponding to strips of area $0.288(\Delta y)$,

like that shown in Fig. 6.7a, where $\Delta F = \tau(\Delta A) = \tau(0.288)\Delta y$. Substituting for τ its value in terms of y, passing to the limit, and integrating, we obtain

$$F = \frac{0.288V}{108.1} \ (2) \int_0^{3.567} (51.86 - 0.5y^2) \, dy = 0.947V,$$

where the factor 2 takes care of the two halves of the web. The preceding result shows that the web accounts for 94.7% of the shear strength, with the remainder of 5.3% being contributed by the flanges.

Ans.

Observe that if V is divided by the area of the web alone, which is the rectangle, 0.288 in. thick and 7.134 in. high, there is obtained $0.487V$ psi, which differs but slightly from the maximum of $0.480V$ psi. This explains the common practice of considering the average value of τ based on the area of the web as the maximum for the entire cross section.

It is interesting to note that the web and the flanges in doubly symmetrical structural shapes complement each other's role in beam action: the flanges furnish practically all the bending strength and the web practically all the shear strength.

PROBLEMS

6.19. In terms of the vertical shear force V that the beam section of Fig. P6.15 is assumed to transmit, determine the maximum transverse shear stress.

6.20. A beam with the box section shown is to transmit a shear force V. If the allowable transverse shear stress is 500 psi, what maximum value can V have, and how should the beam section be oriented relative to V?

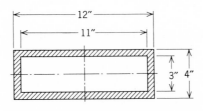

FIG. P6.20

6.21. For each of the beam sections of Fig. P6.11, calculate by integration the contribution of the unshaded area to the total shear strength.

6.22. In Fig. P6.15, determine by integration how much of the total shear strength of the beam section is accounted for by the stem and how much by the bar of the inverted **T**.

6.23. Using the approximation explained in the text, estimate the maximum transverse shear stress in a 15I50 steel section caused by a shear force parallel to the web. Look up the required dimensions in the Appendix tables. Express the result in terms of V. Compare this with the result of a more accurate calculation.

6.24. Do Prob. 6.23 for an 18WF50 steel section.

6.25. Derive Eq. g of Example 3, governing the shear stress τ_{xy} in a beam of rectangular cross section, of width b and depth h, by integrating the first differential equation of equilibrium, Eq. 2.3a. Start with the expression for σ_x which was derived for pure bending, $\sigma_x = -M_z y / I_z$; assume a state of plane stress, so that $\tau_{zx} = 0$, and ignore body forces. Make use of the boundary conditions that, at $y = \pm(h/2)$, τ_{xy} must vanish.

6.26. Using Eq. g of Example 3 in the second differential equation of equilibrium, Eq. 2.3b, show that if a rectangular beam bears a continuously distributed load of local intensity q (uniform across b), then normal stresses on z-x planes arise whose magnitudes are given by

$$\sigma_y = \frac{q}{b}\left(\frac{3y}{2h} - \frac{2y^3}{h^3} + \frac{1}{2}\right).$$

Set both τ_{zy} and the body force to zero, and make use of the boundary condition that, at $y = -(h/2)$, σ_y must vanish. Sketch a graph showing the variation of σ_y across the depth of the rectangular section.

6.5   Shear Stresses in Wide-Flange Sections.   In cross sections whose lateral edges are parallel to the plane of loading, and especially if the thickness is small compared to the depth, it is reasonable to assume: (1) that the transverse shear stresses are parallel to the shear force (understood to be in the Y direction) and (2) that these stresses do not vary across the thickness of the section at the level in question, except at or near abrupt changes in the thickness. Equation 6.5 then gives τ_{xy}. This is the situation in the web of doubly symmetrical structural shapes.

Now let us consider the shear stresses in the flanges of WF-sections. The long edges along these boundaries are parallel to the Z direction, perpendicular to the plane of loading. If the thickness, which is the dimension parallel to the Y axis, is small, shear stresses τ_{xz} will develop that can be more significant than the nominal τ_{xy}. To evaluate τ_{xz} we may still use Eq. 6.5, provided we take A' as shown in Fig. 6.8a; here, one of the sectioning planes which cut out the small block is parallel to the x-y plane, and therefore the coordinate z of this cutting plane locates the "level" at which the particular τ_{xz} exists. The shaded area A' varies directly as the width d of the rectangle, and its centroidal distance $\bar{y}$ is constant; therefore Q, as well as Q/t, varies linearly with d, since the thickness t does not change. Hence τ_{xz} also varies linearly with d.

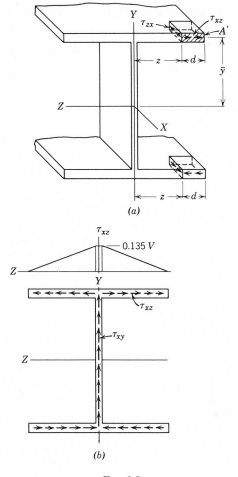

FIG. 6.8

Figure 6.8b indicates the two systems of stresses: τ_{xz} for the flanges, varying linearly, and τ_{xy} for the web, varying parabolically.

At the junction of web and flange in the last example, the dimension d of Fig. 6.8a is (see Fig. 6.7a) $4 - 0.144 = 3.856$ in. Therefore

$$\frac{Q}{t} = \frac{3.856(0.433)(4 - 0.217)}{0.433} = 14.6 \text{ in.}^2$$

and the maximum τ_{xz} becomes, by Eq. 6.5,

$$(\tau_{xz})_{\max} = \frac{V(14.6)}{108.1} = 0.135V \text{ psi.}$$

At the level of the median line of the flange, the nominal τ_{xy} is approximately $0.0078V$ psi. Hence, in the vicinity of the junction of web and flange, τ_{xz} is over seventeen times as large as the nominal τ_{xy}.

PROBLEMS

6.27. The box beam transmits a shear force of 10,000 lb along the Y axis. Isolate a length Δx of the shaded portion ($abcd$) and draw its free-body diagram

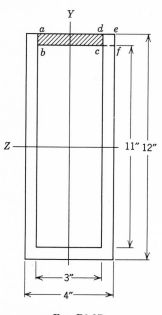

in the manner of Fig. 6.5c. The vertical longitudinal faces (ab and cd) of the small block must have shown acting on them shear stresses τ_{zx}. Assume that τ_{zx} does not vary with y. From basic statics, calculate the average intensity of τ_{zx}.

6.28. Calculate the average τ_{zx} on the vertical longitudinal faces (ab and cd) of the block in Fig. P6.27, using Eq. 6.5. (Note that for the thickness t a total value of $0.5 + 0.5 = 1.0$ in. must be used.) Then calculate τ_{yx} at the level cf. Finally, isolate a length Δx of the portion $cdef$ and in the manner of Fig. 6.5c show that it is indeed in equilibrium.

6.29. In Fig. 6.8b, imagine that the left portions of the two flanges are cut off, leaving a section in the form of a channel or a U on its side, as shown in the sketch. Let us assume that the two sets of stresses, τ_{xz} and τ_{xy}, are distributed in a manner similar to the original, although not necessarily of the same magnitudes. This is like saying that the beam formulas, $\sigma_x = -M_z y/I_z$ and $\tau = VQ/It$, are assumed applicable. Examine the figure carefully.

FIG. P6.27

Without making any calculations, using only your knowledge of statics, show that the resultant action in the plane of the figure must be a force parallel to the web but lying to the left of it. Where this resultant force crosses the Z axis (still an axis of symmetry) is called the *shear center*, or sometimes the *center of flexure*. It is the point through which the transmitted shear force V must pass in order that beam sections *will not twist in their planes*. Again, without doing any computing, show by means of a schematic free body that equilibrium in rotation about the X axis is possible when V is offset from the web (see sketch b).

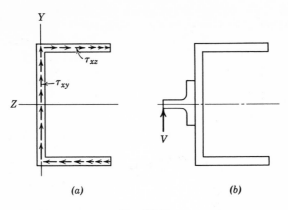

(a)   (b)

Fig. P6.29

A beam with an arbitrary shape cross section will possess a shear center which, in general, will not be the same as the centroid. These points will not coincide whenever shear stresses τ_{xz} (usually not derivable by our elementary theory) give rise to a twisting moment about the X axis. Determination of where the shear center is for any but the most simple of cross sections belongs to more advanced studies.* We take up here only *thin* open sections in which the shear stress at any "level" may be assumed *constant* across the thickness and hence sections in which τ_{xz} may be evaluated, albeit approximately.

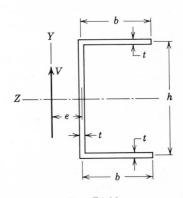

Fig. P6.30

6.30. The open section shown has a uniform thickness t, which is very small compared to the other dimensions b and h, assumed to be those of the median line. Calculate the distance e from the web of the equivalent transmitted shear force V in order that the beam section will not twist in its plane. (*Hint:* Evaluate τ from Eq. 6.5 and then find the moments of all the shear flows q ($= \tau t$) about some convenient moment center.)

6.31. The shear center for this angle section is obviously at the intersection of the median lines. For any point in the cross section, derive the expressions for τ_{xy} and τ_{xz}. Express these in terms of the shear force V and the dimensions a, t, and y.

6.32. Locate the shear center for this open section.

* See Timoshenko and Goodier, *op. cit.* on p. 157 , pp. 333–336.

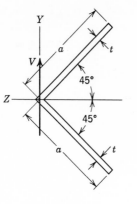

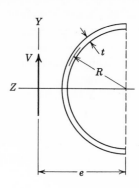

Fig. P6.31   Fig. P6.32

6.6   Further Significance of the Beam Formula, $\tau = VQ/It$.
If the thickness t is large compared to the depth h, or if t varies continuously throughout h, which is true in the circular cross section, for example, then τ_{xy} as given by Eq. 6.5 is only one component of τ_x since τ_{xz} in general differs from zero. On any transverse plane, any nonzero shear stress at points on the boundary must be tangent to the boundary, because otherwise the cross shear stress on the supposedly stress-free periphery becomes an absurdity. For such points on the boundary, the total shear stress τ_x may be computed with the aid of τ_{xy} as given by Eq. 6.5; for interior points, our elementary analysis furnishes no answer. This is shown in the following.

Illustrative Example 5.   Determine the maximum transverse shear stress in a beam of circular cross section due to a shear force V.

SOLUTION.   Consider the circular section shown in Fig. 6.9a. At the level y above the neutral axis, let us assume that the transverse shear stress on the periphery is parallel to the shear force V. Resolve this stress into two rectangular components in the tangential and radial directions, τ_{xt} and τ_{xr}, as shown in the left-hand side of Fig. 6.9a. From the fact that cross shears on perpendicular planes must exist concomitantly, if at all, we conclude that τ_{xr} cannot exist because there is nothing to exert the necessary accompanying cross shear stress τ_{rx} on the free surface of the beam. Hence it follows that τ_{xt} is itself the *total* transverse shear stress at this point, and that the vertical shear stress τ_{xy} is merely its vertical orthographic component as indicated in the right-hand side of the sketch.

Regarding the shear stress at some point on this same level other than at the periphery, we need to make some assumption relative to the inclination of the total τ_x before we can evaluate its magnitude. Two reasonable suppositions are: (1) the total stress vector passes through the point where the tangents to the periphery intersect and (2) that the vertical component τ_{xy} is constant in magnitude. (See Fig. 6.9b.) The horizontal component τ_{xz} then goes through the value zero at the vertical diameter, where it also changes sense; this is consistent with symmetry. With these assumptions we may now proceed as follows.

For the shaded area in Fig. 6.9a, $Q = (2/3)R^3 \sin^3 \theta$, and $t = 2R \sin \theta$. Therefore

$$\frac{Q}{t} = \frac{R^2 \sin^2 \theta}{3},$$

and
$$\tau_{xy} = \frac{VQ}{It} = \frac{VR^2 \sin^2 \theta}{3I}. \tag{a}$$

The total shear stress τ_x has a maximum inclination relative to τ_{xy} at the periphery; hence τ_x is greatest there for any given level, and its

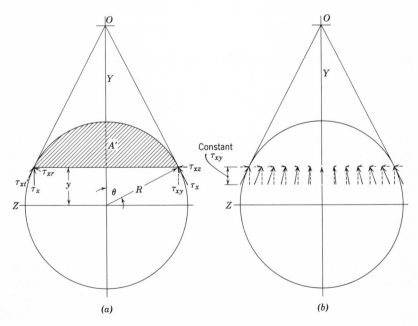

(a)   (b)

FIG. 6.9

magnitude is

$$\tau_x = \frac{\tau_{xy}}{\sin\theta} = \frac{VR^2\sin\theta}{3I}. \tag{b}$$

Introducing y in the relation $R\sin\theta = \sqrt{R^2 - y^2}$, we finally obtain for τ_x at the periphery:

$$\tau_x = \frac{VR\sqrt{R^2 - y^2}}{3I}. \tag{c}$$

Equation c shows that the maximum transverse shear stress occurs at the level of the neutral axis, where $y = 0$. Substituting for I its value $\pi R^4/4$, we find for this maximum

$$(\tau_x)_{\max} = \frac{VR^2}{3\pi R^4/4} = \frac{4V}{3\pi R^2}. \qquad Ans. \tag{d}$$

The rigorous mathematical solution of this problem gives the following results.* The transverse shear stress takes on its maximum value at the center of the circle, and this is

$$(\tau_x)_{\max} = \frac{3 + 2\nu}{2(1 + \nu)}\left(\frac{V}{\pi R^2}\right). \tag{e}$$

At the ends of the horizontal diameter, the transverse shear stress is

$$\tau_x = \frac{1 + 2\nu}{1 + \nu}\left(\frac{V}{\pi R^2}\right). \tag{f}$$

If for the Poisson ratio ν the approximate value of 0.3 is substituted, Eqs. e and f lead to, respectively, $1.384V/\pi R^2$ and $1.230V/\pi R^2$. Comparing Eq. d with these results, we note that our elementary theory gives $(\tau_x)_{\max}$ to within less than 4% of the correct maximum.

PROBLEMS

6.33. After the manner of Example 5, determine and locate the maximum transverse shear stress τ_x in a beam, whose cross section is an isoceles triangle of base b and altitude h, due to a shear force V in its plane of symmetry.

* See I. S. Sokolnikoff, *Mathematical Theory of Elasticity*, p. 214, McGraw-Hill Book Company, New York, 1956.

6.34. In terms of V, calculate and locate the maximum transverse shear stress in this beam section.

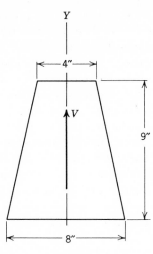

FIG. P6.34

6.7 Applications. Having developed elementary expressions for the bending strength and the shearing strength of a beam section, we naturally would like now to apply these to entire beams. It must be remembered that Eq. 6.5 was derived on the basis of an extrapolation, namely, that Eq. 6.2 applies even when the bending moment is accompanied by shear force. In applying the two formulas to whole beams, we must make the additional extrapolation that they both hold even when the local load intensity is not zero. We are in effect saying that, on any transverse beam section, the stress distribution given by Eq. 6.2, when superimposed on the stress distribution given by Eq. 6.5, will define the resultant stress distribution due to the combined action of shear force and bending moment, *even in the presence of externally distributed lateral forces.* The immediately obvious implication of this extension is that Eq. *c* of Article 6.2 should be modified: both σ_y and σ_z, as well as τ_{xy} and τ_{xz}, must not be assumed zero. Consider, for instance, the beam element of Fig. 6.5; if a continuously distributed system of downward forces were acting on top of the beam, then upward normal stresses σ_y must be shown acting on the underside of the free body in Fig. 6.5*b* in order to preserve equilibrium. Furthermore, the boundary conditions at the top and bottom surfaces of the beam suggest that σ_y must be some function of y. (See Prob. 6.26.) Fortunately, these pressures on horizontal longitudinal planes are usually small and, except

in the immediate vicinity of concentrated loads, they may be ignored.*
Equation 6.3, $\sigma = Mc/I$, tells us that we should look for the maximum
bending stresses at those points where the product Mc is greatest. In
beams whose cross sections are doubly symmetrical, the two values of c
are equal and the maximum bending stresses invariably occur in those
sections where M is greatest. On the other hand, in beams whose cross
sections have only one axis of symmetry, that in the plane of loading,
the two sections with the largest bending moments of opposite signs
must, in general, be investigated for maximum stresses; then a comparison of the products of the four possible pairs of M and c will quickly
indicate where the largest bending stresses occur. Bending-moment
diagrams facilitate the location of these critical sections.

In contrast to the bending stresses, the maximum transverse shear
stresses always occur in those sections where V is greatest. The shear-
force diagram shows where such sections are. There remains only the
evaluation of $(Q/t)_{max}$ and then Eq. 6.5, $\tau = VQ/It$, will give the maximum transverse shear stress.

Illustrative Example 6. A beam whose cross section is shown in Fig.
6.10*b* is to be loaded as in Fig. 6.10*a* when in the inverted-**T** position.
It is desired to analyze the beam for maximum bending and shearing
stresses.

SOLUTION. The centroid of the cross-sectional area is found to be 2.33
in. from the bottom; therefore the two values of c are 5.67 in. and 2.33
in. The second moment of area with respect to the neutral axis is

$$I_z = \frac{1(6)^3}{12} + 1(6)(2.67)^2 + \frac{6(2)^3}{12} + 6(2)(1.33)^2$$

$$= 86 \text{ in.}^4$$

The load-intensity, shear-force, and bending-moment diagrams are
shown in Figs. 6.10*c*, *d*, and *e*. Sketch *e* reveals the two greatest bending
moments of opposite signs to be +23,945 ft-lb, 7.3 ft from the left end,
and −11,200 ft-lb, 16 ft from the left end. Pairing off each of these
moments with the two values of c in turn, thus:

For Tension	For Compression
23,945(2.33) = 55,800	23,945(5.67) = 135,700
11,200(5.67) = 63,500	11,200(2.33) = 26,100

* See S. Timoshenko, *Strength of Materials, Part I,* pp. 146–148, D. Van Nostrand
Company, Princeton, New Jersey, 1930.

we see that the maximum tensile stress is

$$(\sigma_t)_{\max} = \frac{63,500(12)}{86} = 8860 \text{ psi}; \qquad Ans.$$

it occurs in the uppermost fibers at the section 16 ft from the left end. The maximum compressive stress is

$$(\sigma_c)_{\max} = \frac{135,700(12)}{86} = 18,960 \text{ psi} \qquad Ans.$$

in the topmost fibers at the section 7.3 ft from the left end.

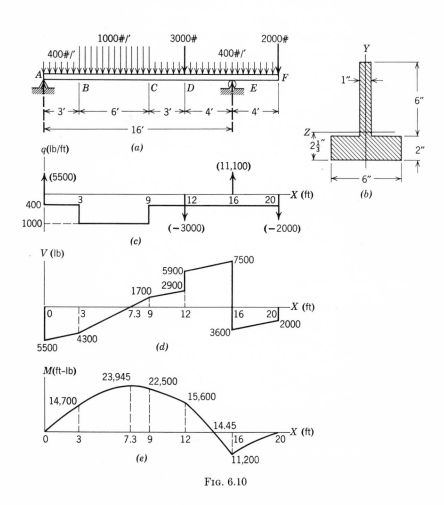

FIG. 6.10

Since the neutral axis crosses the narrowest part of the cross section, Q/t is maximum there and is equal to

$$\left(\frac{Q}{t}\right)_{max} = \frac{1(5.67)^2/2}{1} = 16.06 \text{ in.}^2$$

Using $V_{max} = 7500$ lb from Fig. 6.10d, we find

$$\tau_{max} = \frac{7500(16.06)}{86} = 1400 \text{ psi.} \qquad\qquad Ans.$$

This occurs at the neutral axis of the section immediately to the left of $x = 16$ ft.

Illustrative Example 7.   For the beam shown in Fig. 6.11a, determine the maximum value that W may have if the following stresses in any

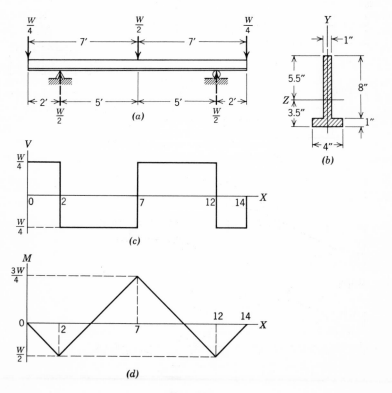

Fig. 6.11

transverse plane are not to be exceeded: 6000 psi in tension, 10,800 psi in compression, and 750 psi in shear. Ignore the weight of the beam.

SOLUTION. The neutral axis locates at 3.5 in. from the base, and $I_z = 97$ in.[4] The two values of c are 5.5 in. and 3.5 in. Equation 6.3′ now gives the usable bending strength of the beam section. With the top in compression, we have

$$M_1 = \frac{10,800(97)}{5.5} = 190,500 \text{ in.-lb.}$$

With the top in tension, we find

$$M_2 = \frac{6000(97)}{5.5} = 105,800 \text{ in.-lb.}$$

Noting that the neutral axis crosses the narrowest part of the cross section, we obtain $(Q/t)_{max} = 5.5(5.5)/2(1) = 15.13$ in.[2] Hence, by Eq. 6.5′, the usable shear strength is

$$V = \frac{750(97)}{15.13} = 4810 \text{ lb.}$$

From Fig. 6.11d we see that the maximum demand for that kind of resisting moment which requires the upper fibers to be in compression, and of which M_1 is the usable limit, is $0.75W$ ft-lb. Equating this to M_1, using proper units, we get

$$0.75W(12) = 190,500,$$

whence $W_1 = 21,180$ lb.

The maximum demand for the other kind of resisting moment, of which M_2 is the usable limit, is $0.5W$ ft-lb. Equating this to M_2, thus

$$0.5W(12) = 105,800,$$

we obtain $W_2 = 17,640$ lb.

Finally, the maximum demand for V is $0.25W$, by Fig. 6.11c. Equating this to the usable shear strength, we write

$$0.25W = 4810,$$

from which $W_3 = 19,240$ lb.

Of these three values we select the smallest one, W_2, for our answer, since this is the least load which, when distributed as in Fig. 6.11a, will induce one of the allowable values of stress: 6000 psi in tension. This controlling stress will occur in the top fibers of the beam where it is supported.

Illustrative Example 8. A steel beam, 40 ft long and supported at two points whose locations are adjustable, is to carry a uniformly distributed load of 1000 lb/ft. Determine the smallest WF or   structural shape that will carry this load without the bending stresses exceeding 20,000 psi.

SOLUTION. From our understanding of strength as a measure of usefulness, we conclude that the smallest beam is that which will function most efficiently within the prescribed limits. This will happen when the greatest number of transverse sections can fully develop their usable bending capacities. The ideal is, of course, for *all* sections of the beam to participate fully. With a finite number of supports, however, this ideal can never be realized; we will, accordingly, have to be content with exploiting a limited number of beam sections. Moreover, since we are not yet in a position to handle statically indeterminate beams, we are further limited to a maximum of *three* sections. This number is arrived at as follows.

If the beam were supported at one end only, as a cantilever, only *one* section, that at the wall, would develop its full measure of usefulness. If the beam were simply supported at the two ends, again only *one* section, that at midspan, could deliver its full strength. By moving one of the supports nearer the center, however, we could make *two* sections deliver full strength; these are the section immediately above the reaction near the overhang and that one between the two supports where the shear force is zero. Finally, by moving the other support nearer the center, we could make the maximum number of *three* sections develop full usefulness; these are the two sections at the supports and the one section between them where the shear force is zero. This number of sections of fully developed strength can be increased to four or more only by imposing additional restraints (supports) on the beam, making it statically indeterminate. Such beams are discussed in Chapter 8.

In order for these three sections to develop their usable capacities simultaneously, it is necessary that the bending moments there be of the same magnitude. Hence the beam with two overhangs must be supported symmetrically as shown in Fig. 6.12*a*. The length *a* of each overhang is determined from the numerical equality of the bending moment at each support and that at midspan, thus:

$$\frac{pa^2}{2} = \frac{pL}{2}\left(\frac{L}{2} - a\right) - \frac{pL^2}{8}.$$

This yields the equation

$$4a^2 + 4La - L^2 = 0,$$

from which we find $a = 0.207L$. Substituting 40 ft for L, we obtain for the overhang $a = 8.28$ ft.

The three greatest bending moments are therefore each equal to $pa^2/2$ $= 1000(8.28)^2/2 = 34,300$ ft-lb. From Eq. 6.3 we now find the necessary section modulus

$$\frac{I}{c} = \frac{M}{\sigma} = \frac{34,300(12)}{20,000} = 20.6 \text{ in.}^3$$

The Appendix tables show that either an 8WF31 ($I/c = 27.4$ in.³) or a 10I25.4 ($I/c = 24.4$ in.³) would be satisfactory, although an 8WF24 ($I/c = 20.8$ in.³) would be more economical. *Ans.*

If the dead weight of the beam is to be considered an added load, the beam being assumed supported in a horizontal position, a check will be in order, especially if the chosen section has a bending strength that is just slightly larger than the required value. It is instructive to do this, first for the 10I25.4 and then for the 8WF24. In the I-beam, whose weight per foot is 25.4 lb, the maximum bending moment will increase by pro-

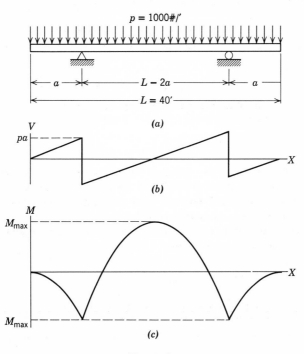

Fig. 6.12

portion to the value: 34,300(1025.4/1000) = 35,170 ft-lb. Hence the maximum bending stresses will become: σ = 35,170(12)/24.4 = 17,300 psi; this is still less than 20,000 psi. In the W-beam, whose weight is 24 lb/ft, the maximum bending moment will increase to 34,300($\frac{1024}{1000}$) = 35,130 ft-lb. Then the maximum bending stress will be: σ = 35,130(12)/20.8 = 20,270 psi, which is slightly in excess of the allowable value of 20,000 psi.

In a design problem like this last example, it should be noted that, if it is desired to take into account the dead weight of the beam itself in the computations, then it is not possible to avoid altogether a certain amount of trial and error in the solution. This is because the weight per unit length of beam, among the various sizes of commercially available structural shapes, varies not continuously but in stepwise fashion.

PROBLEMS

6.35. What percent more uniformly distributed load will a beam carry when its two supports are at optimum locations, compared to when they are at the ends? Assume the allowable stresses in tension and compression to be equal in magnitude.

6.36. This beam has a 3-in. thick rectangular cross section. If the maximum bending stress is not to exceed 3200 psi, what least depth may the beam have?

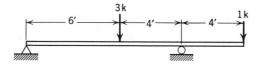

FIG. P6.36

6.37. A 12-ft rectangular beam, simply supported at both ends, bears a uniformly distributed load of 100 lb per ft. If the allowable bending stress is 2000 psi, and if the depth-to-width ratio of its cross section is 1.55, what are the dimensions of the smallest satisfactory beam?

6.38. Select a W-section for this beam, using an allowable bending stress of 16,000 psi. Ignore the beam's weight.

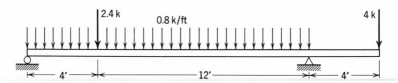

FIG. P6.38

6.39. Investigate whether the beam of Example 7 (Fig. 6.11a) would carry more or less load if used in the upright-**T** position.

6.40. If the maximum transverse shear stress induced by P is 500 psi, what are the maximum tensile and compressive bending stresses?

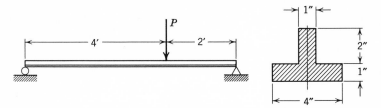

Fɪɢ. P6.40

6.41. This built-up wood beam consists of three 3 in. by 4 in. pieces glued together. If the glue has a maximum shear strength of 500 psi, what load P will make the beam come apart?

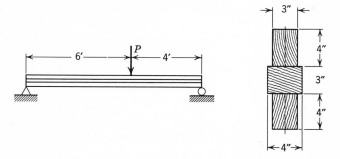

Fɪɢ. P6.41

6.42. Where should the two supports of a uniformly loaded beam be placed in order that the transverse shear stresses will be the least possible? Explain.

6.43. The section modulus of this uniform beam is 18 in.^{3} If the allowable bending stress is 10,000 psi, what maximum load P may be applied when the roller support is placed at the optimum location?

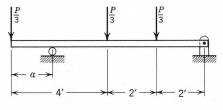

Fɪɢ. P6.43

6.44. Of the two supports holding up this book shelf, only one may have its location adjusted. Where should this support be placed for optimum conditions, it being assumed that the shelf will be fully loaded with uniform size books? For the same load on the shelf, how much larger would the bending stresses be if the adjustable support were at the left end?

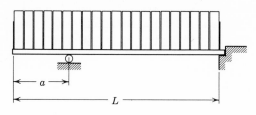

FIG. P6.44

6.45. How far from the ends should the supports be placed so that the beam of Example 7 would carry the greatest possible load distributed as shown, when the section is used in the inverted-**T** position? Consider bending stresses only. Calculate the maximum load.

6.46. The same as Prob. 6.45, except that the section is to be used in the upright-**T** position.

6.47. The forces P_1 and P_2, a fixed distance apart, represent a pair of moving loads, such as those exerted by the wheels of a vehicle. As they move across the simple span L, the bending moment at the site of one and then at the other will pass through its maximum. Show that the bending moment at P_1, say, occurs when the action line of the resultant, $R = P_1 + P_2$, is as far to one side of mid-span as that of P_1 is to the other side; that is, when $x_1 = L/2 - d/2$, where d is the distance of P_1 from R. Show further that this is the same criterion regardless of the number of discrete loads, at fixed distances relative to one another, provided R is the resultant of all loads *then on the span.*

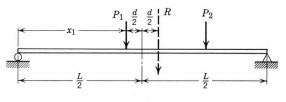

FIG. P6.47

6.48. The carriage of a crane rides on two wheels 6 ft apart. The wheel pressures may be assumed equal to 12,000 lb apiece. Select a suitable I-beam for a 24-ft simply supported span over which the crane can move back and forth without exceeding a bending stress of 10,000 psi.

6.8   Efficiencies of Symmetrical Beam Sections.   Earlier in this chapter we made comparisons between the strengths of different cross sections.   Let us now make another kind of comparison, that of the actual strength of a beam section with its ideal strength, its potential usefulness which, because of practical considerations, can never be fully realized.

For a given depth h of a doubly symmetrical beam section, the ideal distribution of area for bending is one in which each half of the area is spread out in the form of a strip of zero thickness and infinite width, at a distance of $h/2$ to either side of the neutral axis, it being assumed that the allowable stresses in tension and compression are of equal magnitudes.   Then all the material would be subject to the same maximum stress and would have maximum leverage.   The section modulus for such an ideal section would be

$$\left(\frac{I}{c}\right)_{\text{ideal}} = \frac{2(A/2)(h/2)^2}{h/2} = \frac{Ah}{2}. \tag{a}$$

The measure of the section's efficiency, or the factor of utilization α, is then determined as the ratio of its actual section modulus to the ideal value, thus:

$$\alpha_{\text{bending}} = \frac{I/c}{Ah/2} = \frac{2I/h}{Ah/2} = \frac{4I}{Ah^2} = 4\left(\frac{k}{h}\right)^2, \tag{b}$$

where k is the radius of gyration of area relative to the neutral axis.

A given cross section is most efficiently utilized in shear when all the area uniformly bears the maximum shear stress.   Hence the ideal strength in shear is

$$V_{\text{ideal}} = \tau A. \tag{c}$$

Since the actual shear strength is $V = \tau I/(Q/t)_{\text{max}}$, the factor of utilization in shear is

$$\alpha_{\text{shear}} = \frac{\tau I/(Q/t)_{\text{max}}}{\tau A} = \frac{k^2}{(Q/t)_{\text{max}}}. \tag{d}$$

Comparing Eqs. b and d, we observe that for a given depth of beam an increase in α_{bending} is not accompanied by a similar increase in α_{shear}. In fact, $(Q/t)_{\text{max}}$ may even increase faster than k^2, resulting in an actual decrease in α_{shear}.   The following table illustrates this.

FACTORS OF UTILIZATION

	Circle	Rectangle	8W^F31
Bending	0.250	0.333	0.752
Shear	.750	.667	.232

This points up the old truism that advantages are almost always attended by disadvantages. The saving feature is that, except in very short and deep beams, the shear stresses and the shear strength seldom play prominent roles in the functioning of actual beams. Beams are normally designed to have the necessary bending strengths first and are only later checked for shear stresses.

PROBLEMS

6.49. Calculate the efficiencies in bending of a square cross section (a) when the neutral axis is parallel to an edge, and (b) when the neutral axis coincides with a diagonal.

6.50. Determine the efficiencies in bending of an elliptical cross section (a) when the neutral axis coincides with the major diameter, and (b) when the neutral axis coincides with the minor diameter.

6.9   Beams of Variable Cross Sections.   In discussing the bending strength of a beam section, we pointed out that it is possible to improve the efficiency of material utilization by changing the form of the cross section, redistributing the material so that most of it is at maximum distance from the neutral axis. From the nature of beam loading as typified in the solved examples, it should be clear that the demand for bending strength as reflected in the bending-moment diagram is, in general, a variable quantity; hence, if the beam has uniform strength throughout its length, its potential usefulness can be utilized only at a limited number of locations, the critical or controlling sections, and at a great many others it remains idle and unused.   This represents waste. The philosophy of optimization suggests that material utilization could be greatly improved by so varying the cross section at different locations along the beam that the supply of strength there will match the demand for it.

If a beam may be subjected to different patterns of loading throughout the expected useful life of the structure, many of which cannot be accurately predicted, then it is obviously impractical to design it as a variable cross section beam.   The sensible act in such a situation is to design the beam with a uniform cross section whose strength should be governed by the probable maximum bending moment or the maximum shear force that could be expected.   On the other hand, if the loading may be assumed to remain of a fixed pattern, then the sound engineering approach to its design is that which will optimize material utilization through the variable cross section.   In view of the remarks made in the preceding article, we shall confine this discussion of optimization to bending only; later we shall indicate modifications needed to take care of the shear. Implicit in Eq. 6.3 is the design relationship

$$\frac{I}{c} = \frac{M}{\sigma}. \tag{6.3''}$$

This suggests that in order to achieve the ideal of a *uniformly stressed* beam we must vary the section modulus I/c as dictated by the bending moment M. It must be particularly noted that this statement just made is an out and out extrapolation which cannot possibly be rigorously justified. Specifically, the fundamental Eq. 6.2, $\sigma_x = -M_z y/I_z$, which was derived expressly for beams of uniform cross section, is now being assumed to apply to beams of variable cross section. We make these remarks and call attention to every extrapolation by way of emphasizing the nature of an engineer's way of thinking. By this token, however, we are not suggesting that, being made aware of these liberties, the budding engineer need feel apologetic. As the old saying goes, the proof of the pudding is in the eating. Our rather crude theory of bending has led us already to the extremely useful structural shapes, the I- and the WF-sections. Let us then strike out boldly and find out where this latest extrapolation will take us.

Since there is a limitless variety of means whereby the form factor I/c may be varied, even for a fixed shape of cross section, the uniformly stressed beam can be achieved in numerous ways. Let us limit the discussion to beams of rectangular cross section, and let us further restrict the variation of I/c to two modes only: the first one for its historical interest and the second for its practical implications.

Consider a cantilever beam of length L, bearing a transverse load P at its free end. The cross section is assumed to be rectangular, of width b and depth h, and the effect of the earth pull on the beam is to be ignored. Setting up our reference system as shown in Fig. 6.13a, we define the bending moment as $M = -Px$. Since we are interested only in the numerical variation of M, we need not carry the minus sign along; then by Eq. 6.3'' $I/c = Px/\sigma$. For a rectangle, $I/c = bh^2/6$. Therefore we must have

$$\frac{bh^2}{6} = \frac{Px}{\sigma},$$

or $$bh^2 = Cx, \tag{a}$$

to achieve a uniformly stressed beam. The two variations that we shall discuss are: (1) keep b constant and vary h, and (2) keep h constant and vary b.

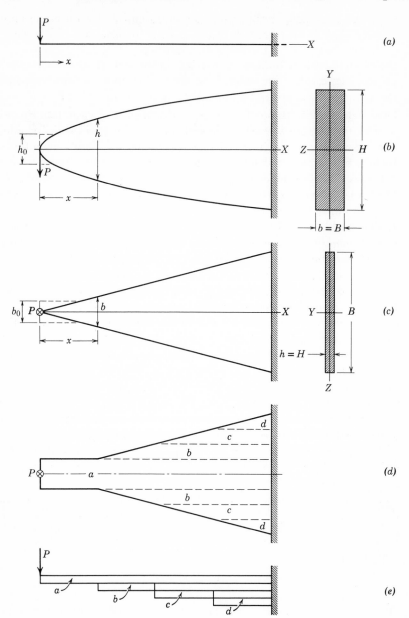

FIG. 6.13

If b is held constant and h allowed to vary, the equation

$$h^2 = C'x \qquad (b)$$

shows that such a uniformly stressed beam should have a parabolic profile, Fig. 6.13b. The value H at the wall support is calculated from the numerical values of P, L, and σ, the constant value $b = B$ being fixed at a certain ratio to H.

This form of cantilever beam has been known for more than 300 years, since the time of Galileo Galilei, regarded as the father of strength theory, who first discussed it in his famous book, translated *Two New Sciences*, originally published in 1638. In arriving at this form of beam profile, Galilei considered, as we have done, bending action only. Note that at $x = 0$ the beam of Fig. 6.13b has no strength in shear. The profile should therefore be modified to provide the minimum shear strength. This is done as follows. If the allowable transverse shear stress τ is known, then from Eq. 6.5, rewritten in the form

$$\frac{I}{(Q/t)_{\max}} = \frac{V}{\tau} \qquad (6.5'')$$

we can find the needed initial depth h_0. Substituting $Bh_0{}^3/12$ for I, $h_0{}^2/8$ for $(Q/t)_{\max}$, P for V, and simplifying, we find from Eq. 6.5$''$ that

$$h_0 = \frac{3P}{2B\tau}. \qquad (c)$$

The dotted lines in Fig. 6.13b show the modified profile. Obviously, the resulting beam is no longer uniformly stressed in bending near its free end, and quite as obviously a compromise is unavoidable.

Let us now hold the depth h constant and vary b. Equation a then becomes

$$b = C''x, \qquad (d)$$

which shows that a uniformly stressed beam of constant depth should have the form of a wedge, Fig. 6.13c. As before, the dimension B at the wall is determined from numerical data, $h = H$ being held at a constant ratio to B. The necessary initial width b_0 to take care of the shear is found as above to be

$$b_0 = \frac{3P}{2H\tau}. \qquad (e)$$

The modified top view is indicated by the dotted lines in Fig. 6.13c.

The wedge-shaped uniformly stressed beam is the basis for a useful practical device. Imagine that the plate, shown in the plan in Fig. 6.13d, is cut into longitudinal strips of equal width, except the center piece $2a$ which is left intact. If the corresponding pieces were joined edge to edge, b to b, c to c, d to d, and so on, and the successively shorter pieces placed one below the other, as shown in Fig. 6.13e, there would result the familiar leaf spring, or at least, half of it. The action of the transformed piece in sketch e would be approximately the same as that of the original wedge in sketch d only if there were no friction between adjacent leaves. Without the stiffening effect of interleaf shear stresses, the individual leaves would act as beams in parallel, the effective width b for any x being the sum of the individual widths of all leaves involved. Thus, for a constant depth h, the section modulus I/c would still vary linearly with x, matching the variation of the bending moment. On the other hand, with friction between leaves, the interleaf shear stresses would have the effect of increasing the equivalent depth, and since I/c is proportional to h^2, the resulting beam would no longer be uniformly stressed in bending. The stresses would then decrease toward the wall, and the greatest stresses would be concentrated in the thinnest overhang. Therefore, in order that the stress distribution be as favorable as in the original design, the leaves of a spring should always be properly lubricated.

PROBLEMS

6.51. Design this constant depth (rectangular cross section) beam for optimum bending strength, using an allowable bending stress of 10,000 psi. Then modify the dimensions to take care of shear, assuming an allowable transverse shear stress of 2500 psi. Show the plan view of the beam.

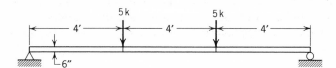

FIG. P6.51

6.52. The stepped shaft is used as a simply supported beam bearing one concentrated load as shown. Based on an allowable bending stress of 10,000 psi, what maximum value may P have?

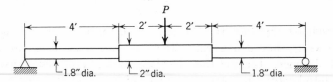

FIG. P6.52

6.53. In the beam of Prob. 6.52, for the same span of 12 ft and the same diameters of 1.8 in. and 2 in., what are the optimum lengths of the various segments? The manner of loading is the same.

6.54. What is the optimum shape of a constant depth cantilever beam bearing a uniformly distributed (along its length) load?

6.10 Beams of Two or More Materials. Among the important and widely used structural materials, some are markedly weaker in tension than in compression. Outstanding examples are the light metals and their alloys, cast iron, wood, and concrete. When such materials are used in beams, it becomes necessary for the most efficient utilization of the strength properties to modify the cross section in such a way that the neutral axis in bending shifts toward the tension side; this allows the compressive side to be stressed more highly than the weaker tension side.

One obvious way of effecting this shift is to use a T-shaped section, where the bar of the T and a small part of the stem are to be stressed in tension and the remaining, deeper part of the stem stressed in compression. A larger part of the cross-sectional area can then transmit tension to compensate for the lower allowable tensile stress. (See Probs. 6.14 to 6.17.)

An alternative method is to help the weaker tension side with another material having a higher tensile strength. Thus we have reinforced beams. Everyone certainly has heard of reinforced concrete; its theory is based on the one fact that concrete is much stronger in compression than in tension. In order to exploit this high compressive strength for bending, we embed in the tension side of the beam a material like steel, which has greater tensile strength than concrete. Large tension forces can then develop to balance the potentially large compression forces, making it possible for the reinforced concrete beam to have optimum strength.

The elementary theory of bending of nonhomogeneous beam sections is handled in much the same way as that of homogeneous sections. Essentially the same assumptions are made as detailed in Article 6.2, with the exception of the fourth one which is now modified to read simply: the materials obey Hooke's law. The assumption of symmetry implies that the several materials comprising the beam are to be arranged symmetrically relative to the plane of loading. Assumption 6, the deformation mechanism of transverse planes remaining plane, now implies that no relative sliding takes place at the interface of any two adjacent materials. Equation d, page 145, then marks the point of departure.

For convenience in explaining the remainder of the theory, let us assume that the beam is composed of two materials, A and B. Equation d, page 145, is now replaced by the pair of equations

$$\sigma_{xA} = C_1 E_A y_A = C_A y_A \tag{a}$$

and
$$\sigma_{xB} = C_1 E_B y_B = C_B y_B, \tag{b}$$

where, for example, y_A denotes the y coordinate of all points in the cross section within the limits of material A. Now we consider two points with the same y, one in region A and the other in region B; by virtue of the assumption that transverse planes remain plane, these two points experience the same strain ϵ_x whether or not they are at an interface. This is to say that when $y_A = y_B$,

$$\frac{\sigma_{xA}}{E_A} = \frac{\sigma_{xB}}{E_B}. \tag{c}$$

Hence by Eqs. a and b

$$\frac{C_A}{E_A} = \frac{C_B}{E_B}, \tag{d}$$

whence
$$C_B = \frac{E_B}{E_A} C_A = n_{BA} C_A, \tag{e}$$

or, alternatively,
$$C_A = \frac{E_A}{E_B} C_B = n_{AB} C_B. \tag{e'}$$

The equilibrium equation $\Sigma F_x = 0$ then leads to

$$0 = C_A \int y_A (dA)_A + C_B \int y_B (dA)_B$$

or
$$0 = C_A \bar{y}_A A_A + C_B \bar{y}_B A_B. \tag{f}$$

By virtue of Eq. e, this becomes

$$0 = C_A \bar{y}_A A_A + n_{BA} C_A \bar{y}_B A_B,$$

which simplifies to

$$0 = \bar{y}_A A_A + \bar{y}_B (n_{BA} A_B); \tag{g}$$

or, alternatively, by Eq. e',

$$0 = \bar{y}_A (n_{AB} A_A) + \bar{y}_B A_B. \tag{g'}$$

Introducing the notion of "weighted area" that is implied in the quantities $n_{BA} A_B$ and $n_{AB} A_A$, we rewrite Eqs. g and g' thus:

$$0 = \bar{y}_{eq} A_{eq}, \tag{h}$$

where A_{eq} stands for the equivalent or "transformed" area. Proceeding as in Article 6.2, we derive from Eq. h the significant result

$$\bar{y}_{eq} = 0. \tag{6.1}$$

The rest of the theory is developed as before, and the final result of interest to us, namely,

$$\sigma_x = -\frac{M_z y}{(I_z)_{eq}}, \tag{6.2}$$

means that the pure bending of nonhomogeneous beams may be handled in exactly the same way as that of homogeneous beams, provided the cross section is first transformed into an equivalent one. In this transformation, the y and z coordinates of all points remain unchanged; owing to the relative weighting of the component areas, however, the location of the centroid (hence of the neutral axis) will generally differ from that in the homogenous section.

It makes no difference whatsoever into which material the beam is transformed—into all A or into all B—but care must be exercised in interpreting Eq. 6.2. Suppose that we have transformed the beam cross section into an all-A one; let $(I_z)_{eq}^A$ denote the second moment of the transformed area. Then the bending stress at some point in the A-region of the original beam is given directly by Eq. 6.2 as

$$\sigma_x = -\frac{M_z y_A}{(I_z)_{eq}^A}.$$

On the other hand, suppose that we have transformed the beam into an all-B one, for which $(I_z)_{eq}^B$ is the second moment of the transformed area. Then the bending stress at some point in the B-region of the original beam is

$$\sigma_x = -\frac{M_z y_B}{(I_z)_{eq}^B}.$$

What interpretation are we now to give the expressions

$$\sigma_x = -\frac{M_z y_B}{(I_z)_{eq}^A} \quad \text{and} \quad \sigma_x = -\frac{M_z y_A}{(I_z)_{eq}^B} ?$$

These are fictitious stress values which must be corrected through multiplication by the pertinent n ratio: n_{BA} and n_{AB}, respectively. They are fictitious because in the all-A beam section the B material that has been transformed into equivalent A is limited to the actual B boundaries of the original beam: there is no weighted-B material within the original A boundaries. Similarly, in the all-B beam, there is no weighted-A material within the original B boundaries.

To make this clearer, let us backtrack a little to the point where we set up the differential force $\Delta F = \sigma_x(\Delta A)$ preparatory to applying the equilibrium conditions. (See Article 6.2.) Since, no matter what we do, we may not disturb equilibrium, any differential force ΔF must remain unchanged in the transformation of the section. If the differential area ΔA of the actual beam section is transformed by a weighting multiplier n, then the corresponding stress on this transformed area must necessarily be $1/n$ times its actual value. This is shown quantitatively, thus:

$$\Delta F = \sigma_{\text{actual}}(\Delta A)_{\text{actual}} = \sigma_{\text{transformed}}(\Delta A)_{\text{transformed}}$$

$$= \sigma_{\text{transformed}} n (\Delta A)_{\text{actual}}.$$

Hence
$$\sigma_{\text{actual}} = \sigma_{\text{transformed}} \frac{n(\Delta A)_{\text{actual}}}{(\Delta A)_{\text{actual}}}$$

$$= n\sigma_{\text{transformed}}$$

or
$$\sigma_{\text{transformed}} = \frac{1}{n} \sigma_{\text{actual}}.$$

Illustrative Example 9. A rectangular wood beam, 4 in. by 8 in. in cross section, is reinforced with a $\frac{1}{4}$-in. thick steel plate 2 in. wide, glued to the 4-in. face. Under a bending moment of 100,000 in.-lb in a plane parallel to the 8-in. face such that the steel is in tension, what maximum bending stresses are set up in the wood and in the steel? For steel, $E = 30 \times 10^6$ psi, and for wood, $E = 1.5 \times 10^6$ psi.

SOLUTION. We transform the section into an all-wood one, using for n, $30/1.5 = 20$. Measuring all distances along the axis of symmetry from the edge of the steel plate, we locate (see Fig. 6.14a) the centroid of the transformed area to be at a distance

$$d = \frac{0.125[20(0.5)] + 4.25(32)}{20(0.5) + 32} = 3.27 \text{ in.}$$

This locates the neutral axis Z. The second moment of area relative to Z is

$$I_z = \frac{4(4.98)^3}{3} + \frac{4(3.02)^3}{3} + \left[\frac{2(0.25)^3}{12} + 0.5(3.045)^2 \right] 20$$

$$= 294.6 \text{ in.}^4$$

In the wood, the maximum compressive stress is

$$(\sigma_c)_{\text{wood}} = \frac{100,000(4.98)}{294.6} = 1690 \text{ psi}, \qquad \qquad Ans.$$

and the maximum tensile stress is

$$(\sigma_t)_{\text{wood}} = \frac{100,000(3.02)}{294.6} = 1025 \text{ psi.} \qquad Ans.$$

In the steel, the maximum tensile stress is

$$(\sigma_t)_{\text{steel}} = (20)\frac{100,000(3.27)}{294.6} = 22,200 \text{ psi.} \qquad Ans.$$

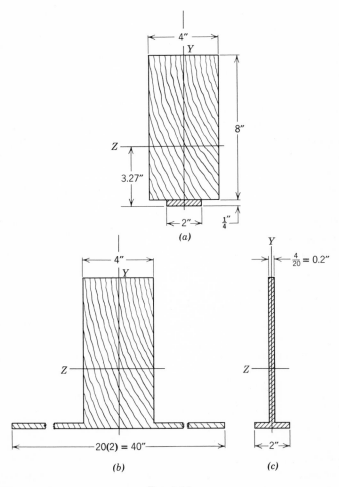

Fig. 6.14

Owing to the fact that the part of the cross-sectional area which is transformed becomes merely n times its original value, without any change in its shape, and the further fact that the second moment of a rectangular area is proportional to the first power of the width b parallel to the Z axis, the transformed area may be represented as being n times as *wide* as the original. Thus, Fig. 6.14b suggests an all-wood transformed section and Fig. 6.14c an all-steel transformed section for the preceding example. These representations are helpful visual aids: they make it easier to understand the shift of the neutral axis. It must be emphasized, however, that they are merely aids and nothing more; they are NOT to replace the original cross section. Observe that the two figures are valid only for bending about the Z axis, but are not valid for bending about the Y axis.

The bending of reinforced concrete beams is treated somewhat differently from the foregoing. In view of the peculiar characteristic of concrete that its tensile strength is very much smaller than its compressive strength, any slight contribution to the bending strength which the concrete in the tension side might make is ignored altogether; it is assumed instead that the necessary balancing tension force is furnished exclusively by the embedded steel. This consititues the first principal difference in the analysis. The other departure consists in considering the cross-sectional area of the steel to be concentrated, as it were, at the centroid of the steel area within the beam cross section. This is equivalent to ignoring the slight variation in the tensile stresses with the depth, which variation is shown in the original beam theory. Resulting from these slight modifications is a considerably simplified theory which makes it relatively easy to achieve that ideal objective of all structural design: optimum material utilization.

Illustrative Example 10.   The 10 in. by 4 in. concrete beam in Fig. 6.15a is to be reinforced with steel rods embedded 8 in. below the top. The allowable compressive stress in the concrete is 1000 psi and the allowable tensile stress in the steel is 20,000 psi. A value of $n = 15$ may be assumed for the ratio of the elasticity moduli, steel to concrete. Determine (1) how much steel is needed for a balanced design and (2) the usable bending strength of such an optimum section.

SOLUTION. For convenient reference, the solution will be brought out in algebraic form first. Let b denote the width of the cross section and d the depth to the centroid of the steel area A_s. Since the concrete in the tension side is assumed completely ineffective in bending, that edge of the rectangular area in compression where the stress is nil (the lower edge) automatically locates the neutral axis Z. Let kd be the depth of this compression area.

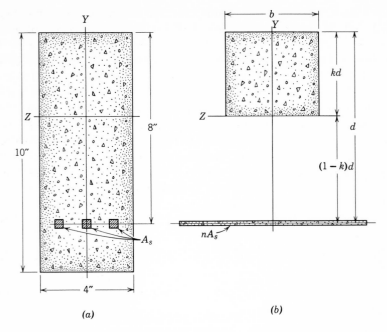

(a)   *(b)*

FIG. 6.15

Figure 6.15*b* represents the transformed section, where the weighted or equivalent tension area is shown as being *n* times the original steel area A_s. The condition that the neutral axis is a centroidal axis of the transformed section yields the following equation:

$$b(kd) \frac{kd}{2} = nA_s(d - kd), \tag{a}$$

which simplifies to

$$bdk^2 + 2nA_s k - 2nA_s = 0. \tag{b}$$

Dividing through by *bd* and replacing the *steel ratio* A_s/bd by the symbol *p*, we transform Eq. *b* to

$$k^2 + 2npk - 2np = 0. \tag{c}$$

Solved for *k*, Eq. *c* gives

$$k = -np + \sqrt{(np)^2 + 2np}; \tag{d}$$

solved for *np*, it yields

$$np = \frac{k^2}{2(1 - k)}. \tag{e}$$

If the steel ratio p and the modulus ratio n are given, Eq. d shows immediately where the neutral axis lies in the beam section. With all the dimensions known, it then becomes a simple matter to evaluate I_z and, from a given or assumed bending moment, to analyze the section for maximum bending stresses. In reinforced concrete theory, Eq. d is called the *checker's equation*.

When the allowable stresses in both concrete and steel are known, the philosophy of optimization dictates that there should be a balance between the concrete and the steel; that is, the beam should be neither overreinforced, thus wasting steel, nor underreinforced, thus not fully exploiting the concrete. This condition of balanced reinforcement will be satisfied if the neutral axis is so located that

$$\frac{\sigma_c}{kd} = \frac{\sigma_s}{n(1-k)d}. \qquad (f)$$

This is an expression of the condition that the allowable stress in the concrete, σ_c, is developed simultaneously with the allowable stress in the steel, σ_s, which in the transformed section becomes σ_s/n. Solving for k, we obtain from Eq. f

$$k = \frac{n\sigma_c}{\sigma_s + n\sigma_c} = \frac{1}{1 + \dfrac{\sigma_s}{n\sigma_c}}. \qquad (g)$$

Thus, if the allowable stresses and the modulus ratio n are given, with the aid of Eq. g we can directly locate the neutral axis, and from Eq. e, we can then find the necessary steel ratio p. Accordingly, Eq. g is known as the *designer's equation*.

Substituting the given numerical data in Eq. g, we obtain

$$k = \frac{1}{1 + \dfrac{20,000}{15(1000)}} = 0.429.$$

From Eq. e, we find

$$np = \frac{(0.429)^2}{2(0.571)} = 0.161.$$

Then

$$p = \frac{0.161}{15} = 0.01073 \quad \text{and} \quad A_s = 0.01073(4)8 = 0.3435 \text{ in.}^2$$

Ans.

With k known, we find $kd = 0.429(8) = 3.43$ in., and $d - kd = 4.57$ in. Next we calculate the second moment of area I_z, thus:

$$I_z = \frac{b(kd)^3}{3} + nA_s(d - kd)^2 \qquad (h)$$

$$= \frac{4(3.43)^3}{3} + 15(0.3435)(4.57)^2 = 161.9 \text{ in.}^4$$

Finally, from the strength formula, $M = \sigma I/c$, we find the bending strength,

$$M = \frac{1000(161.9)}{3.43} = 47{,}200 \text{ in.-lb,}$$

or, alternatively,

$$M = \frac{20{,}000(161.9)}{15(4.57)} = 47{,}200 \text{ in.-lb.} \qquad Ans.$$

The first value, which is based on the allowable stress in the concrete, should, of course, coincide with the second value, which is based on the allowable stress in the steel, since the beam has been designed for optimum conditions.

In closing, we note that the additional concrete in the tension side below the steel serves two purposes. First, it makes possible the bond between steel and concrete which is necessary when the beam section must transmit shearing force along with bending moment; second, it provides a shield from extreme heat in case of a fire, thus minimizing the danger of the steel softening and losing strength sufficiently to cause collapse.

Before we leave the subject of beam strength, we remark that the observant reader should have had thoughts as to whether, in the manner of Probs. 3.41 and 4.26, optimization of material utilization may be achieved even more fully by introducing initial misfit in the composite beam. Indeed, this is possible and it is done. For instance, although it is not practical, a steel plate used to reinforce a timber beam could be pre-shrunk before being joined to the wood; then subsequent loading would make it possible for the allowable stresses in the steel to develop fully at the same time the allowable stresses in the wood are reached.

In the case of reinforced concrete beams, it certainly is not impractical to prestretch the steel before it is bonded to the concrete. This would have the effect of setting up: (1) initial tensile (slight) stresses in the concrete where the bending stresses in actual service are normally compressive, (2) initial compressive stresses in the concrete where the bending stresses in actual service are normally tensile (assumed nil in the elementary theory), and (3) initial tensile stresses in the steel itself. When the service loads are applied, the steel experiences additional tensile stresses (this makes it mandatory to use special high-strength steel for the reinforcement) while the surrounding concrete is relieved of its compressive stresses first before going over into slight tension, and at the same time the concrete on the other side of the neutral axis is relieved of its initial tension first before going over into full compression. In this manner, with proper prestraining, tremendous bending strength can be built into the composite beam.

The preceding, in capsule form, is the theory of prestressed concrete, the success of which in practice has long since been recognized and acclaimed. The interested reader should look up any recent book on reinforced concrete.

PROBLEMS

6.55. Why is Eq. c of Article 6.10 not quite correct, if there is bond between adjacent materials in a composite beam? (See Prob. 3.37.) Note that in the subsequent parts of the theory any slight discrepancy which arises out of using the simplest form of Hooke's law is disregarded.

6.56. This 8 in. by 6 in. timber beam is reinforced with four 2 in. by 2 in. by $\frac{1}{4}$ in. steel angles (see Appendix tables for properties). How much uniformly distributed load can the beam carry on a simply supported span of 10 ft if the allowable stresses are 1500 psi in the wood and 15,000 psi in the steel? $E_{\text{wood}} = 1.5 \times 10^6$ psi and $E_{\text{steel}} = 30 \times 10^6$ psi.

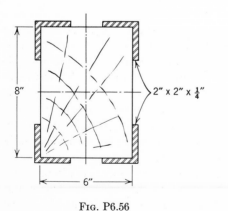

FIG. P6.56   FIG. P6.58

6.57. Solve the above problem without the top steel angles.

6.58. This composite beam section transmits a bending moment of 500,000 in.-lb in its plane of symmetry. What maximum stresses are induced in each of the three components? $E_{\text{steel}} = 30 \times 10^6$ psi, $E_{\text{aluminum}} = 10 \times 10^6$ psi, and $E_{\text{brass}} = 15 \times 10^6$ psi.

6.59. In a reinforced concrete beam, the width b is 6 in., the depth d to the steel is 10 in., and the total steel area A_s is 0.574 in.^{2} Assume a modulus ratio n of 15 and allowable stresses of 1000 psi in the concrete and 18,000 psi in the steel. Determine the usable bending strength of the section.

6.60. A concrete beam is 10 in. wide and 20 in. deep and is reinforced with four $\frac{3}{4}$-in. diameter steel rods with their centers 2 in. above the bottom face. With a bending moment of 400,000 in.-lb being transmitted, what maximum stresses may be expected in the concrete and in the steel? Assume $n = 15$.

6.61. A 12-in. wide simply supported reinforced-concrete beam with a 20-ft span is to carry a uniformly distributed load of 1500 lb per foot. The allowable stresses are 900 psi in the concrete and 18,000 psi in the steel, and n is 12. How much steel should be used and where should it be embedded? If the above load is to include the beam's weight, how much "pay load" (also called "live load") can the beam carry? Concrete weighs 150 lb per cubic foot. Disregard the weight of the steel and assume there is an extra 3-in. layer of concrete on the steel side.

6.62. From basic principles, in the manner of Example 10, (a) locate the neutral axis of this beam section, (b) evaluate the equivalent I_z, and (c) calculate the bending strength. The following are given: $n = 12$, allowable stresses of 18,000 psi in the steel and 1000 psi in the concrete. Note that the equations developed for the rectangular section are not necessarily applicable. When would they be applicable?

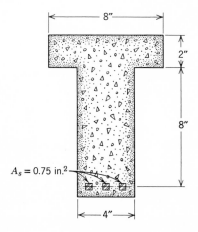

FIG. P6.62

CHAPTER

7

BENDING: BEAM DEFLECTIONS

7.1 Introduction. With few exceptions, all points in a beam undergo shifts in position as a result of impressed forces in equilibrium. Referred to the cartesian X, Y, Z frame, the displacement of each point from its original position has the three components u, v, and w. The complete picture of a beam's deformation is fully defined only when for its every point correct expressions for u, v, and w are found as functions of the position coordinates x, y, and z.

Complete solutions have been found only for elementary beam cross sections and uncomplicated loadings. Even for the innocuously simple problem of a cantilever beam with a circular cross section, bearing a transverse load at its free end, a complete solution exists only if the point end load is replaced by a statically equivalent system of forces distributed over the end face. It is no exaggeration to say that complete solutions in closed form cannot, in general, be found for the kind of beams and the kind of loadings which the engineer must contend with. And, quite obviously, he must make do with some approximate solution to the deflection problem.

Before stating the principal problem dealt with in this chapter, we will first make some observations regarding the pure bending deformation of a beam with a rectangular cross section. These concern the change in shape of the cross section.

7.2 Deformations in a Transverse Plane. For a prismatic beam with a longitudinal plane of symmetry, subject only to bending moments in this plane, the system of stresses,

$$\sigma_x = -\frac{M_z y}{I_z}, \qquad (a)$$

$$\sigma_y = \sigma_z = \tau_{xy} = \tau_{yz} = \tau_{zx} = 0, \qquad (b)$$

is the correct one provided the end external moments are due to forces distributed according to Eq. a. If the end moments are only statically equivalent to the system of σ_x, then the preceding distribution is valid only for sections removed at least a few beam depths away from the ends (Saint-Venant's principle).

The statement that the stresses are correct means that the attendant strains are geometrically compatible. Every point in the cross section experiences these strains:

$$\epsilon_x = -\frac{M_z y}{EI_z}, \qquad (c)$$

$$\epsilon_y = \epsilon_z = \frac{\nu M_z y}{EI_z}, \qquad (d)$$

$$\gamma_{xy} = \gamma_{yz} = \gamma_{zx} = 0. \qquad (e)$$

That these satisfy the compatibility equations (Eqs. 2.7) is obvious.

Consider a rectangular cross section b by h, Fig. 7.1. As the beam bends, all elements of length h parallel to the Y axis remain the same length. We show this as follows. From $\epsilon_y = \partial v/\partial y = \nu M_z y/EI_z$, we find

$$v = \frac{\nu M_z}{EI_z}\frac{y^2}{2} + f(z).$$

For a fixed z, $(v)_{y=h/2} - (v)_{y=-h/2} = 0$; this shows that the ends of a vertical strip do not move relative to each other.

On the other hand, elements of length b parallel to the Z axis do not remain of the same length. From $\epsilon_z = \partial w/\partial z = \nu M_z y/EI_z$, we find

$$w = \frac{\nu M_z yz}{EI_z} + g(y).$$

For a fixed y,

$$(w)_{z=b/2} - (w)_{z=-b/2} = \frac{\nu M_z yb}{2EI_z} + \frac{\nu M_z yb}{2EI_z} = \frac{\nu M_z b}{EI_z}y.$$

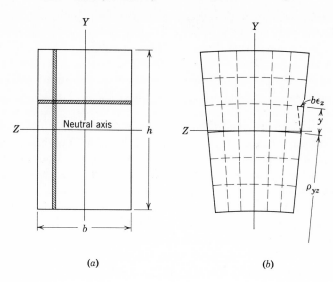

FIG. 7.1

This shows that the *change* in the length of a horizontal strip varies linearly as its distance from the Z axis: lengths below this axis contract, whereas those above elongate.

The preceding mode of deformation can only mean that the cross section will not remain a rectangle but will assume a shape like that shown in Fig. 7.1b. The originally vertical and horizontal elements will form a system of orthogonal lines in order to satisfy the strain equation, $\gamma_{yz} = 0$. Therefore the neutral axis, although remaining of length b, will no longer be a straight line, but rather will assume the shape of a circular arc. Its radius of curvature ρ_{yz} can be found by similar triangles, thus:

$$\frac{b\epsilon_z}{y} = \frac{\nu M_z y b / EI_z}{y} = \frac{b}{\rho_{yz}},$$

whence $\qquad\qquad \rho_{yz} = \dfrac{EI_z}{\nu M_z}, \qquad\qquad\qquad (f)$

or $\qquad\qquad \dfrac{1}{\rho_{yz}} = \dfrac{\nu M_z}{EI_z}. \qquad\qquad\qquad (g)$

As stated briefly in Article 6.2, and as will be pointed out more explicitly in the next article, a positive bending moment M_z will bend the beam in the x-y plane such that it will be concave in the positive sense of y. On the other hand, in the y-z plane, under the influence of this same positive M_z, the beam cross section will so deform as to be concave in the negative sense of y, Fig. 7.1b. The beam will therefore assume the shape of a saddle. This deformation in transverse planes that accompanies the deformation in longitudinal planes is called an *anticlastic* effect. The anticlastic curvature can be easily demonstrated with a rubber model like an eraser.

7.3 Deformations in a Longitudinal Plane. The Bernoulli-Euler Equation.

In the plane of symmetry of the beam, which is also its plane of loading, a rectangular slice of original dimensions Δx by h (Fig. 7.2a) will, owing to the positive bending moment, deform as shown in Fig. 7.2b: all (vertical) elements originally parallel to the Y axis will retain their lengths h and all (longitudinal) elements originally parallel to the X axis will change their lengths in proportion to their distances from the neutral surface. These lines will form an orthogonal net so that $\gamma_{xy} = 0$. The *neutral line* (the original X axis), which is the intersection of the neutral plane and the plane of loading, will no longer be a straight line, but will assume the shape of a circular arc that is concave upward. The radius of curvature of this neutral line ρ_{xy} is

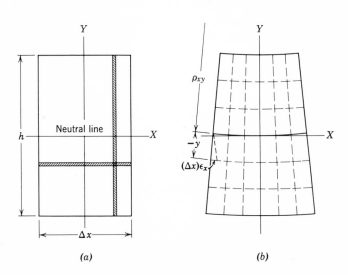

(a)   (b)

FIG. 7.2

found by similar triangles (Fig. 7.2b), thus:

$$\frac{(\Delta x)\epsilon_x}{-y} = \frac{-M_z y (\Delta x)/EI_z}{-y} = \frac{\Delta x}{\rho_{xy}}$$

from which

$$\rho_{xy} = \frac{EI_z}{M_z},$$ (a)

or

$$\frac{1}{\rho_{xy}} = \frac{M_z}{EI_z}.$$ (7.1)

Formula 7.1 is the celebrated Bernoulli-Euler equation, originally derived for thin elastic rods. It gives the curvature * of the neutral line in terms of the bending moment M and the *section stiffness EI*.

Combining Eq. *g* of Article 7.2 with the preceding, we derive the interesting relation between the two curvatures,

$$\frac{1}{\rho_{yz}} = \frac{\nu}{\rho_{xy}}.$$ (b)

From the discussion up to this point, it should be evident that, of all the longitudinal lines lying in the neutral surface, only the neutral line will continue to lie in its original plane, the plane of loading, which is also its osculating plane; all other lines in the doubly curved neutral surface will have osculating planes that are inclined to the plane of symmetry.

PROBLEMS

7.1. To what minimum radius of curvature may an originally straight piano wire with a diameter of 0.05 in. be bent without the elastic-limit stress of 300,000 psi being exceeded? $E = 30 \times 10^6$ psi.

7.2. This bimetallic strip, made up of two identical pieces of stainless steel and aluminum, is subjected to a pure moment load of 25 in.-lb in its plane of symmetry. Calculate the radius of curvature of its neutral line. For the steel $E = 31.5 \times 10^6$ psi and for the aluminum $E = 10.5 \times 10^6$ psi.

---

* The sign convention for curvature employed here is the same as that defined for right-handed systems in analytic geometry and the calculus: that, as one moves along the arc in the increasing sense of the position coordinate, if the curve is concave to one's left, then the curvature is positive. Thus the curvature of the neutral axis in Fig. 7.1b, as well as that of the neutral line in Fig. 7.2b, is positive.

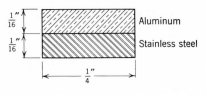

$\frac{1}{16}''$ — Aluminum

$\frac{1}{16}''$ — Stainless steel

$\frac{1}{4}''$

FIG. P7.2

7.4 Beam Deflections. By "deflections of a beam" we shall understand the deflections of its neutral line under the influence of applied loads. For strictly elastic behavior to which this chapter is devoted, the form assumed by the neutral line is referred to as the *elastic curve* of the beam.

We study beam deflections for two reasons. First, they are important for their own sake: We must be able to determine whether or not the deflections of a beam fall within prescribed limits. For example, a beam in an office building must not deflect more than a certain small fraction of its span in order that the plastered ceiling underneath will not separate in unsightly cracks. Second, the expressions for certain known deflections in terms of unknown reaction components lead to equations that are independent of the equilibrium equations. By making use of such additional relationships, we are able to solve statically indeterminate beam problems.

Transverse forces deflect a beam in two ways. First, on account of the bending moments at the various cross sections that these forces give rise to, curvatures are produced which are proportional directly to the bending moments and inversely to the section stiffness, as expressed by Eq. 7.1. Second, owing to the shear forces transmitted at the various sections, adjacent sections tend to slide with respect to each other, producing additional deflections that are not accountable directly by the Bernoulli-Euler equation. These additional deflections must obviously depend on the transverse shear forces. As we did with the beam stresses, we now evaluate first the deflections produced by the bending moments only, then those by the shear forces, and finally superpose the two to obtain the total deflections.

The several methods available for determining beam deflections fall into two groups. One comprises those methods based on the geometry of the elastic curve; three of the best-known of these are the "double-integration method," the "area-moment method," and the "conjugate-beam method." The other group includes those methods based on the principle of work and energy, of which popular techniques are "Castigliano's theorem," "elastic energy theory," and "unit-load method." Generally speaking, we remark that energy methods are the more powerful and are all inclusive; we shall discuss some of them in Chapter 13. This chapter is devoted to one of the geometry methods.

7.5 Differential Equation of the Elastic Curve. The implied simplification, whereby the beam is assumed equivalent to a thin rod whose center line is defined by the neutral line, is the necessary first step toward an approximate solution of the deflection problem. Conversion of the Bernoulli-Euler equation into a differential equation, whose solution is made easy by another approximation, is the next step. This is done as follows.

For any plane curve, the curvature is given by the formula *

$$\frac{1}{\rho} = \frac{d^2y/dx^2}{[1 + (dy/dx)^2]^{3/2}}.$$

In any actual beam, the curvature involved is extremely slight, which means that the slope dy/dx is very small compared to unity. Hence the term $(dy/dx)^2$, which is smaller yet, may be ignored when substituting the preceding in Eq. 7.1. Doing this, we simplify the exact equation to the equivalent approximate form,

$$\frac{d^2y}{dx^2} = \frac{M_z}{EI_z}. \tag{7.2}$$

This is the differential equation of the elastic curve. Note that y rather than v now gives the deflection; this is consistent with the approximation of the beam by a thin rod, since it is understood that all points in the rod have the initial value $y = 0$ corresponding to the unstrained state. In comparing engineering solutions with those exact mathematical ones which exist, the expression one should look for is that for v when $y = z = 0$.

With M expressed as a function of x as explained in Chapter 5, the successive integration of Eq. 7.2 leads to the equation of the elastic curve. The different geometry methods effect this integration in different ways, and it is in this respect primarily that they differ from one another. The one that accomplishes the analytic integration, which we

---

* See any standard work on the calculus.

will discuss, is the oldest, and at the same time the newest, of the various methods; among them it certainly is the most basic.

7.6   Differential Relations between y, θ, M, V, q, and x.   Before going into the details of the method, let us relate Eq. 7.2 to the fundamental equations derived in Chapter 5.   Inasmuch as dy/dx is very small, and since $dy/dx = \tan \theta$, where θ is the inclination with respect to the X axis of the tangent line to the elastic curve, we may replace the slope dy/dx by the angle θ itself in radian measure.   Thus $dy/dx = \theta$ and $d^2y/dx^2 = d\theta/dx = M/EI$.   Noting that $dM/dx = -V$ and $dV/dx = -q$ (see Eqs. 5.2 and 5.1), we may write the following successive relationships:

$$y = y(x), \qquad\qquad (a)$$

$$\frac{dy}{dx} = \theta, \qquad\qquad (b)$$

$$\frac{d^2y}{dx^2} = \frac{d\theta}{dx} = \frac{M}{EI}, \qquad\qquad (c)$$

$$\frac{d^3y}{dx^3} = \frac{d}{dx}\left(\frac{M}{EI}\right) = -\frac{V}{EI}, \qquad\qquad (d)$$

and
$$\frac{d^4y}{dx^4} = \frac{d}{dx}\left(-\frac{V}{EI}\right) = \frac{q}{EI}. \qquad\qquad (e)$$

These equations suggest that if (q/EI)-x, (V/EI)-x, (M/EI)-x, θ-x, and y-x diagrams were plotted, each curve in turn would represent an integral of the preceding one and the geometrical relations between any two successive diagrams would be as discussed in the last example of Chapter 5.   For instance, the slope at any point of the θ-x curve gives the corresponding ordinate of the (M/EI)-x diagram, whereas the change between any two ordinates of the θ-x curve is given by the corresponding area under the (M/EI)-x diagram.

The sketches in Fig. 7.3 depict these relationships qualitatively; they are for a uniformly loaded beam with a constant EI.   Observe that, following the sign convention associated with right-handed systems, we finally arrive at the elastic curve (sketch f) in a form we would naturally expect: the downwardly loaded beam should deflect downward and should be concave upward throughout its length.   Herein lies the final justification for the sign convention we have selected.

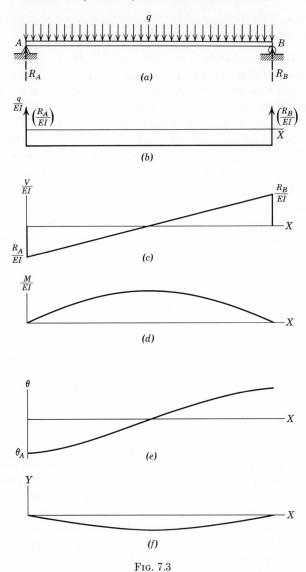

FIG. 7.3

PROBLEMS

7.3. In the manner of Fig. 7.3, sketch the (V/EI)-x, (M/EI)-x, θ-x, and y-x curves for a simply supported uniform beam bearing a point load at the center of its span. Then, evaluating the maximum ordinates of each curve from the area enclosed by the preceding diagram, calculate the maximum deflection of the beam. Disregard the beam's weight and leave the result in terms of P, L, and EI.

7.4. Repeat the above for a cantilever beam bearing a point load at its free end.

7.7 The Double Integration Method. This method is so named because two successive integrations of the second-order differential equation 7.2 result in the equation of the elastic curve. Examining Eqs. a to e of the preceding article, we see that these are but the last two such steps in the "repeated-integration technique." It should be clear that the integration process could be started just as well with, say, the (q/EI)-x equation or the (V/EI)-x one, depending on the nature of the loading. Beginning with the (M/EI)-x equation, when this can be set up directly by applying Rule 2, can, of course, save time.

That this method is the oldest among the first group is understandable; the systematic study of beam deflections began with the Bernoulli-Euler equation (1757), the solution of which by the earliest students of the subject, who were primarily mathematicians, necessarily entailed analytic integration. For many years since, engineers have tended to shy away from the repeated integration method, primarily because the piecewise-continuous load patterns encountered in actual structural beams have meant writing and solving several sets of equations for just one beam. As the graphical and semigraphical techniques based on the area-moment and conjugate-beam methods gained in popularity, the analytical method was looked upon with increasing disfavor. This was in part symptomatic of the continuing unsureness engineers felt about their own mathematical abilities, which appears curious indeed when we consider that the mathematics involved in solving Eq. 7.2 certainly is most elementary for run-of-the-mill beam problems. This prejudice persisted and even now continues to persist in some quarters, many years after Föppl introduced the "comma technique" of handling several discrete loads in one equation (1905 or earlier), and Macaulay the clever device of the braced term to take care of point as well as piecewise-continuous loads (1919).* With the more comfortable formulation of the singularity functions explained in Chapter 5, and with the increasing mathematical sophistication among engineers, the earlier objections to the repeated-integration method have largely been overcome. This return to the fundamental approach then makes this method also the newest.

Two examples should suffice to illustrate the utmost simplicity and ease of the double integration method. Notice the fact that the two

* See footnote, p. 125.

integration constants involved in every solution have the following fixed meanings. The first constant always represents the slope of the elastic curve at the left end, the second always the deflection there, it being understood that $x = 0$ at the left end.

Illustrative Example 1. The beam on unyielding supports shown in Fig. 7.4a has a constant section stiffness EI. Ignoring the weight of the beam, derive the equation of its elastic curve. Locate and evaluate the maximum deflection.

SOLUTION. From equilibrium considerations, R_1 and R_2 are found to be each equal to 1500 lb. Applying Rule 2 directly, and using braced terms as explained in Chapter 5, we write the bending moment equation

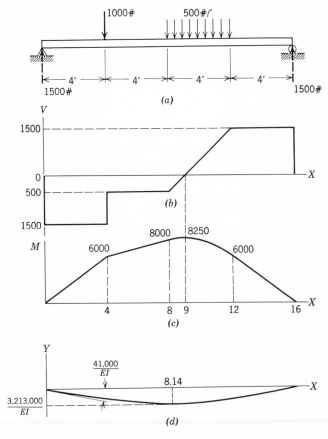

FIG. 7.4

as follows:

$$M = 1500x - 1000\{x - 4\}^1 - \tfrac{500}{2}\{x - 8\}^2 + \tfrac{500}{2}\{x - 12\}^2,$$

$$0 < x < 16.$$

Note that the first ramp need not be indicated with braces since it starts at $x = 0$, and that the last ramp which would correspond to R_2 need not be included because x will never exceed 16. Dividing by EI and equating the result to the second derivative of y with respect to x, we obtain the differential equation,

$$\frac{d^2y}{dx^2} = \frac{1}{EI}[1500x - 1000\{x - 4\}^1 - \tfrac{500}{2}\{x - 8\}^2 + \tfrac{500}{2}\{x - 12\}^2].$$

Integrating once, we get

$$\frac{dy}{dx} = \frac{1}{EI}[750x^2 - 500\{x - 4\}^2$$
$$- \tfrac{250}{3}\{x - 8\}^3 + \tfrac{250}{3}\{x - 12\}^3] + C_1. \quad (a)$$

Integrating a second time, we obtain

$$y = \frac{1}{EI}[250x^3 - \tfrac{500}{3}\{x - 4\}^3 - \tfrac{250}{12}\{x - 8\}^4 + \tfrac{250}{12}\{x - 12\}^4]$$
$$+ C_1x + C_2. \quad (b)$$

The two integration constants must be of such value that the boundary conditions in terms of deformation are satisfied. These are: at $x = 0$, $y = 0$; at $x = 16$, $y = 0$. Observe that these are merely symbolic descriptions of the unyielding nature of the supports. Substituting the first statement in Eq. b gives $C_2 = 0$. The second leads to:

$$0 = \frac{1}{EI}[250(16)^3 - \tfrac{500}{3}(12)^3 - \tfrac{250}{12}(8)^4 + \tfrac{250}{12}(4)^4] + C_1(16),$$

from which we get $C_1 = -41,000/EI = \theta_0$. The minus sign indicates that the slope at the left end is negative, as shown in Fig. 7.4d. Putting these values of C_1 and C_2 in Eqs. a and b, we finally obtain the slope and deflection equations:

$$\theta = \frac{1}{EI}[-41,000 + 750x^2 - 500\{x - 4\}^2$$
$$- \tfrac{250}{3}\{x - 8\}^3 + \tfrac{250}{3}\{x - 12\}^3], \quad (c)$$

and
$$y = \frac{1}{EI}[-41,000x + 250x^3 - \tfrac{500}{3}\{x - 4\}^3$$
$$- \tfrac{250}{12}\{x - 8\}^4 + \tfrac{250}{12}\{x - 12\}^4]. \quad (d)$$

To locate the point of maximum deflection, which obviously is somewhere between the two supports, we equate θ to zero, keeping, in addition to the constant term, only those terms corresponding to the forces that lie within the region between $x = 0$ and near where we estimate this maximum to occur. Suppose that we suspect this to be in the region $4 < x < 8$; we then use only the first three terms in the right-hand side of Eq. c in equating θ to zero, thus:

$$0 = -41{,}000 + 750x^2 - 500(x - 4)^2.$$

This reduces to $x^2 + 16x - 196 = 0,$ (e)

which yields $x = 8.12$. This value is outside the suspected range, but is near enough to 8 to suggest that the maximum deflection occurs most likely in the neighboring region, $8 < x < 12$. Repeating the preceding process, this time retaining the fourth term also, we get

$$0 = -41{,}000 + 750x^2 - 500(x - 4)^2 - \tfrac{250}{3}(x - 8)^3,$$

which simplifies to the cubic

$$x^3 - 27x^2 + 144x + 76 = 0. \qquad (f)$$

A cut-and-try solution gives $x = 8.14$, which value is in the correct range and therefore gives the sought for location. Substitution of this value of x in Eq. d gives the maximum deflection:

$$(y)_{x=8.14} = \frac{1}{EI}\,[-41{,}000(8.14) + 250(8.14)^3$$

$$- \tfrac{500}{3}(4.14)^3 - \tfrac{250}{12}(0.14)^4]$$

$$= -\frac{3{,}213{,}000}{EI}, \qquad\qquad Ans.$$

where the minus sign indicates a downward displacement.

It is to be hoped that our use of the word maximum has not caused, and will in the future not occasion, any confusion. From the context, and for obvious practical reasons, maximum refers to the numerically largest magnitude. In the preceding example, this happens to be an algebraic minimum. When uncertainty is made probable by the presence of inflection points and reversed curvatures in the elastic curve, we shall be more precise in our terminology.

A word about units is in order here. In the preceding expressions for θ and y, E is assumed to be in lb/ft^2 and I in ft^4 Then θ is in radians and y is in feet. If, as is more usual, E is in $lb/in.^2$ and I in $in.^4$, the expression for θ must be multiplied by 144 and that for y by 1728; then θ will still be in radians, but y will be in inches. These are easily verified by dimensional checks.

A sketch of the bending-moment diagram is not essential in the solution for the elastic curve, although such a diagram would be useful in visualizing the shape of the bent beam. Figure 7.4c shows the bending-moment diagram for the preceding example; all its ordinates are positive. Accordingly, the elastic curve, shown in Fig. 7.4d, is upwardly concave throughout the entire length of the beam. We remark that there is *no* particular correlation between the location of the section of maximum bending moment and that of maximum deflection. If these locations happen to coincide, as in the beam of Fig. 7.3, no special significance should be attached to this fortuitous result. The uninitiated are often prone to associate these two with each other.

Illustrative Example 2.   For the beam shown in Fig. 7.5a, calculate the slope and deflection at section C where the concentrated moment load acts. Leave these in terms of EI, assumed constant, and ignore the weight of the beam.

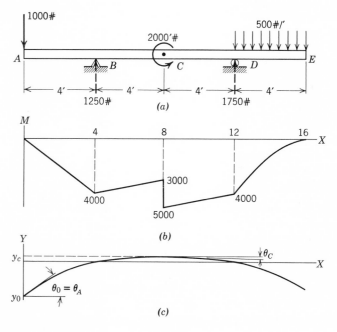

Fig. 7.5

SOLUTION. The reactions of the supports are found to be $R_1 = 1250$ lb and $R_2 = 1750$ lb. Writing the expression for the bending moment, dividing it by EI, and equating the result to d^2y/dx^2, we have

$$\frac{d^2y}{dx^2} = \frac{1}{EI}[-1000x + 1250\{x-4\}^1 - 2000\{x-8\}^0$$
$$+ 1750\{x-12\}^1 - 250\{x-12\}^2], \qquad 0 < x < 16.$$

Note that the concentrated 2000 ft-lb moment load occurs as a step downward at $x = 8$ in the bending-moment diagram, Fig. 7.5b. Integrating the preceding equation once, we get

$$\frac{dy}{dx} = \frac{1}{EI}[-500x^2 + 625\{x-4\}^2 - 2000\{x-8\}^1$$
$$+ 875\{x-12\}^2 - \tfrac{250}{3}\{x-12\}^3] + C_1. \qquad (g)$$

Integrating once again, we obtain

$$y = \frac{1}{EI}[-\tfrac{500}{3}x^3 + \tfrac{625}{3}\{x-4\}^3 - 1000\{x-8\}^2$$
$$+ \tfrac{875}{3}\{x-12\}^3 - \tfrac{250}{12}\{x-12\}^4] + C_1x + C_2. \qquad (h)$$

At $x = 4$, $y = 0$. Therefore, by Eq. h,

$$0 = \frac{1}{EI}[-\tfrac{500}{3}(4)^3] + C_1(4) + C_2.$$

At $x = 12$, $y = 0$. Hence, by Eq. h again,

$$0 = \frac{1}{EI}[-\tfrac{500}{3}(12)^3 + \tfrac{625}{3}(8)^3 - 1000(4)^2] + C_1(12) + C_2.$$

Solved simultaneously, these two equations yield:

$$C_1 = \theta_0 = \frac{70,000}{3EI} \quad \text{and} \quad C_2 = y_0 = -\frac{248,000}{3EI}.$$

Putting these back in Eqs. g and h, we finally obtain:

$$\theta = \frac{1}{EI}\left[\frac{70,000}{3} - 500x^2 + 625\{x-4\}^2 - 2000\{x-8\}^1\right.$$
$$\left. + 875\{x-12\}^2 - \tfrac{250}{3}\{x-12\}^3\right], \qquad (i)$$

and
$$y = \frac{1}{EI}\left[-\frac{248,000}{3} + \frac{70,000}{3}x - \tfrac{500}{3}x^3 + \tfrac{625}{3}\{x-4\}^3\right.$$
$$\left. - 1000\{x-8\}^2 + \tfrac{875}{3}\{x-12\}^3 - \tfrac{250}{12}\{x-12\}^4\right]. \qquad (j)$$

At $x = 8$,

$$\theta = \frac{1}{EI}\left[\frac{70,000}{3} - 500(64) + 625(16)\right] = \frac{4000}{3EI} = \theta_c, \qquad Ans.$$

and $\quad y = \frac{1}{EI}\left[-\frac{248,000}{3} + \frac{70,000}{3}(8) - \frac{500}{3}(512) + \frac{625}{3}(64)\right]$

$$= \frac{32,000}{EI} = y_c. \qquad\qquad\qquad\qquad\qquad Ans.$$

Figure 7.5c shows the elastic curve. It is observed that the curve is concave downward everywhere; this is consistent with the fact that the bending moment is negative throughout the beam. The slope at the left end is positive, the deflection negative. At section C both the slope and deflection are positive.

PROBLEMS

7.5. Derive the expression for the end deflection of a uniform cantilever beam due to an end load P. Express in terms of P, the length L, and EI.

7.6. Derive the expression for the end deflection of a uniform cantilever beam due to a uniformly distributed load of intensity q over its entire length. Express in terms of q, L, and EI.

7.7. (a) Derive the expression for the end deflection of a uniform cantilever beam due to a concentrated load P at a distance a from the fixed end. (b) Using superposition, derive the expression for the end deflection of a uniform cantilever beam due to a uniformly distributed load over its entire length. (*Hint:* Consider a differential load $q(dx)$, at a distance x from the fixed end, equivalent to the point load P.)

7.8. If the maximum bending stress in this 6W20 cantilever beam is 10,000 psi, what is the deflection of its free end? Ignore the beam's weight. $E = 30 \times 10^6$ psi.

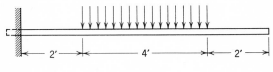

Fig. P7.8

7.9. Derive the equation of the elastic curve for the beam of Fig. 7.3. Evaluate the maximum deflection.

7.10. One specification regarding maximum deflections of beams commonly observed in connection with plastered ceilings is that the deflection shall not exceed $\frac{1}{360}$ of the span. Assuming a simply supported 16-ft uniform beam bearing a uniform live load of 500 lb per foot, select the lightest WF-section that will satisfy this requirement. What maximum bending stresses may be expected? $E = 29 \times 10^6$ psi.

For each of the following beams, assume a constant EI. Ignoring the weight of the beam, derive the equation of the elastic curve, evaluating all integration constants. Use the symmetry argument where applicable. Leave all expressions in terms of EI and P and L when no numbers are given for them.

7.11. Beam of Fig. P6.51.
7.12. Beam of Fig. P5.26.
7.13. Beam of Fig. P5.27.
7.14. Beam of Fig. P6.36.
7.15. Beam of Fig. P6.38.
7.16. Beam of Fig. P5.1.
7.17. Beam of Fig. P5.3.
7.18. Beam of Fig. P5.4.
7.19. Beam of Fig. P5.19.
7.20. Beam of Fig. P5.20.
7.21. Beam of Fig. P5.21.
7.22. Beam of Fig. P5.22.
7.23. Beam of Fig. P5.23.
7.24. Beam of Fig. P5.24.
7.25. Beam of Fig. P5.25.

7.26. In a uniformly loaded beam of constant EI, resting on two supports that are symmetrically located for optimum bending strength (see Example 8, Chapter 6), compare the deflection at the overhanging ends with that at midspan.

7.27. Derive the equation of the elastic curve for the beam of Fig. 6.10, and from it locate and evaluate the two greatest deflections of opposite senses. EI is constant.

7.28. Do the same for the beam of Fig. 5.9.

7.8   Deflections Due to Shear. Warping of Transverse Sections. In addition to the deflections associated with curvatures caused by bending moments, there are deflections due to the relative sliding of adjacent transverse sections as they transmit shear forces.   Just as bending deflections are proportional to the bending moments, so we must expect that shear deflections are proportional to the shear forces. In those regions where the shear force is constant, the adjacent beam sections clearly must slide a constant amount relative to each other. Figure 7.6a displays this schematically for a simply supported beam bearing one concentrated load at midspan. Shown in Fig. 7.6b is a small element of differential length Δx from this beam, where the trans-

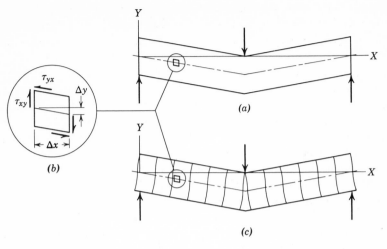

Fɪɢ. 7.6

verse shift is denoted by Δy; in the limit, the ratio $\Delta y/\Delta x$ becomes dy/dx $= \gamma = \tau/G$.

The mode of deformation depicted in Fig. 7.6a would require that the shear stress τ did not vary across the depth of the beam section; such a distribution of shear stress would be at variance with the one derived in Article 6.4. We learned there that transverse shear stresses do vary from top to bottom, always being zero at both extremes from the neutral axis. For example, in a rectangular section, the magnitudes of these shear stresses vary parabolically, reaching a maximum at the neutral axis. Consequently, the magnitudes of the shear strains also vary parabolically. Therefore a square element from either the top or bottom of the beam in profile remains a square, whereas a similar element at the neutral line deforms into a rhombus. As a result, the beam section under shear, instead of remaining plane, warps as indicated in Fig. 7.6c. For elements at the neutral line, Fig. 7.6b would still be a reasonable picture of deformation geometry.

Before proceeding with the shear deflection, we digress briefly to point out two things. The first one is the disturbing implication of the conclusion that beam sections warp when they transmit shear force. Evidently we have the following curious situation. Starting out with the assumption that transverse planes remain plane during bending, we derived Eq. 6.2 for bending stress, $\sigma_x = -M_z y/I_z$, which we then used to derive Eq. 6.3 for shear stress, $\tau_{xy} = VQ/It$; now this last expression tells us, in effect, that the beam section cannot possibly remain plane. Does this mean then that, since our reasoning has led us to an absurdity, the first expression for bending stress is necessarily wrong? *If* the assumed deformation pattern were necessary for the derivation of the bending stress, then this would be so. The assumption, however, was made merely as a convenience to help us arrive at a reasonable stress pattern. For that matter, we could have immediately assumed a linear stress distribution, bypassing the matter of strain altogether. Actually, the necessary condition for the correctness of the stresses is equilibrium, and the sufficient condition is that the compatibility equations be satisfied. Since equilibrium is not violated and inasmuch as the compatibility equations are satisfied, at least in a thin rectangular section (see Prob. 7.29), the conclusion that transverse planes warp does not in any way invalidate Eq. 6.2. Longitudinal elements of original length Δx will still elongate or contract in proportion to their distances from the neutral surface; and the development of small shear strains γ_{xy} will not result in additional linear strains ϵ_x and normal stresses σ_x (see description of Hooke's law, Article 2.5). (Or almost so. See Prob. 7.30.)

The other item concerns the impossibility of the situation in the vicinity of the concentrated load as depicted in Fig. 7.6c. A discontinuity in the deformation geometry at this section cannot take place, and what is suggested in the sketch must be considered as much an abstraction as that of a point force, which cannot in reality exist. In more sophisticated language, we say that the system of strains, which is valid for sections in those regions of the beam free of external force, is not geometrically compatible in the vicinity of point forces. If instead the beam carried a uniformly distributed load, we would find that the warping of transverse sections will vary uniformly from maximum amounts at the ends to zero at the center and will consequently present no geometric incompatibility.

Returning to Fig. 7.6b, we may now write for the slope of the elastic curve due to shear forces,

$$\frac{dy}{dx} = \frac{\tau_{\max}}{G}, \tag{a}$$

It being assumed that the maximum transverse shear stress occurs at the level of the neutral surface. Because we can always express the maximum shear stress in the form $\tau_{\max} = KV/A$, where V/A represents an average value and K a form or correction factor, Eq. *a* may be written

$$\frac{dy}{dx} = \frac{KV}{AG}. \tag{7.3}$$

(Note that the slope agrees in sign with the shear force. In Fig. 7.6b the slope $\Delta y/\Delta x$ is negative; in Fig. 7.6a the shear force is also negative.) Then, in order to obtain the shear deflection, all we need do is substitute for V its expression as a function of x, integrate once, and evaluate the lone integration constant, which now stands for the shear deflection at the end where $x = 0$.

Illustrative Example 3.   Determine the deflections due to shear in the beam of Example 1.

SOLUTION. The shear-force equation is

$$V = -1500 + 100\{x - 4\}^0 + 500\{x - 8\}^1 - 500\{x - 12\}^1.$$

Substituting this in Eq. 7.3, we get

$$\frac{dy}{dx} = \frac{K}{AG}[-1500 + 1000\{x - 4\}^0 + 500\{x - 8\}^1 - 500\{x - 12\}^1],$$

from which, taking into account that $y_0 = 0$, we finally obtain

$$y = \frac{K}{AG}[-1500x + 100\{x - 4\}^1 + 250\{x - 8\}^2 - 250\{x - 12\}^2].$$

Ans.

This equation, combined with Eq. d of Article 7.7, gives the total deflection as a function of x.

Illustrative Example 4.   For the symmetrically loaded beam of Fig. 7.6a, calculate approximately what fraction of the total maximum deflection is due to shear. Investigate for rectangular and circular cross sections. Ignore the weight of the beam and assume constant E, I, and A.

SOLUTION. Considering bending moments only, we have

$$\frac{d^2y_1}{dx^2} = \frac{1}{EI}\left[\frac{P}{2}x - P\left\{x - \frac{L}{2}\right\}^1\right],$$

whence $$\frac{dy_1}{dx} = \theta_{1_0} + \frac{1}{EI}\left[\frac{P}{4}x^2 - \frac{P}{2}\left\{x - \frac{L}{2}\right\}^2\right], \tag{b}$$

and $$y_1 = y_{1_0} + \theta_{1_0}x + \frac{1}{EI}\left[\frac{P}{12}x^3 - \frac{P}{6}\left\{x - \frac{L}{2}\right\}^3\right]. \tag{c}$$

The constant y_{1_0} is known to be zero. The constant θ_{1_0} is evaluated most readily from the symmetry condition: at $x = L/2$, $dy_1/dx = 0$. Substituting this in Eq. b and solving for θ_{1_0}, we obtain $\theta_{1_0} = -PL^2/16EI$. Using this in Eq. c and putting $x = L/2$, we find the bending deflection at midspan to be

$$(y_1)_{x=L/2} = -\frac{PL^3}{48EI}. \tag{d}$$

We turn now to Eq. 7.3.

$$\frac{dy_2}{dx} = \frac{K}{AG}\left[-\frac{P}{2} + P\left\{x - \frac{L}{2}\right\}^0\right], \tag{e}$$

whence

$$y_2 = y_{2_0} + \frac{K}{AG}\left[-\frac{P}{2}x + P\left\{x - \frac{L}{2}\right\}^1\right]. \tag{f}$$

The constant y_{2_0} is zero. At $x = L/2$ occurs the maximum shear deflection, and is found from Eq. f to be

$$(y_2)_{x=L/2} = -\frac{KPL}{4AG}. \tag{g}$$

The total midspan deflection is now obtained by combining Eqs. d and g. For metals, $G = 0.385E$, approximately; hence, for metallic beams, we obtain for this maximum deflection:

$$(y)_{x=L/2} = -\frac{PL^3}{48EI}\left[1 + 31.2K\left(\frac{k}{L}\right)^2\right], \tag{h}$$

where $k^2 = I/A$.

It was shown in Example 3, Chapter 6, that the maximum transverse shear stress in a rectangular section is $\tau_{\max} = 3V/2bh$; therefore, for such a section, $K = 1.5$. Also, $k^2 = bh^3/12bh = h^2/12$. Substituting these values in Eq. h, we find for the rectangular section:

$$(y)_{x=L/2} = -\frac{PL^3}{48EI}\left[1 + 3.9\left(\frac{h}{L}\right)^2\right]. \tag{i}$$

Thus that part of the total deflection due to shear depends on the depth-to-span ratio. When $h/L = \frac{1}{10}$, Eq. i shows that shear contributes only 3.9/103.9 or 3.75% of the *total* deflection; this is certainly no more than 4% of the *bending* effect.   *Ans.*

For a circular cross section, $\tau_{\max} = 4V/3\pi r^2$ (see Example 5, Chapter 6); hence $K = 1.33$. Also, $k^2 = 4\pi d^4/64\pi d^2 = d^2/16$. Therefore, for the circular section,

$$(y)_{x=L/2} = -\frac{PL^3}{48EI}\left[1 + 2.6\left(\frac{d}{L}\right)^2\right]. \qquad (j)$$

For a depth-to-span ratio of $\frac{1}{10}$, Eq. j shows that shear contributes only $2.6/102.6$ or 2.53% of the total deflection; this is less than 3% of the bending deflection. *Ans.*

The preceding results suggest that for such stout cross sections as the rectangular and the circular, deflections due to shear may be ignored with little error in beams whose span-to-depth ratios exceed 10. For structural shapes such as I- and W-sections, the span-to-depth ratio above which shear deflections may be ignored should be increased to 15 or larger because of the considerably higher values of the factor K. Consider the cross section in Fig. 6.4, for example; its K is about 4.3. If such a beam were loaded as in the last example, for a span-to-depth ratio of 10 shear would account for slightly over 20% of the total deflection. Increasing the ratio to 15 will decrease this amount to about 10%.

PROBLEMS

7.29. Show that, for a thin $(b < h)$ rectangular beam transmitting a constant shear force V (no lateral loads), the compatibility equations (Eqs. 2.7) are satisfied by the following system of strains, derived from the stresses on the basis of Hooke's law for plane stress (in which $\sigma_y = 0$):

$$\epsilon_x = -\frac{12M_z y}{Ebh^3}; \quad \epsilon_y = \epsilon_z = \frac{12\nu M_z y}{Ebh^3}; \quad \gamma_{xy} = \frac{6V}{Gbh^2}\left(\frac{h^2}{4} - y^2\right); \quad \gamma_{yz} = \gamma_{zx} = 0.$$

7.30. If the preceding beam bears a uniform lateral load of intensity q in the Y direction, then one possible system of stresses is (see Prob. 6.26):

$$\sigma_x = -\frac{12M_z y}{bh^3}; \quad \sigma_y = \frac{q}{b}\left(\frac{3y}{2h} - \frac{2y^3}{h^3} + \frac{1}{2}\right);$$

$$\tau_{xy} = \frac{6V}{bh^3}\left(\frac{h^2}{4} - y^2\right); \quad \sigma_z = \tau_{yz} = \tau_{zx} = 0.$$

Do the associated strains, based on Hooke's law for plane stress, satisfy the compatibility equations?

7.31. In a simply supported uniform beam that is uniformly loaded throughout the entire span, determine the percent increase over the maximum bending deflection when shear is taken into account: (a) for a beam of rectangular cross section; (b) for a beam of circular cross section. Assume $G = 0.385E$ and a span-to-depth ratio of 10.

7.32. In terms of G, derive an expression for the maximum shear deflection in this beam. Disregard the beam's weight.

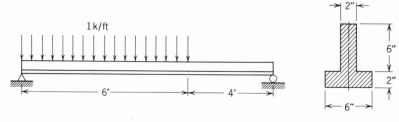

FIG. P7.32

7.9 Deflections of Variable Cross Section Beams. Having made so many simplifications and extrapolations, it is inevitable that we should now extend the approximate method of calculating bending deflections to beams of variable cross section. Where the variation is a uniformly continuous one susceptible to analytical expression, no difficulty should be encountered in solving the reduced Bernoulli-Euler differential equation; the only change made necessary then would be that EI may no longer be factored out.

It is for those beams with sectionally uniform cross sections, commonly called stepped beams, that the method of repeated integration is especially suited. In solving the deflection problem for such cases, we find it convenient to sketch the M-x diagram first; from this we then construct the (M/EI)-x curve, dividing every M ordinate by the local EI. If the (M/EI)-x diagram contains no higher-order singularities than the step, the (M/EI)-x equation can be written down directly; otherwise, it may be desirable first to sketch the derivative curve (V/EI)-x, and even (q/EI)-x, until the highest-order singularity remaining is the step, as explained in Chapter 5. After the (M/EI)-x equation is derived, the rest of the solution will follow the same steps as for prismatic beams.

Illustrative Example 5. Derive the equation of the elastic curve for the simply supported stepped beam shown schematically in Fig. 7.7a. Ignore the weight and assume a constant E.

SOLUTION. The bending-moment diagram is sketched first, Fig. 7.7b, and from this is derived the (M/EI)-x curve, Fig. 7.7c. Since this contains ramps, its derivative curve, (V/EI)-x, is sketched next, Fig. 7.7d, which is seen to consist of steps and impulses. The (V/EI)-x equation can now easily be written

$$\frac{V}{EI} = -\frac{P}{2EI} + \frac{PL}{16EI}\left\{x - \frac{L}{4}\right\}^{-1} + \frac{P}{4EI}\left\{x - \frac{L}{4}\right\}^{0}$$

$$+ \frac{P}{2EI}\left\{x - \frac{L}{2}\right\}^{0} - \frac{PL}{16EI}\left\{x - \frac{3L}{4}\right\}^{-1} + \frac{P}{4EI}\left\{x - \frac{3L}{4}\right\}^{0}. \quad (a)$$

One integration gives us the key (M/EI)-x equation. Performing this integration and equating the result to d^2y/dx^2, we obtain after simplification,

$$\frac{d^2y}{dx^2} = \frac{P}{EI}\left[\frac{x}{2} - \frac{L}{16}\left\{x - \frac{L}{4}\right\}^{0} - \frac{1}{4}\left\{x - \frac{L}{4}\right\}^{1}\right.$$

$$\left. - \frac{1}{2}\left\{x - \frac{L}{2}\right\}^{1} + \frac{L}{16}\left\{x - \frac{3L}{4}\right\}^{0} - \frac{1}{4}\left\{x - \frac{3L}{4}\right\}^{1}\right]. \quad (b)$$

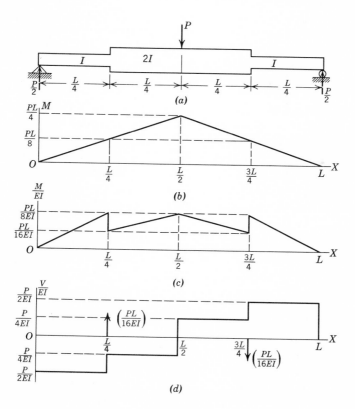

Fig. 7.7

Then,

$$\frac{dy}{dx} = \theta_0 + \frac{P}{EI}\left[\frac{x^2}{4} - \frac{L}{16}\left\{x - \frac{L}{4}\right\}^1 - \frac{1}{8}\left\{x - \frac{L}{4}\right\}^2 \right.$$
$$\left. - \frac{1}{4}\left\{x - \frac{L}{2}\right\}^2 + \frac{L}{16}\left\{x - \frac{3L}{4}\right\}^1 - \frac{1}{8}\left\{x - \frac{3L}{4}\right\}^2 \right]. \quad (c)$$

At this point, if desired, the constant θ_0 may be evaluated from the symmetry condition: at $x = L/2$, $dy/dx = 0$. Substituting $x = L/2$ in Eq. c and putting $dy/dx = 0$, thus:

$$0 = \theta_0 + \frac{P}{EI}\left[\frac{L^2}{16} - \frac{L}{16}\left(\frac{L}{4}\right) - \frac{1}{8}\left(\frac{L}{4}\right)^2\right],$$

we obtain $\theta_0 = -\dfrac{5PL^2}{128EI}.$ $\qquad(d)$

Putting this value of θ_0 back in Eq. c and integrating, we finally obtain the deflection equation

$$y = \frac{P}{EI}\left[-\frac{5L^2 x}{128} + \frac{x^3}{12} - \frac{L}{32}\left\{x - \frac{L}{4}\right\}^2 - \frac{1}{24}\left\{x - \frac{L}{4}\right\}^3 \right.$$
$$\left. - \frac{1}{12}\left\{x - \frac{L}{2}\right\}^3 + \frac{L}{32}\left\{x - \frac{3L}{4}\right\}^2 - \frac{1}{24}\left\{x - \frac{3L}{4}\right\}^3 \right]. \quad Ans. \quad (e)$$

The maximum deflection occurs at midspan, and is found from Eq. e to be

$$(y)_{x=L/2} = \frac{PL^3}{EI}\left[-\frac{5}{256} + \frac{1}{96} - \frac{1}{512} - \frac{1}{1536} \right] = -\frac{7PL^3}{384EI}.$$

PROBLEMS

7.33. Derive an expression for the end deflection of a uniformly stressed cantilever beam of constant depth due to an end load. Compare this with the deflection of a similar uniform cantilever beam similarly loaded. The cross section of the uniform beam is identical to the maximum cross section of the tapered beam. Ignore the effects of shear.

7.34. Determine the maximum deflection of a simply supported uniformly stressed beam of constant depth due to a uniformly distributed load over its entire span. Compare this with the deflection of a similar uniform beam similarly loaded. The cross section of the uniform beam is identical to the maximum cross section of the optimum beam.

7.35. In terms of P, L, B, H, and E, determine the maximum deflection of this uniformly stressed beam. Consider bending action only and ignore the beam's weight.

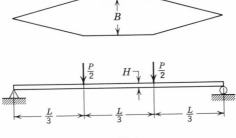

FIG. P7.35

7.36. Derive the equation of the elastic curve for the stepped beam of Fig. P6.52. Evaluate the maximum deflection, using $E = 30 \times 10^6$ psi. Ignore the beam's weight.

7.37. Determine the maximum deflection of this beam. Disregard the beam's weight and use $E = 10.5 \times 10^6$ psi.

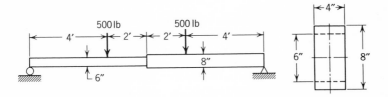

FIG. P7.37

7.38. This stepped beam of rectangular cross section consists of three uniform lengths as shown. First, determine the optimum depths h_1 and h_2 based on allowable bending stresses of 10,000 psi, assuming that the elementary beam formulas apply even where there is a change in cross section. Then calculate the maximum deflection. $E = 6.5 \times 10^6$ psi.

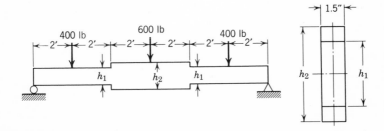

FIG. P7.38

7.39. A beam of uniform rectangular cross section, 4 in. wide by 6 in. deep, consists of a 4-ft long aluminum bar joined to a 4-ft long steel bar. The beam is simply supported at its ends and bears a uniformly distributed load of 1000 lb per foot over the entire 8-ft length. Locate and calculate the maximum deflection due to bending. For steel, $E = 30 \times 10^6$ psi, and for aluminum, $E = 10 \times 10^6$ psi.

7.40. Determine the maximum deflection of this compound beam. For the elastic constants see the preceding problem. Ignore the beam's weight and consider only bending action.

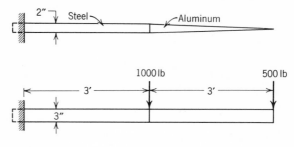

FIG. P7.40

8

REDUNDANTLY SUPPORTED
MEMBERS

8.1 Redundant Constraints. Statical Indeterminateness. A loaded member, so supported that the number of distinct components comprising its reactive force system exceeds the number of available independent equations of equilibrium, is known as a *redundantly supported* or *restrained* member. The corresponding external force system is then *statically indeterminate.* The term redundant has a physical connotation, the term indeterminate a mathematical one. A redundant support or constraint is one that can be dispensed with, without either the equilibrium or the stability of the member being upset. A statically indeterminate force system is one which cannot be solved completely with the use of no equations other than those of static equilibrium.

The degree of redundancy is equal to the greatest number of constraints that can be removed compatible with stability. The degree of statical indeterminateness of a force system equals the number of unknown quantities in excess of the number of independent equilibrium equations available. In this context the two numbers, hence the two degrees, are equal. A member with n redundant constraints yields an external force system that is indeterminate to the nth degree.

Strictly speaking, the expression "statically indeterminate" has a much wider connotation than here implied, and in this respect it differs from redundancy. All problems involving determination of rigorously correct stress patterns are statically indeterminate because the equations of equilibrium, although necessary, are not sufficient for a solution. In the engineering approach that we have repeatedly demonstrated, this indeterminateness is done away with through the simple expedient of *assuming* some reasonable pattern for the stresses, either directly or indirectly through the demonstrable behavior of a physical model. Thus, for example, using only the equations of statics, we are not able to evaluate the stresses across a transverse section of a simple tension bar unless we make some assumption such as their being uniformly distributed. The usage in this chapter is intended to convey a narrower meaning. Accordingly, when we refer to a beam as being statically indeterminate, we are really alluding to the external force system consisting of the loads and the support reactions.

The fact that a support is redundant does not mean it should be removed; there may be a good reason for its being left in. The fact that a force system is statically indeterminate does not mean it is not solvable; a complete solution can be effected by bringing in as many additional equations as the degree of indeterminateness requires, independently of the equilibrium equations.

In an indeterminate system (not necessarily of forces), a group of unknown quantities equal in number to the degree of indeterminateness can always be found in terms of which the remaining unknowns may be expressed mathematically. Then, any set of values arbitrarily assigned to the first group determines the second. In this respect, the set of unknowns is not uniquely determinable—it is *in*determinate. If the equations are of such form that each one contains all the unknowns, then the grouping is completely arbitrary; otherwise it is restricted. For example, in a system of three independent equations, each of which contains the same five unknowns, any three of the unknowns can always be expressed as functions of the other two. On the other hand, equations based on physical facts, such as equilibrium conditions, usually do not involve all the unknowns of the system individually. Thus one equation may contain only some of the unknowns, another equation other unknowns, and so on, with or without overlap. When this happens, the grouping of the unknowns becomes restricted: not just any group of them can be used in terms of which the others may be expressed.

Consider as an example the free-body diagram of the bar in equilibrium shown in Fig. 8.1. This involves a general coplanar force system with five distinct unknown reaction components. Since only three independent equilibrium equations are available, the force system is indeterminate to the second degree. Observe that of the ten possible groupings of the unknowns in two's and three's these three are *not* possible: (1) to express V_1, M_1, and M_2 in terms of any H_1 *and* any R_2; (2)

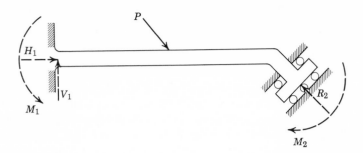

Fɪɢ. 8.1

to express H_1, M_1, and M_2 in terms of any V_1 *and* any R_2; and (3) to express M_1, M_2, and R_2 in terms of any H_1 *and* any V_1. The first is impossible because, by the equation $\Sigma F_H = 0$, H_1 and R_2 may not be arbitrarily chosen; the second because, by the equation $\Sigma F_V = 0$, V_1 and R_2 may not be arbitrarily chosen; and the third because, by the equations $\Sigma F_H = 0$ and $\Sigma F_V = 0$, H_1 and V_1 may not be arbitrarily chosen since the H- and V-components of R_2 bear a fixed ratio to each other. All the other seven groupings are possible. Physically this means that H_1 and R_2 *together*, or V_1 and R_2 *together*, or H_1 and V_1 *together*, may *not* be considered redundant constraints. Any other two constraints together may be considered redundant and hence dispensable.

At this point one may well ask, Why bother with redundant constraints at all if they can be removed anyway? Would it not be far simpler to get rid of the redundants and then solve the resulting determinate system by already familiar methods of analysis? The answers to these questions bear on the concept of strength. In this chapter the strength we will discuss is governed by the proportional limit of the material; in Chapter 14 we will consider strength beyond the proportional limit. In both discussions, the paramount significance of constraint redundancy will be repeatedly brought out.

PROBLEMS

8.1. List the seven groups in two's and three's of the reaction components which, according to the foregoing discussion, are possible for the member of Fig. 8.1.

8.2. What is the degree of redundancy in this beam's system of constraints? Which reaction components together may be considered redundant? List the complete set.

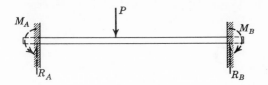

FIG. P8.2

8.3. For this beam, what is the degree of redundancy of its support system? Considering the nature of wires, which of the elements in the support system may together be dispensed with? List the complete set. Ignore the beam's weight.

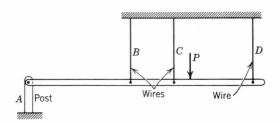

FIG. P8.3

8.4. Sketch the free-body diagram of this space bent, representing the reactions by means of their cartesian components. Note that the end supports are assumed capable of resisting not only thrust and shear but also bending and twist. What is the degree of indeterminateness of the force system? Give at least one set of reaction components that may *not* be considered redundant.

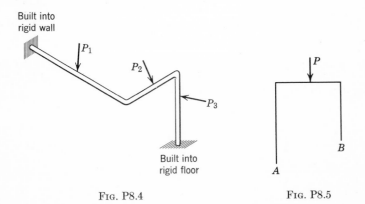

FIG. P8.4   FIG. P8.5

8.5. In this two-dimensional bent, only the ends A and B may be supported. What is the maximum degree of constraint redundancy possible?

8.2 Axially Loaded Members. A straight member acted on by axial loads that induce tension or compression stresses, or both, yields a collinear force system for which only one independent equilibrium equation is available. If only the ends of such a member may be supported, then the maximum degree of indeterminateness possible is one; otherwise it depends on the number of extra constraints that may be imposed between the ends.

When both ends only are constrained, either one of the supports may be considered the redundant. The external force system, indeterminate to the first degree, is solved completely by bringing in an equation which expresses a *known* fact concerning the behavior of the supports. For instance, if there is perfect initial fit and if the supports are unyielding, the known fact is that the total axial deformation of the member is nil. If the expression for the deformation in terms of the external forces is equated to zero, there results an equation (in effect a compatibility equation) which is independent of equilibrium. These two equations then constitute a sufficient set for the complete determination of the unknowns.

Illustrative Example 1. The bar in Fig. 8.2a, assumed of constant A and E, perfectly fits the opening between the two unyielding walls before the localized axial load P is applied. The ends are assumed fastened to the walls in such a manner that each support is capable of exerting either a push or a pull on the bar. Investigate the bar for stresses and deformation within the proportional limit.

ANALYSIS. Figure 8.2b shows the free-body diagram in which the senses of the wall reactions R_1 and R_2 have been assumed. Equilibrium requires that

$$\Sigma F_x = 0 = -R_1 + P - R_2. \qquad (a)$$

The elongation of a differential length Δx of bar, due to a tension load F, is $\Delta \delta = F(\Delta x)/AE$, where $F = R_1 - P\{x - a\}^0$ is the axial force transmitted at any section. Therefore the deflection of any section relative to the left and is

$$\delta = \int_0^x \frac{F}{AE}\, dx = \frac{1}{AE}\left[R_1 \int_0^x dx - P \int_0^x \{x - a\}^0\, dx \right]$$

$$= \frac{1}{AE}[R_1 x - P\{x - a\}^1]. \qquad (b)$$

Since the right end does not deflect relative to the left, upon substitution

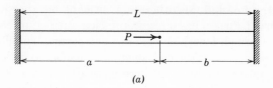

(a)

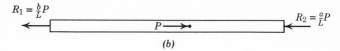

$R_1 = \frac{b}{L}P$ $R_2 = \frac{a}{L}P$

(b)

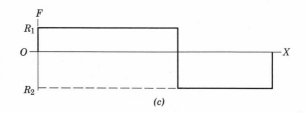

(c)

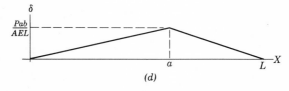

(d)

FIG. 8.2

of the values $x = L$ and $\delta = 0$ we obtain from Eq. b the independent equation

$$0 = \frac{1}{AE}[R_1 L - P(L - a)]. \qquad (c)$$

Between Eqs. a and c we can now solve for the unknown reactions; these are found to be $R_1 = P(L - a)/L = Pb/L$ and $R_2 = Pa/L$, their senses as assumed.

As depicted in the F-x diagram, Fig. 8.2c, the portion of length a is in tension, whereas that of length b is in compression. The maximum deflection, which occurs at $x = a$, Fig. 8.2d, and which numerically equals the total elongation of the length in tension (or the total contraction of the part in compression), is found from Eq. b to be

$$(\delta)_{x=a} = \frac{1}{AE}R_1 a = \frac{Pab}{AEL} = \frac{Pa}{AE}\left(\frac{b}{L}\right) = \frac{Pb}{AE}\left(\frac{a}{L}\right). \qquad (d)$$

Throughout the length a, the normal stresses on transverse planes are tensile, whereas throughout the length b, they are compressive. Their magnitudes are, respectively,

$$\sigma_a = \frac{Pb}{AL} = \frac{P}{A}\left(\frac{b}{L}\right) \quad \text{and} \quad \sigma_b = \frac{Pa}{AL} = \frac{P}{A}\left(\frac{a}{L}\right). \qquad (e)$$

If R_2 were considered the redundant and removed, R_1 would equal P and the total elongation of the bar then would be Pa/AE; the tensile stresses (only throughout a) would have the magnitude P/A. On the other hand, if R_1 were considered the redundant and removed, R_2 would equal P and the contraction of the bar then would be Pb/AE; the compressive stresses (only throughout b) would be of magnitude P/A. Comparing these values with the results shown in Eqs. d and e, we see that the bar, when redundantly supported, would carry the load P with less deformation and lower stresses than when simply supported in either of the two possible ways. The action of the redundantly supported bar may be likened to the simultaneous action of the two simply supported bars; it stands to reason therefore that, for the same allowable stress or the same allowable deformation, *the redundantly supported bar would carry a higher load than either of the simply supported bars.* This is the significant aspect of constraint redundancy that should be kept in mind. It furnishes one answer to the questions posed earlier in the preceding article: that redundancy of constraints, far from being undesirable, is something a designer consciously strives for because it *makes* possible an increase in either (1) the strength of a member based on allowable stresses or (2) the rigidity of the member, or both.

PROBLEMS

8.6. It should be clear from the results of Example 1 (Fig. 8.2) that, except when $a = b$, not every section of the bar can be stressed to its full potential. (*a*) Show that by prestraining the bar optimization of material utilization can be achieved within the proportional limit. (*b*) Assuming that the elastic-limit stresses in compression and tension are equal in magnitude, determine the necessary prestrain that will make this optimum condition possible. Express the result in terms of the dimensions shown in Fig. 8.2, the elastic-limit stress σ_e, and the elasticity modulus E. Assume that $a > b$, and investigate the two cases: when the load P is directed to the right and when it is directed to the left. In each case, specify whether the bar should in effect be initially shorter or longer than the space between the unyielding walls. (*Hint:* The optimum load is $2\sigma_e A$.)

8.7. The homogeneous bar has a uniform cross-sectional area of 2 in.^{2} Assuming perfect initial fit and unyielding supports, analyze the bar for stresses and deflections.   Sketch the graphs depicting the variation of axial force and deflection.   Can the maximum stress be minimized by prestrain?   If so, what kind and how much prestrain should be introduced? $E = 10.5 \times 10^6$ psi.

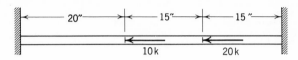

Fig. P8.7

8.8. Aside from the unyielding wall supports, this magnesium alloy ($E = 6.5 \times 10^6$ psi) bar, with a uniform cross-sectional area of 2 in.^{2}, has an additional constraint in the form of a rigid collar bearing against very stiff springs whose equivalent constant is 10^6 lb per inch.   What axial load P will induce stresses of 2000 psi in the bar?   Sketch the variation in the axial force transmitted.   (*Hint:* Make use of the fact that if R is the external reaction at the collar, then the deflection of the bar at this site is $R/10^6$ in.)

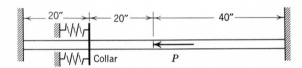

Fig. P8.8

8.9. What is the smallest cross-sectional area that this uniform homogeneous bar may have if the maximum stresses are not to exceed 10,000 psi?   The effective spring constant of the collar support is 2×10^6 lb per inch and $E = 10 \times 10^6$ psi.   There is no prestrain.

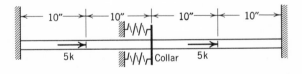

Fig. P8.9

8.10. This stepped bar is of steel for which $E = 30 \times 10^6$ psi.   Analyze it for stresses and deflections, assuming perfect initial fit and unyielding supports. (*Hint:* Write out the (F/AE)-x equation from the (F/AE)-x diagram.)

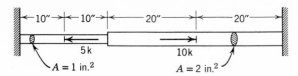

FIG. P8.10

8.11. This compound bar, with a uniform cross-sectional area of 1.5 in.^{2}, consists of a 10-in. length of aluminum joined to a 10-in. length of steel. It is held between two unyielding walls without prestrain. Where should the axial load P be applied in order that the allowable stresses of 5000 psi in the aluminum and 12,000 psi in the steel will develop simultaneously? For aluminum, $E = 10 \times 10^6$ psi, and for steel, $E = 30 \times 10^6$ psi. (*Hint:* Sketch (F/AE)-x diagram and from it derive the (F/AE)-x equation, using step functions.)

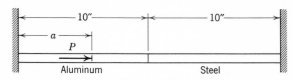

FIG. P8.11

8.12. This 1-in. thick uniformly tapered bar of aluminum alloy ($E = 10.5 \times 10^6$ psi) fits between rigid wall supports without prestrain. What maximum value may P have if the nominal stress is not to exceed 5000 psi? Sketch the deflection diagram and calculate the deflection where P is applied. (*Hint:* when

$$0 < x < 20, \frac{F}{A} = \frac{R_1}{1 + x/40}; \quad \text{when } 20 < x < 40, \frac{F}{A} = -\frac{R_2}{1 + x/40};$$

where $R_1 + R_2 = P$.)

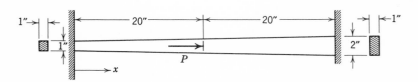

FIG. P8.12

8.13. Where should the axial load P be applied on the bar of Prob. 8.12 in order that it can be a maximum? How much is this P? (*Hint: P* will be greatest when *two* transverse sections of the bar are stressed to the maximum; one of these will be at the left wall, the other will be adjacent to P on the right.)

8.3   Torsion Members.   The analysis of a redundantly supported straight torsion member is similar to that of a redundantly supported straight axially loaded tension or compression member. There is only one equilibrium equation available, $\Sigma M_x = 0$. Consequently, the maximum degree of redundancy is one, if only the ends may be restrained; otherwise it could be any number equal to the number of restraints less one.

Illustrative Example 2.   Figure 8.3a represents a solid shaft of uniform circular cross section, subjected to an external twisting moment T_0 and held against rotation by the two unyielding walls. Before the load is applied, there are no reactive twisting moments at the walls. Analyze the shaft for reactions, stresses, and deformation.

ANALYSIS.   Figure 8.3b shows the free-body diagram, where the twisting moments are represented by doubleheaded arrows whose senses are

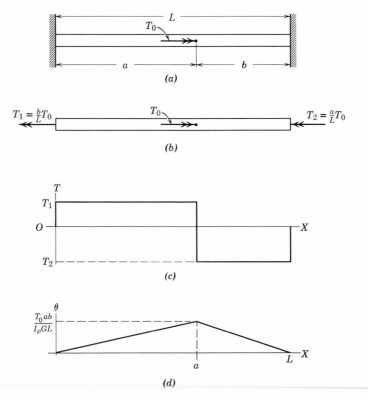

Fig. 8.3

consistent with the right-hand rule. Note that, except for the double arrowheads, Fig. 8.3b is identical to Fig. 8.2b. The twisting moment transmitted across any section is $T = T_1 - T_0\{x - a\}^0$, and the angle of twist for a differential length Δx is $T(\Delta x)/I_pG$. Therefore the angular deflection of any section relative to the left end is

$$\theta = \int_0^x \frac{T}{I_pG} \, dx = \frac{1}{I_pG} [T_1x - T_0\{x - a\}^1]. \qquad (a)$$

Since the walls are unyielding in rotation, the angular deflection of the right end relative to the left is zero. Putting $x = L$ and $\theta = 0$ in the preceding equation, we obtain

$$0 = T_1L - T_0b. \qquad (b)$$

The other independent equation comes from equilibrium, thus:

$$\Sigma M_x = 0 = T_1 - T_0 - T_2. \qquad (c)$$

From Eqs. b and c we find the reactive twisting moments to be $T_1 = T_0b/L$ and $T_2 = T_0a/L$. Figure 8.3c displays the torque-distribution diagram.

The greatest shear stresses are

$$\tau = \frac{16T_0}{\pi d^3} \left(\frac{b}{L}\right) \quad \text{or} \quad \tau = \frac{16T_0}{\pi d^3} \left(\frac{a}{L}\right), \qquad (d)$$

depending on which is larger, b or a.

The maximum angular deflection occurs where the external twisting moment T_0 is applied (Fig. 8.3d) and is found from Eq. a when for x the value a is substituted, thus:

$$(\theta)_{x=a} = \frac{T_1a}{I_pG} = \frac{T_0a}{I_pG}\left(\frac{b}{L}\right) = \frac{T_0b}{I_pG}\left(\frac{a}{L}\right). \qquad (e)$$

The rest of the analysis follows lines similar to those in the example of the preceding article. Thus, if either restraint is considered the redundant and removed, the maximum shear stresses become $\tau = 16T_0/\pi d^3$ and the maximum angular deflection is either $\theta = T_0a/I_pG$ or $\theta = T_0b/I_pG$. These values are clearly larger than those shown in Eqs. d and e. Again we remark that redundancy of constraint improves not only the strength but also the rigidity of the member.

PROBLEMS

8.14. In the torsion bar of Example 2 (Fig. 8.3), so long as a does not equal b, only part of the entire length of shaft can be stressed fully. (a) Show that pre-twisting the shaft before it is secured to the unyielding supports makes optimization possible without the elastic limit being overstepped. (b) Determine the necessary pretwist that will make this optimum condition possible. Express the pretwist angle in terms of the dimensions shown in Fig. 8.3, the diameter d of the shaft, the elastic-limit stress τ_e, and the elasticity modulus G. Assume that $a > b$. Specify the sense of the pretwist in relation to the external load T_0. (*Hint:* The optimum load is $2T_e = 4\tau_e I_p/d$.)

8.15. This uniform and homogeneous solid round shaft is built into the un-yielding walls without any pretwist. Evaluate the reactive twisting moments. Sketch the torque-variation and twist-deformation diagrams, giving key values. Use the letter symbols given, including G and I_p, where needed.

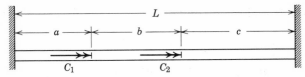

FIG. P8.15

8.16. Do Prob. 8.15, with $a = b = c = L/3$ and $C_1 = C_2$.
8.17. Do Prob. 8.15, with $a = b = c = L/3$ and $C_1 = -C_2$.
8.18. This uniform and homogeneous solid round shaft is loaded and sup-ported symmetrically. Determine the ratio a/L for optimum conditions (so that the maximum shear stresses develop at the largest number of sections). (*Hint:* First sketch the torque-variation diagram.)

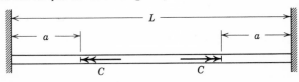

FIG. P8.18

8.19. Determine the lengths b and c in terms of L so that the maximum shear stresses will be the least possible in this uniform and homogeneous round shaft.

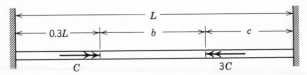

FIG. P8.19

8.20. The 2-in. round solid aluminum alloy shaft is held between two un-yielding walls and is further constrained against rotation through a thin disk welded to it at its center section as shown. The equivalent torsional spring constant of the middle support is 10^6 in.-lb per radian. What maximum stresses are induced by the torsional loads C, each equal to 10,000 in.-lb? Sketch the twisting-moment and twist-deformation diagrams, giving key values. $G = 4 \times 10^6$ psi.

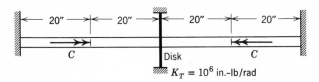

FIG. P8.20

8.21. The composite shaft, consisting of a 40-in. length of aluminum alloy rod joined to a 30-in. length of titanium alloy rod, both 2 in. in diameter, is built into the unyielding walls without any pre-strain. Where should the external torque load T_0 be applied, and what is its magnitude in order that the allowable shear stresses of 5000 psi in the aluminum and 8000 psi in the titanium be in-duced simultaneously? For aluminum, $G = 4 \times 10^6$ psi, and for titanium, $G = 6 \times 10^6$ psi. (*Hint:* Assume the maximum allowable reactions, then sketch the (T/GI_p)-x diagram and from it derive the (T/GI_p)-x equation.)

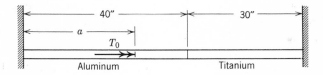

FIG. P8.21

8.22. The stepped composite shaft made up of two 20-in. lengths of alumi-num and titanium alloy cylinders is loaded and supported as shown. Assuming perfect initial fit, determine the diameter of the aluminum portion and the magnitude of the load T_0 that will make it possible for the allowable shear stresses of 5000 psi in the aluminum and 8000 psi in the titanium to develop simultaneously. See Prob. 8.21 for the elastic constants.

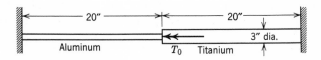

FIG. P8.22

8.23. Assume that the equations developed for uniform cylinders apply to this gently tapered shaft built into two unyielding walls. Determine the reactive torques. What is T_0 if the maximum nominal stress is 5000 psi?

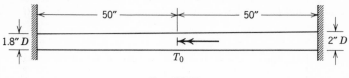

FIG. P8.23

8.4   Beams of One Span. Beams may be classified according to the number of their spans. Single-span beams include those with overhangs. Multispan beams are continuous over the inner supports and for this reason are called continuous beams; they are taken up in the next article.

If the only loads acting on a beam are transverse forces lying in one plane, and if the supports are such that they do not exert appreciable longitudinal restraint, then the forces involved constitute essentially a coplanar parallel system for which only two independent equilibrium equations are available. In beams of only one span, the greatest number of components that the reactive system can have is four: one shear force and one moment at each end. Hence, in such beams, the maximum degree of redundancy possible is two; the two additional equations necessary for a complete solution of the force system must express known facts, aside from the usual boundary conditions for statically determinate beams. For instance, additional values of linear or angular deflection at the ends or elsewhere must be known beforehand, or values of the shear force or the bending moment at two sections must be specified; these extra equations must then account for these conditions. Then they, together with the equilibrium equations, will suffice for a complete solution of the beam's force system.

Illustrative Example 3.   The uniform beam of length L shown in Fig. 8.4a is fixed at one end and simply supported at the other and carries a uniformly distributed downward load of intensity p. Analyze the beam for stresses and deformation within the proportional limit, assuming perfect initial fit (that is, the beam was not sprung into position).

ANALYSIS. Figure 8.4b shows the free-body diagram. Since the reactive force system has three components, all unknown, and there are only two independent equations from equilibrium, the beam is statically

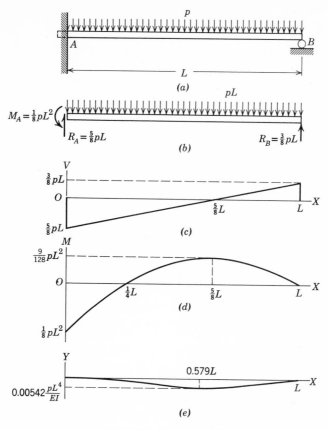

FIG. 8.4

indeterminate to the first degree. Any one of the three components may be assumed the redundant, although for practical reasons this choice may be only between M_A and R_B. By equilibrium, we may write

$$\Sigma F_V = 0 = R_A + R_B - pL \tag{1}$$

and

$$\Sigma M_B = 0 = -M_A + R_A L - \frac{pL^2}{2}. \tag{2}$$

A third equation follows from the fact that at B the deflection is zero.

The next immediate task therefore is to derive an equation for the deflection. We proceed as follows. The bending moment at any section x distant from the left end is $M = -M_A + R_A x - px^2/2$. Therefore the differential equation of the elastic curve is

$$\frac{d^2y}{dx^2} = \frac{1}{EI}\left[-M_A + R_A x - \frac{px^2}{2} \right], \tag{a}$$

whence $\theta = \theta_0 + \frac{1}{EI}\left[-M_A x + \frac{R_A x^2}{2} - \frac{px^3}{6} \right], \tag{b}$

and $y = y_0 + \theta_0 x + \frac{1}{EI}\left[-\frac{M_A x^2}{2} + \frac{R_A x^3}{6} - \frac{px^4}{24} \right]. \tag{c}$

Both θ_0 and y_0 are zero from the given conditions. Using the additional boundary condition that the deflection at B is zero, we obtain from Eq. c the third independent equation

$$0 = \frac{1}{EI}\left[-\frac{M_A L^2}{2} + \frac{R_A L^3}{6} - \frac{pL^4}{24} \right]. \tag{3}$$

Solution of Eqs. 1, 2, and 3 yields

$$M_A = \frac{pL^2}{8}, \qquad R_A = \frac{5pL}{8}, \qquad \text{and} \qquad R_B = \frac{3pL}{8}.$$

Figure 8.4c shows the V-x curve; it crosses the X axis at a distance of $\frac{5}{8}$ the span from A. The M-x curve, Fig. 8.4d, reveals the two largest bending moments: $pL^2/8$ at the wall and $9pL^2/128$, where V is zero. The elastic curve, Fig. 8.4e, displays a point of inflection. To locate the maximum deflection, we equate θ to zero and solve for x from Eq. b, thus:

$$0 = -M_A x + \frac{R_A x^2}{2} - \frac{px^3}{6} = -\frac{pL^2 x}{8} + \frac{5pLx^2}{16} - \frac{px^3}{6} \tag{d}$$

after using the above values of M_A and R_A. The value $x = 0$ satisfies the equation as it should. The reduced and simplified equation

$$0 = 8x^2 - 15Lx + 6L^2 \tag{e}$$

gives $x = \frac{15L \pm \sqrt{225L^2 - 192L^2}}{16} = 0.579L.$

Substituting this in Eq. c and using the previously obtained values of

M_A and R_A, we get

$$(y)_{x=0.579L} = \frac{1}{EI}\left[-\frac{pL^2(0.579L)^2}{16} + \frac{5pL(0.579L)^3}{48} - \frac{p(0.579L)^4}{24}\right]$$

$$= \frac{(0.579)^2 pL^4}{48EI}(-3 + 2.895 - 0.671)$$

$$= -\frac{0.00542pL^4}{EI},$$

where the minus sign indicates a downward deflection.

If R_B were considered the redundant and removed, the resulting cantilever beam would experience a maximum bending moment of $pL^2/2$ at
the wall and a maximum downward deflection of $0.125pL^4/EI$ at the
free end. On the other hand, if M_B were considered the redundant
constraint and removed, the resulting simply supported beam would
have a maximum bending moment of $pL^2/8$ and a maximum downward
deflection of $0.013pL^4/EI$, both at midspan. Comparing these with the
maximum values of bending moment and deflection in the redundantly
supported beam, we see once again that redundancy of constraints makes
the beam considerably more rigid and, for the same allowable bending
stress, at least as strong as or stronger than a similarly loaded statically
determinate beam of the same length.

PROBLEMS

In the following problems, unless mentioned to the contrary, perfect initial fit
(no prestrain) is understood and the member is assumed to be of uniform cross
section and negligible weight and made of a homogeneous material. "Solve
completely" means that all reaction components must be determined and the
shear-force and bending-moment diagrams sketched, with key values to be
given. If only the reactions are desired, it shall be so stated.

8.24. Solve completely. Determine the maximum deflection.

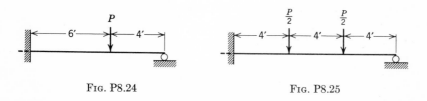

FIG. P8.24   FIG. P8.25

8.25. Solve completely. Determine the maximum deflection.

8.26. Solve completely.

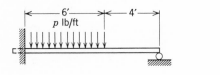

FIG. P8.26

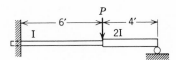

FIG. P8.27

8.27. Solve completely. Determine the maximum deflection. (*Hint:* Sketch a tentative M-x curve first, using the unknown reaction components. From this derive the (M/EI)-x diagram and write out the Bernoulli-Euler equation.)

8.28. Solve for the reactions.

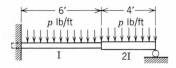

FIG. P8.28

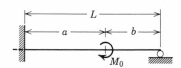

FIG. P8.29

8.29. Solve completely.

8.30. Show that the bending moment at the wall is $-Pab(a + 2b)/2L^2$. Solve for the other reaction components.

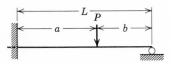

FIG. P8.30

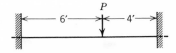

FIG. P8.34

8.31. Using the result of Prob. 8.30, derive by superposition the bending moment at the wall in the beam of Example 3 (Fig. 8.4). (*Hint:* Consider the differential force $p(dx)$ equivalent to the point load P.)

8.32. Using the result of Prob. 8.30, evaluate by superposition the wall bending moment in the beam of Fig. P8.25.

8.33. Using the result of Prob. 8.30, evaluate the wall bending moment for the beam of Fig. P8.26.

8.34. Solve completely. Determine the maximum deflection.

8.35. Solve completely. Determine the maximum deflection.

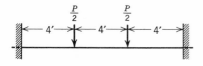

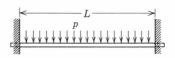

Fɪɢ. P8.35   Fɪɢ. P8.36

8.36. Solve completely. Determine the maximum deflection.

8.37. Solve completely. Determine the maximum deflection. (*Hint:* First sketch a tentative M-x diagram and from it derive the (M/EI)-x curve. Take advantage of symmetry.)

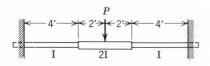

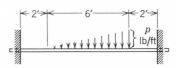

Fɪɢ. P8.37   Fɪɢ. P8.38

8.38. Solve for the reactions.

8.39. Solve for the reactions.

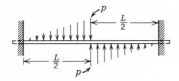

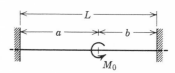

Fɪɢ. P8.39   Fɪɢ. P8.40

8.40. Solve completely.

8.41. Show that the bending moment at the left wall is $-Pab^2/L^2$ and that at the right wall is $-Pa^2b/L^2$.

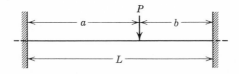

Fɪɢ. P8.41

8.42. Using the results of Prob. 8.41, evaluate the wall bending moments in the beam of Fig. P8.36.

8.43. Using the results of Prob. 8.41, evaluate the wall bending moments in the beam of Fig. P8.38.

8.44. These are three identical beams, rectangular in cross section, 4 in. deep and 3 in. thick. The allowable bending stress is 10,000 psi. Compare the load-carrying capacities of the three beams, noting the influence of the degree of constraint redundancy.

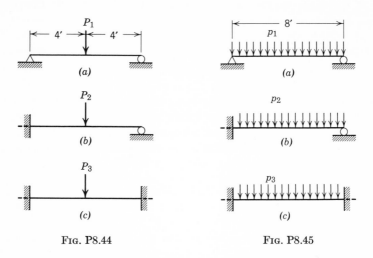

FIG. P8.44   FIG. P8.45

8.45. These are the same three beams of Prob. 8.44, but now bearing uniformly distributed loads. Compare their load-carrying capacities.

8.46. Each of the beams of Fig. P8.44 carries a load of 10 kips. Select for each the smallest WF-section. Compare the weights of the three beams. The allowable bending stress is 10,000 psi.

8.47. Each of the beams of Fig. P8.45 carries a load of 2 kips per foot. Select for each the smallest WF-section. Compare the weights of the three beams. The allowable bending stress is 10,000 psi.

8.48. Adjust the elevation of the roller support of the beam in Fig. P8.44b for optimum conditions in regard to bending. (This represents a prestrain.) Calculate the adjustment and the maximum P corresponding to this optimum. What is the percent increase in P over that for the perfectly aligned beam? (*Hint:* Find the reactions from statics and then calculate the end deflection consistent with the reactions.)

8.49. Can the beam of Fig. P8.44c be optimized in regard to bending by prestraining?

8.50. Adjust the elevation of the roller support of the beam in Fig. P8.45b for optimum conditions in regard to bending. Calculate the adjustment and the maximum p corresponding to this optimum. What is the percent increase in p

over that for the perfectly aligned beam? (*Hint:* Locate the section of maximum bending moment between supports first, using statics only. Take advantage of the fact that M peaks where V goes through zero. Then evaluate the reactions. Finally, calculate the end deflection from the known force system.)

8.51. How can the beam of Fig. P8.45c be optimized for bending? Calculate the optimum load-carrying capacity and compare it with that of the perfectly aligned beam.

8.5 Continuous Beams. In beams of several spans, the maximum degree of indeterminateness possible equals the number of spans plus one when only the ends may be restrained externally against rotation; the minimum is one less than the number of spans when neither end is restrained against rotation. This number of extra equations must then be brought in, independently of the equilibrium equations, in order to effect a complete solution of the force system. The technique of the preceding article for single-span beams may still be used, although it may not be the most convenient approach. Note that in this method the components of the external reactive system are carried along as the unknowns.

Illustrative Example 4. For the three-span beam of constant cross section and constant E shown in Fig. 8.5a, derive a complete set of equations for determining the unknown reactions. Assume perfect initial fit, unyielding supports at the same level, and ignore the weight of the beam.

ANALYSIS. From the free-body diagram in Fig. 8.5b we note that the system is statically indeterminate to the second degree. Equilib-

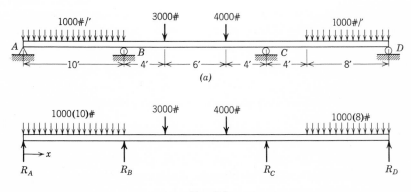

Fɪɢ. 8.5

rium requires that

$$\Sigma F_V = 0 = R_A + R_B + R_C + R_D - 10,000 - 3000 - 4000 - 8000, \quad (1)$$

and

$$\Sigma M_D = 0 = R_A(36) + R_B(26) - 10,000(31) - 3000(22) \\ - 4000(16) - 8000(4). \quad (2)$$

The differential equation of the elastic curve is

$$\frac{d^2y}{dx^2} = \frac{1}{EI}[R_A x - 500x^2 + 500\{x - 10\}^2 + R_B\{x - 10\}^1 \\ - 3000\{x - 14\}^1 - 4000\{x - 20\}^1 \\ + R_C\{x - 24\}^1 - 500\{x - 28\}^2], \quad (a)$$

whence

$$\theta = \frac{1}{EI}\left[\frac{R_A x^2}{2} - \frac{500x^3}{3} + \frac{500}{3}\{x - 10\}^3 + \frac{R_B}{2}\{x - 10\}^2 \\ - 1500\{x - 14\}^2 - 2000\{x - 20\}^2 + \frac{R_C}{2}\{x - 24\}^2 \\ - \tfrac{500}{3}\{x - 28\}^3\right] + \theta_0, \quad (b)$$

and

$$y = \frac{1}{EI}\left[\frac{R_A x^3}{6} - \frac{125x^4}{3} + \frac{125}{3}\{x - 10\}^4 + \frac{R_B}{6}\{x - 10\}^3 \\ - 500\{x - 14\}^3 - \tfrac{2000}{3}\{x - 20\}^3 + \frac{R_C}{6}\{x - 24\}^3 \\ - \tfrac{125}{3}\{x - 28\}^4\right] + \theta_0 x, \quad (c)$$

since y_0 is zero. Note that Eq. b introduces the additional unknown θ_0. The *three* additional equations independent of Eqs. 1 and 2 make use of the conditions that at B, C, and D the deflections are zero. Accordingly, from Eq. c we obtain

$$(y)_{x=10} = 0 = \frac{1}{EI}\left[\frac{500R_A}{3} - \frac{1,250,000}{3}\right] + 10\theta_0, \quad (3)$$

$$(y)_{x=24} = 0 = \frac{1}{EI}\left[2304R_A - 55,296,000 + \frac{4,802,000}{3}\right. \\ \left. + \frac{1372R_B}{3} - 500,000 - \frac{128,000}{3}\right] + 24\theta_0, \quad (4)$$

and

$$(y)_{x=36} = 0 = \frac{1}{EI}\left[7776R_A - 69{,}984{,}000 + \frac{57{,}122{,}000}{3} + \frac{8788R_B}{3}\right.$$

$$\left. - 5{,}324{,}000 - \frac{8{,}192{,}000}{3} + 288R_C - \frac{512{,}000}{3}\right] + 36\theta_0. \quad (5)$$

Clearing fractions and collecting terms, we rewrite the preceding equations as follows:

$$R_A + R_B + R_C + R_D = 25{,}000, \quad (1')$$

$$36R_A + 26R_B + 12R_C = 472{,}000, \quad (2')$$

$$500R_A + 30EI\theta_0 = 1{,}250{,}000, \quad (3')$$

$$6912R_A + 1372R_B + 72EI\theta_0 = 162{,}714{,}000, \quad (4')$$

$$23{,}328R_A + 8788R_B + 864R_C + 108EI\theta_0 = 177{,}510{,}000. \quad (5')$$

All five equations are independent of one another; they constitute a sufficient set for the unique determination of the five unknowns: four components of the reactive system and one deformation constant. With these quantities known, the shear force, bending moment, slope or deflection of the elastic curve at any location can be readily determined.

Note the large numbers that inevitably become involved in this method. This is because the successively increasing distances of the various supports from the left end enter into the equations. It should be clear that for beams of even only a few spans the disparate magnitudes of the numbers involved could make ordinary slide rule computation awkward and unsatisfactory.

PROBLEMS

8.52. This uniform and homogeneous beam just rests on all three supports before any load is applied. (a) Solve for the reactions. (b) Sketch the V-x and M-x diagrams, giving key values. (c) If this were an 8WF20 beam, how large could P be based on a design bending stress of 18,000 psi?

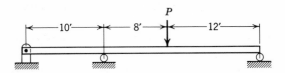

FIG. P8.52

8.53. For the beam of Prob. 8.52, how large could P be under optimum conditions for bending, brought about by adjusting the elevation of one of the supports? Calculate the necessary adjustment. $E = 30 \times 10^6$ psi.

8.54. This uniform and homogeneous beam just rests on all three supports before any load is applied. (a) Solve for the reactions. (b) Sketch the V-x and M-x diagrams, giving key values. (c) In terms of an elastic-limit resisting moment M_e, how large can P be?

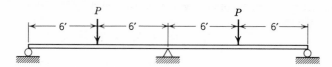

FIG. P8.54

8.55. For the beam of Prob. 8.54, how large can P be under optimum conditions compared to the P for the perfectly aligned beam?

8.56. Solve for the reactions. Assume E is constant and there is no prestrain. (*Hint:* Working from the left, sketch each component of the bending-moment diagram using the unknown reactions. Divide each one by the proper EI, and then derive the (M/EI)-x equation. You should get the following (see Probs. 5.41 and 5.45):

$$\frac{M}{EI} = \frac{1}{4EI} [2R_1(x + \{x - 20\}^1 + 20\{x - 20\}^0)$$

$$- p(x^2 + \{x - 20\}^2 + 40\{x - 20\}^1 + 400\{x - 20\}^0) + 4R_2\{x - 20\}^1].$$

Check this, at least at the end points, before proceeding with the solution.)

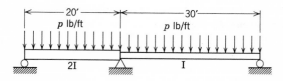

FIG. P8.56

8.6 The Three-Moment Equation.

A technique that avoids these large numbers makes use of the bending moments at the supports as the unknowns. With such moments evaluated, the components of the external reactive system can be easily determined either from equilibrium considerations or by applying the definition of bending moment (Rule 2). This method is based on the *three-moment equation* which we now derive.

Let Fig. 8.6a represent two adjacent spans of a uniform continuous beam on unyielding supports. Neither P nor R is necessarily an ex-

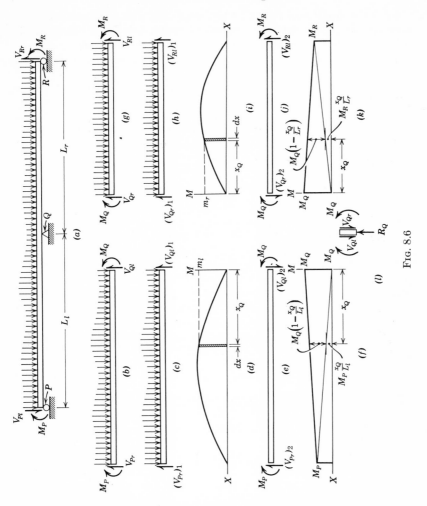

FIG. 8.6

terior support. The shear and moment immediately to the left of P and to right of R will, in general, differ from zero.

Figure 8.6b shows the free-body diagram of the left span isolated by sectioning transverse planes very close to the supports. The force system may be resolved into two components: one involving the external loads and the accompanying reactions but without the restraining moments at the ends, as shown in Fig. 8.6c; the other one accounts for the restraining moments (assumed positive, that is, so as to cause compression in the upper side of the beam), considered as external loads with the necessary reactions, as shown in Fig. 8.6e. The beam represented in Fig. 8.6c is in effect the left span considered simply supported. The bending-moment diagram for the beam of Fig. 8.6c is shown schematically in Fig. 8.6d, in which m_l stands for the bending moment at any section a distance x_Q from Q. Observe that the coordinate system is a *left-handed* one. The bending-moment diagram for the beam in Fig. 8.6e is shown in Fig. 8.6f; it consists of a trapezoidal figure which has been divided into two triangles. This division allows expressing the bending moment as a function exclusively of the end moments. The coordinate system is also left handed. The bending moment at any section in the left span may now be written

$$M_l = m_l + M_Q + (M_P - M_Q)\frac{x_Q}{L_l}. \qquad (a)$$

This process is repeated for the right span, for which the corresponding diagrams are shown in sketches g to k of Fig. 8.6. Note that the coordinate systems in sketches i and k are both *right handed*. Then the bending moment at any section in the right span is

$$M_r = m_r + M_Q + (M_R - M_Q)\frac{x_Q}{L_r}. \qquad (b)$$

Using the preceding expressions for the bending moment, we now derive the equation of the elastic curve. First, for the left span, by Eq. a we have

$$\frac{d^2y}{dx^2} = \frac{1}{EI}\left[m_l + M_Q + (M_P - M_Q)\frac{x_Q}{L_l}\right], \qquad (c)$$

whence

$$\theta = \theta_{Ql} + \frac{1}{EI}\left[\int_0^{x_Q} m_l\,dx + M_Q x_Q + (M_P - M_Q)\frac{x_Q{}^2}{2L_l}\right], \qquad (d)$$

and

$$y = y_Q + \theta_{Ql}x_Q + \frac{1}{EI}\left[\int_0^{x_Q}\int_0^{x_Q} m_l\,dx\,dx + \frac{M_Q x_Q{}^2}{2}\right.$$
$$\left. + (M_P - M_Q)\frac{x_Q{}^3}{6L_l}\right]. \qquad (e)$$

At P, $x_Q = L_l$ and $y = y_P$; therefore Eq. e becomes

$$y_P = y_Q + \theta_{Ql}L_l + \frac{1}{EI}\left[\int_0^{L_l}\int_0^{x_Q} m_l\,dx\,dx\right.$$
$$\left. + \frac{M_Q L_l{}^2}{2} + (M_P - M_Q)\frac{L_l{}^2}{6}\right]. \qquad (f)$$

Solving for θ_{Ql}, we obtain

$$\theta_{Ql} = -\frac{1}{EI}\left[\frac{1}{L_l}\int_0^{L_l}\int_0^{x_Q} m_l\,dx\,dx + \frac{M_Q L_l}{2} + (M_P - M_Q)\frac{L_l}{6}\right]$$

$$+ \frac{y_P - y_Q}{L_l}. \quad (g)$$

Repeating the preceding steps for the right span, we find at R

$$y_R = y_Q + \theta_{Qr}L_r + \frac{1}{EI}\left[\int_0^{L_r}\int_0^{x_Q} m_r\,dx\,dx\right.$$

$$\left.+ \frac{M_Q L_r^2}{2} + (M_R - M_Q)\frac{L_r^2}{6}\right]. \quad (h)$$

Solving for θ_{Qr}, we find

$$\theta_{Qr} = -\frac{1}{EI}\left[\frac{1}{L_r}\int_0^{L_r}\int_0^{x_Q} m_r\,dx\,dx + \frac{M_Q L_r}{2} + (M_R - M_Q)\frac{L_r}{6}\right]$$

$$+ \frac{y_R - y_Q}{L_r}. \quad (i)$$

Owing to the continuity of the elastic curve at Q, the slope at that section when approached from the left must be the same as when approached from the right; that is, there are no kinks in the elastic curve of a continuous beam. This means that θ_{Ql} as given by Eq. g must numerically equal θ_{Qr} as given by Eq. i. Taking into account the fact that a positive slope in a right-handed coordinate system appears negative in a left-handed one, we equate the right-hand sides of Eqs. g and i, putting a minus sign in front of one, thus:

$$-\frac{1}{EI}\left[\frac{1}{L_l}\int_0^{L_l}\int_0^{x_Q} m_l\,dx\,dx + \frac{M_Q L_l}{2} + (M_P - M_Q)\frac{L_l}{6}\right] + \frac{y_P - y_Q}{L_l}$$

$$= \frac{1}{EI}\left[\frac{1}{L_r}\int_0^{L_r}\int_0^{x_Q} m_r\,dx\,dx + \frac{M_Q L_r}{2} + (M_R - M_Q)\frac{L_r}{6}\right] - \frac{y_R - y_Q}{L_r}.$$

$$(j)$$

Collecting terms and rearranging, we obtain the *three-moment equation* for a continuous uniform beam on unyielding supports.

$$M_P L_l + 2M_Q(L_l + L_r) + M_R L_r = -\frac{6}{L_l}\int_0^{L_l}\int_0^{x_Q} m_l\,dx\,dx$$

$$-\frac{6}{L_r}\int_0^{L_r}\int_0^{x_Q} m_r\,dx\,dx + 6EI\left(\frac{y_P - y_Q}{L_l} + \frac{y_R - y_Q}{L_r}\right). \quad (8.1)$$

For the special case when the unyielding supports are all at the same level, the preceding reduces to

$$M_P L_l + 2M_Q(L_l + L_r) + M_R L_r$$

$$= -\frac{6}{L_l}\int_0^{L_l}\int_0^{x_Q} m_l \, dx \, dx - \frac{6}{L_r}\int_0^{L_r}\int_0^{x_Q} m_r \, dx \, dx. \quad (8.2)$$

The various symbols in the preceding equations have the following meanings:

P, Q, and R are any three consecutive (left to right) supports;

M_P, M_Q, and M_R are the bending moments at these supports, assumed positive (associated with upward concavity);

L_l is the length of the left span, or the distance from Q to P;

L_r is the length of the right span, or the distance from Q to R;

m_l is the bending moment at any section in the *simply supported* left span x_Q distant from Q;

m_r is the bending moment at any section in the *simply supported* right span x_Q distant from Q;

$y_P - y_Q$ is the difference in elevation between the supports P and Q; and

$y_R - y_Q$ is the difference in elevation between the supports R and Q.

In applying Eq. 8.2, one writes as many such equations as there are successive pairs of adjacent spans; then there emerges a complete set of independent equations for the unique determination of the internal moments. If the beam has a built-in end, an imaginary span of infinite stiffness is added beyond the fixed end; the remote moment as well as the loads on this imaginary span are all zero. Hence for a beam with n spans, the maximum number of unknown moments at the supports (therefore the maximum number of three-moment equations) is $n + 1$ when both ends are fixed; the minimum number is $n - 1$ when both ends are simply supported.

Illustrative Example 5.   Determine the reactive system for the beam of Fig. 8.5a and sketch the shear-force and bending-moment diagrams, giving significant numerical values.   Assume unyielding supports at the same level and ignore the weight of the beam.

SOLUTION.   First, the simply supported spans are solved for their reactions.   These are shown in sketches a, b, and c of Fig. 8.7.   The bending-moment equations are:

From B to A: $m_l = 5000x - 500x^2$.

From B to C: $m_r = \dfrac{23{,}000}{7} x - 3000\{x - 4\}^1 - 4000\{x - 10\}^1$.

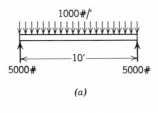

(a)

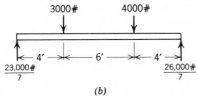

(b)

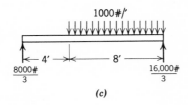

(c)

FIG. 8.7

From C to B: $m_l = \dfrac{26,000}{7} x - 4000\{x - 4\}^1 - 300\{x - 10\}^1.$

From C to D: $m_r = \frac{8000}{3} x - 500\{x - 4\}^2.$

Next, the double integrals are evaluated as follows:

$$\int_0^{10} \int_0^x (5000x - 500x^2)\, dx\, dx = \int_0^{10} \left(2500x^2 - \tfrac{500}{3}x^3\right) dx$$

$$= \left. \tfrac{2500}{3}x^3 - \tfrac{125}{3}x^4 \right|_0^{10} = \frac{1,250,000}{3}.$$

$$\int_0^{14} \int_0^x \left[\frac{23,000}{7} x - 3000\{x - 4\}^1 - 4000\{x - 10\}^1\right] dx\, dx$$

$$= \int_0^{14} \left[\frac{11,500}{7} x^2 - 1500\{x - 4\}^2 - 2000\{x - 10\}^2\right] dx$$

$$= \left.\frac{11,500}{21} x^3 \right|_0^{14} - \left. 500(x - 4)^3 \right|_4^{14} - \left.\tfrac{2000}{3}(x - 10)^3 \right|_{10}^{14}$$

$$= 960,000.$$

$$\int_0^{14} \int_0^{x} \left[\frac{26,000}{7} x - 4000\{x - 4\}^1 - 3000\{x - 10\}^1 \right] dx\, dx$$

$$= \int_0^{14} \left[\frac{13,000}{7} x^2 - 2000\{x - 4\}^2 - 1500\{x - 10\}^2 \right] dx$$

$$= \frac{13,000}{21} x^3 \Big|_0^{14} - \tfrac{2\,0\,0\,0}{3}(x - 4)^3 \Big|_4^{14} - 500(x - 10)^3 \Big|_{10}^{14}$$

$$= 1,000,000.$$

$$\int_0^{12} \int_0^{x} [\tfrac{8\,0\,0\,0}{3} x - 500\{x - 4\}^2]\, dx\, dx = \int_0^{12} [\tfrac{4\,0\,0\,0}{3} x^2 - \tfrac{5\,0\,0}{3}\{x - 4\}^3]\, dx$$

$$= \tfrac{4\,0\,0\,0}{9} x^3 \Big|_0^{12} - \tfrac{1\,2\,5}{3}(x - 4)^4 \Big|_4^{12} = \frac{1,792,000}{3}.$$

The three-moment equations are now written. Thus, for the spans AB and BC, Eq. 8.2 becomes

$$0 + 2M_B(10 + 14) + M_C(14) = -\frac{6}{10}\left(\frac{1,250,000}{3}\right) - \tfrac{6}{14}(960,000)$$

or $$48M_B + 14M_C = -\frac{4,630,000}{7}.$$ (a)

For the spans BC and CD, we get

$$M_B(14) + 2M_C(14 + 12) + 0 = -\tfrac{6}{14}(1,000,000) - \frac{6}{12}\left(\frac{1,792,000}{3}\right)$$

or $$14M_B + 52M_C = -\frac{15,272,000}{21}.$$ (b)

Solution of Eqs. a and b gives

$$M_B = -10,527 \text{ ft-lb} \qquad \text{and} \qquad M_C = -11,151 \text{ ft-lb.}$$

The reaction R_A now follows from the definition of the bending moment at B (Rule 2), thus:

$$M_B = R_A(10) - 10,000(5) = -10,527,$$ (c)

whence $R_A = 3947$ lb.

Similarly, we find R_D from the bending moment at C, thus:

$$M_C = R_D(12) - 8000(8) = -11,151,$$ (d)

from which $R_D = 4404$ lb.

The reaction R_B may be obtained in either of two ways. One is to express the bending moment at C in terms of the forces to the left of C; then

R_B is the only unknown. The other is to find the shear forces V_{Bl} and V_{Br} first and then add them (see Fig. 8.6*l*). This second method is more convenient for beams of many spans. Using the first method, we write

$$M_C = 3947(24) + R_B(14) - 10,000(19) - 3000(10) - 4000(4)$$

$$= -11,151, \tag{e}$$

which gives $\qquad\qquad R_B = 9294 \text{ lb.}$

Finally, expressing the bending moment at B in terms of the forces to the right of B, we have

$$M_B = 4404(26) + R_C(14) - 8000(22) - 4000(10) - 3000(4)$$

$$= -10,527, \tag{f}$$

whence $\qquad\qquad R_C = 7355 \text{ lb.}$

With the reactive force system completely solved, there is now enough information for calculating the shear force and the bending moment at any section of the continuous beam. The shear-force and bending-moment diagrams, whose construction the reader should be able to follow without difficulty, are displayed in sketches *a* and *b* of Fig. 8.8. It is seen that the largest bending moment of 11,151 ft-lb occurs at section C; this causes downward concavity of the beam in this vicinity.

In discussing the details of a method, one could easily overlook the major objectives. As the saying goes, one loses sight of the forest because of the trees. Let us then try to view the forest. We observe from Fig. 8.8*b* that peaks in the bending-moment diagram occur at the supports and in between; this is typical of continuous beams. It should not be difficult to understand that, by suitable adjustments of the levels of the supports or the lengths of the spans, the magnitudes of these peak bending moments could be made nearly equal to one another. This would make for a more efficient utilization of the material since the maximum number of beam sections could be made simultaneously to contribute approximately their full potential strengths within the proportional limit. Once more we remark that redundancy of constraints can give added strength and rigidity, hence added usefulness, to a beam over and above that which it possesses when statically determinate.

The next example explains the use of the three-moment equation method when either or both ends of a beam are fixed. The single-span beam is purposely chosen to show that, although this method is especially useful for multispan beams, it can be cumbersome, although by no means invalid, for single-span beams. The reader should demonstrate to himself the directness of the method of Article 8.4.

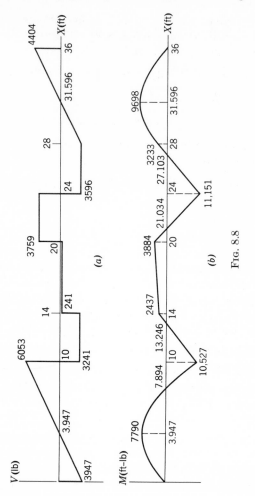

Fig. 8.8

Illustrative Example 6. Determine the reactions for the uniform beam shown in Fig. 8.9a. Assume perfect initial fit and unyielding built-in supports, and ignore the weight of the beam.

SOLUTION. The free-body diagram of the simply supported span is shown in Fig. 8.9b. The bending-moment equations are

$$m_r = 700x - 50x^2 + 50\{x - 6\}^2 - 600\{x - 12\}^1,$$

$$m_l = 500x - 600\{x - 6\}^1 - 50\{x - 12\}^2.$$

Then $\displaystyle\int_0^{18}\int_0^x [700x - 50x^2 + 50\{x - 6\}^2 - 600\{x - 12\}^1]\,dx\,dx$

$$= \int_0^{18} [350x^2 - \tfrac{50}{3}x^3 + \tfrac{50}{3}\{x - 6\}^3 - 300\{x - 12\}^2]\,dx$$

$$= \tfrac{350}{3}x^3 - \tfrac{25}{6}x^4 \Big|_0^{18} + \tfrac{25}{6}(x - 6)^4 \Big|_6^{18} - 100(x - 12)^3 \Big|_{12}^{18}$$

$$= 307{,}800.$$

And $\displaystyle\int_0^{18}\int_0^x [500x - 600\{x - 6\}^1 - 50\{x - 12\}^2]\,dx\,dx$

$$= \int_0^{18} [250x^2 - 300\{x - 6\}^2 - \tfrac{50}{3}\{x - 12\}^3]\,dx$$

$$= \tfrac{250}{3}x^3 \Big|_0^{18} - 100(x - 6)^3 \Big|_6^{18} - \tfrac{25}{6}(x - 12)^4 \Big|_{12}^{18} = 307{,}800.$$

The three-moment equation for the imaginary span to the left of A and the span AB is

$$0 + 2M_A(0 + 18) + M_B(18) = 0 - \tfrac{6}{18}(307{,}800)$$

or $\qquad\qquad 36M_A + 18M_B = -102{,}600. \qquad\qquad (g)$

The three-moment equation for the span AB and the imaginary span to the right of B is

$$M_A(18) + 2M_B(18 + 0) + 0 = -\tfrac{6}{18}(307{,}800) - 0$$

or $\qquad\qquad 18M_A + 36M_B = -102{,}600. \qquad\qquad (h)$

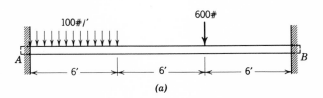

(a)

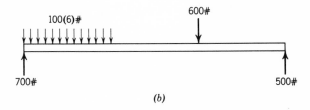

(b)

FIG. 8.9

Solving Eqs. g and h, we get

$$M_A = -1900 \text{ ft-lb} \quad \text{and} \quad M_B = -1900 \text{ ft-lb}.$$

The reaction component R_A is found from the expression for the bending moment at B, thus:

$$M_B = 18R_A - 1900 - 600(15) - 600(6) = -1900, \qquad (i)$$

whence $\qquad\qquad\qquad R_A = 700 \text{ lb}.$

Similarly, from the expression for the bending moment at A,

$$M_A = 18R_B - 1900 - 600(12) - 600(3) = -1900, \qquad (j)$$

we find $\qquad\qquad\qquad R_B = 500 \text{ lb}.$

Either or both of the equilibrium equations may be used to check the final results, or, alternatively, they may be used instead of Eqs. i and j.

From the foregoing it appears that, when applied to multispan beams, the three-moment equation method not only reduces the number of equations that have to be solved *simultaneously as a group* but also avoids the large numbers which arise from the use of lever arms two or more spans in length; it accomplishes this by dealing singly with simple spans. The slight lengthening of the solution is offset by the simplicity of the intermediate steps. For other techniques, especially the powerful relaxation methods that lend themselves better to numerical work (hence to approximate solutions), the reader is referred to books on structural theory.

PROBLEMS

8.57. Solve Prob. 8.52a using the three-moment equation.

8.58. Solve Prob. 8.54a using the three-moment equation.

8.59. Assume perfect initial fit for this uniform and homogeneous continuous beam, fixed at one end and overhanging the last support at the other. Solve for the reactions using the three-moment equation. Sketch the V-x and M-x diagrams and give key values.

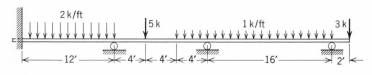

FIG. P8.59

8.60. Derive from Eq. j the three-moment equation for the case when the span PQ has a section stiffness $E_l I_l$ and the span QR a section stiffness of $E_r I_r$.

8.61. Using the results of Prob. 8.60, solve for the reactions of the beam in Fig. P8.56.

COLUMN ACTION

9.1 The Short Post. A short post of uniform cross section, subjected to axial compression, presents nothing new and may be treated as explained in Chapter 3. If, however, the compression forces, although parallel to the initial position of the centroidal axis of the member, have a line of action that is slightly displaced from this axis, then a new problem arises.

Figure 9.1a represents such a member. In order not to detract unduly from the main ideas being developed, let us assume (1) that P is the resultant of a continuously distributed force system consistent with the transverse planes of the member remaining plane, and (2) that the action line of the forces P and the longitudinal centroidal axis are parallel and lie in the plane of symmetry. The force system in Fig. 9.1a is statically equivalent to that in Fig. 9.1b. As a first approximation in the analysis, we assume that the member is so stiff in bending that the moment Pe does not change the form enough to affect the lever arm of P. This is like saying that we ignore the curvatures due to bending in order to compute them, which is really nothing new in our procedures since we have done substantially the same thing in analyzing beam deflections: we have assumed the deflections to have no effect on the bending moments which are the cause of such deflections. There is, however, this important difference: Whereas the lever arms of transverse forces are little affected by transverse deflections, those of longitudinal forces are most certainly affected by transverse deflections.

We will now evaluate the stresses and deformations by superposing the

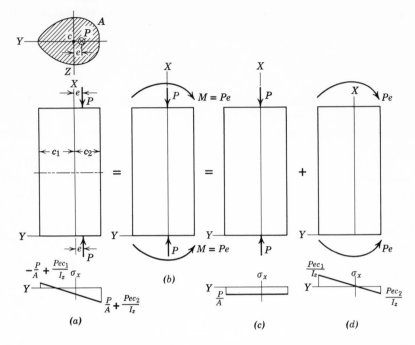

effects of P on those of Pe. Figures 9.1b, c, and d suggest this superposition; the coordinate system in each is right handed with the origin at the lower end of the sketch. Since P has a centroidal action line (Fig. 9.1c), the uniformly distributed normal stresses on transverse planes are of magnitude P/A; and since the bending moment Pe lies in the plane of symmetry, the bending stresses are given by $-My/I = (Pe)y/I_z$. Then the stresses on transverse planes of the member in Fig. 9.1a are given by

$$\sigma = -\frac{P}{A} - \frac{My}{I} = -\frac{P}{A} + \frac{(Pe)y}{I_z}. \qquad (a)$$

Along the left edge of the member,

$$\sigma = -\frac{P}{A} + \frac{Pec_1}{I_z}, \qquad (b)$$

whereas along the right edge,

$$\sigma = -\frac{P}{A} - \frac{Pec_2}{I_z} = -\frac{P}{A} - \frac{Pec_2}{Ak_z^2}, \qquad (c)$$

where k_z is the radius of gyration of area relative to the axis of bending. Solving for P, and dropping the minus sign and subscripts, we get

$$P = \frac{\sigma A}{1 + ec/k^2},\qquad(9.1)$$

in which the proper c and k to use should be determined by inspection. Equation c indicates the greatest compression stress; Eq. 9.1 gives a measure of the strength as governed by some allowable value of this stress.

The centroidal axis in Fig. 9.1c suffers no transverse deflection. The longitudinal displacement of any transverse section relative to the bottom is given by $\delta = Px/AE$; hence the maximum contraction of the member is $\delta_{\max} = PL/AE$. The centroidal axis of Fig. 9.1d does not change in length; its transverse deflection is found in the manner explained in Chapter 7. Using Y to denote transverse deflection, as distinguished from y which denotes distance from the centroidal axis, we have

$$\frac{d^2 Y_1}{dx^2} = \frac{1}{EI}(-Pe),\qquad(d)$$

whence

$$\frac{dY_1}{dx} = \frac{1}{EI}(-Pex) + \theta_{1_0},\qquad(e)$$

and

$$Y_1 = \frac{1}{EI}\left(-\frac{Pex^2}{2}\right) + \theta_{1_0}x + y_{1_0}.\qquad(f)$$

The end deflection Y_{1_0} is zero, and the end slope θ_{1_0} is found from either symmetry considerations $(dY_1/dx = 0$ at $x = L/2)$ or the other boundary condition $(Y_1 = 0$ at $x = L)$: $\theta_{1_0} = PeL/2EI$. Hence

$$Y_1 = \frac{Pe}{2EI}(Lx - x^2).\qquad(g)$$

The maximum deflection of the centroidal axis, which occurs at the center section of the member, is

$$(Y_1)_{\max} = \frac{PeL^2}{8EI}.\qquad(h)$$

An improved value of the maximum moment may now be obtained by considering $(Y_1)_{\max}$ as a lever arm of P in Fig. 9.1b. Therefore the moment that enters into Eq. c, instead of being Pe, is now

$$M_{\max} = Pe + PY_{1_{\max}} = Pe\left(1 + \frac{PL^2}{8EI}\right).\qquad(i)$$

To improve upon our approximation, we must now take into account the effect of Pe on the lever arm of P. Doing this, we write

$$\frac{d^2 Y_2}{dx^2} = \frac{1}{EI}(-Pe - PY_1) = \frac{1}{EI}\left[-Pe - \frac{P^2 e}{2EI}(Lx - x^2) \right]$$

$$= -\frac{Pe}{EI}\left[1 + \frac{P}{2EI}(Lx - x^2) \right]. \tag{j}$$

Upon integration, this becomes

$$\frac{dY_2}{dx} = -\frac{Pe}{EI}\left[x + \frac{P}{2EI}\left(\frac{Lx^2}{2} - \frac{x^3}{3}\right) \right] + \theta_{2_0}, \tag{k}$$

which gives $\theta_{2_0} = \dfrac{PeL}{2EI}\left(1 + \dfrac{PL^2}{12EI}\right) = \theta_{1_0}\left(1 + \dfrac{PL^2}{12EI}\right).$

A second integration gives

$$Y_2 = \frac{Pe}{2EI}\left[L\left(1 + \frac{PL^2}{12EI}\right)x - x^2 - \frac{P}{12EI}(2Lx^3 - x^4) \right], \tag{l}$$

since $Y_{2_0} = Y_{1_0} = Y_0 = 0$. From this last equation we obtain $Y_{2_{\max}}$ at $x = L/2$, thus:

$$(Y_2)_{\max} = \frac{PeL^2}{8EI}\left(1 + \frac{5PL^2}{48EI}\right) = (Y_1)_{\max}\left(1 + \frac{5PL^2}{48EI}\right). \tag{m}$$

Hence a third and better approximation of the maximum moment to use in Eq. c is

$$M_{\max} = Pe + PY_{2_{\max}} = Pe\left[1 + \frac{PL^2}{8EI}\left(1 + \frac{5PL^2}{48EI}\right) \right]. \tag{n}$$

This *iteration* process can be carried on indefinitely until the desired accuracy is attained. The forms of Eqs. i and n suggest two things: first, that for small L and large EI, the corrected maximum moment would differ but slightly from Pe; second, that for such proportions in the dimensions of the member there is a limiting value of the corrected $M_{\max}$ (or the corrected maximum deflection).

Illustrative Example 1. The short post of rectangular cross section carries an eccentrically applied compression load as shown in Fig. 9.2a. How large may the eccentricity be without tension stresses being induced in the post? Ignore the deflection due to bending.

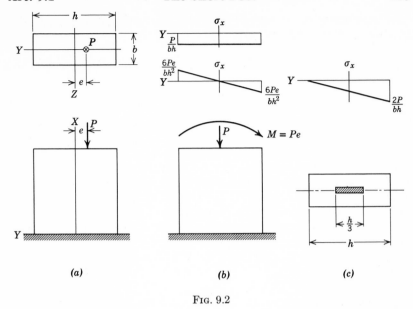

FIG. 9.2

SOLUTION. The force P in Fig. 9.2a is replaced by the statically equivalent system of Fig. 9.2b consisting of a centrally applied P and a moment Pe. The uniformly distributed normal stresses on transverse planes due to P are $\sigma = -P/A = -P/bh$; the uniformly varying stresses due to Pe are $\sigma = -My/I = +Pey/(bh^3/12)$, tensile where y is positive and compressive where y is negative (see Fig. 9.2b). Along the left face of the post the maximum tensile bending stresses are induced; they have the magnitude $(Peh/2)/(bh^3/12) = 6Pe/bh^2$. Superposing the bending stresses on the uniformly distributed compressive stresses, and equating their sum to zero at the left face, we obtain

$$-\frac{P}{bh} + \frac{6Pe}{bh^2} = 0,$$

whence $$e = \frac{h}{6}.$$ *Ans.*

The stress distribution corresponding to the limiting position that P may have is shown in Fig. 9.2c.

The preceding result shows that the action line of P should pass through the *middle third* of the cross section (shaded in Fig. 9.2c) in order that no tensile stresses will be induced across the rectangular area. This information is put to practical use in the design of gravity dams.

Since granular material cannot resist tension, even when compacted, special precautions are taken to insure that the resultant of the forces transmitted across the base of the dam will pass within its middle third.

PROBLEMS

9.1. A 10-in. long steel bar, with a 1 in. by 1 in. square cross section, is subjected to two 1000-lb compressive forces at an eccentricity of 0.1 in. (a) Find Pe. (b) Using Eq. i, determine the first corrected M_{max}. (c) Then using Eq. m, calculate the second corrected M_{max}. (d) Finally, for each degree of approximation, calculate the maximum compressive stress in the bar. Use $E = 30 \times 10^6$ psi.

9.2. Do the above for a 100-in. long steel bar.

9.3. How large a compressive load may a 50-in. long 1-in. diameter rod carry at an eccentricity of 0.25 in., if the maximum compressive stress must not exceed 20,000 psi? For a first approximation, ignore bending of the rod.

9.4. Solve the preceding problem taking bending into account by the use of Eq. i in Eq. c. Use $E = 10.5 \times 10^6$ psi.

9.2   The Column.   A slender member in compression is generally (and loosely) referred to as a *column*, or sometimes a *strut*, to distinguish it from a short post or compression block.   When the length L of such a member is relatively large and the section stiffness EI relatively small, the effect of the deflection on the bending moment may no longer be ignored, even as an approximation.   Figure 9.3a represents a column originally straight before the eccentric compression forces P are applied. In order to focus attention on the main aspects of column action, we will assume that the action line of the forces P is parallel to the centroidal axis and lies in the longitudinal plane of symmetry; we will assume further that this plane of loading is perpendicular to the axis of minimum second moment of area, and that the two principal centroidal second moments of area are comparable in magnitudes.   Figure 9.3b shows the bent form of the column.   The force system is now replaced by the statically equivalent one in Fig. 9.3c.

Referred to the coordinate system in Fig. 9.3c, the bending moment is

$$M = Pe - Py, \qquad (a)$$

where the minus sign takes care of the fact that when y is negative the bending moment Py is positive according to previous convention. Owing to symmetry, the maximum deflection δ is at midspan; therefore, the maximum moment has the magnitude

$$M_{max} = P(e + \delta). \qquad (b)$$

Hence the maximum compressive stress is

$$\sigma_{\max} = \frac{P}{A} + \frac{P(e + \delta)c}{I} = \frac{P}{A}\left[1 + \frac{(e + \delta)c}{k^2}\right]. \qquad (c)$$

When solved for P as an explicit function of $\sigma_{\max}$ and δ, Eq. c gives

$$P = \frac{\sigma_{\max}A}{1 + (e + \delta)c/k^2}. \qquad (d)$$

This expression, like Eq. 9.1, gives a measure of the strength of the slender member as governed by some characteristic value of the stress. Unfortunately, this perfectly reasonable formula is of little use without the value of δ being known beforehand. But δ itself depends on P, since P determines the bending moment which causes δ. Hence we have here a vicious circle, since in order to find δ we must first know δ!

One way of breaking this circularity is to assume some form of curve for the bent column. We could make this quite an intelligent guess rather than a completely wild one, using as our guide the Bernoulli-Euler equation, $1/\rho = M/EI$, which in this instance means that the curvature is proportional to the deflection. This, however, would presuppose an expert knowledge of curves. In the absence of such expertness, one could instead make a guess at the solution of the differential equation which arises out of the Bernoulli-Euler equation.

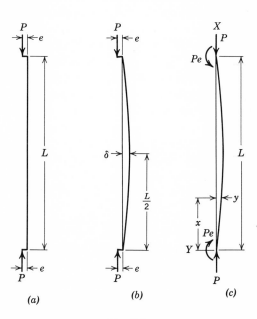

Fig. 9.3

Making the assumption of small curvatures, we have using Eq. a

$$\frac{d^2y}{dx^2} = \frac{1}{EI}(Pe - Py),$$

which rearranged becomes

$$\frac{d^2y}{dx^2} + \frac{Py}{EI} = \frac{Pe}{EI}. \qquad (e)$$

The homogeneous equation

$$\frac{d^2y}{dx^2} + \frac{Py}{EI} = 0 \qquad (f)$$

is of standard form whose solution had been guessed a long time ago and hence is well known. This solution, called the complementary function, is

$$y_{\text{C.F.}} = A \cos \sqrt{P/EI}\, x + B \sin \sqrt{P/EI}\, x. \qquad (g)$$

Since the right-hand side of Eq. e is a constant, we try for the particular integral

$$y_{\text{P.I.}} = C, \qquad (h)$$

which when substituted in Eq. e gives $C = e$. Therefore the complete solution of Eq. e is

$$y = A \cos \sqrt{P/EI}\, x + B \sin \sqrt{P/EI}\, x + e. \qquad (i)$$

The two integration constants A and B are evaluated from the two boundary conditions: at $x = 0$, $y = 0$, and at $x = L$, $y = 0$ (or, alternatively, for the second one: at $x = L/2$, $dy/dx = 0$). After some algebra, we find these constants to be

$$A = -e$$

and
$$B = \frac{e(\cos \sqrt{P/EI}\, L - 1)}{\sin \sqrt{P/EI}\, L} = -e \tan \sqrt{P/EI}\, \frac{L}{2}.$$

Hence the equation of the elastic curve is

$$y = e\left[1 - \cos \sqrt{P/EI}\, x - \left(\tan \sqrt{P/EI}\, \frac{L}{2}\right) \sin \sqrt{P/EI}\, x\right]. \qquad (j)$$

If the value $L/2$ is substituted for x, Eq. j gives the maximum deflection δ, which after some manipulation reduces to

$$\delta = e\left(\sec \sqrt{P/EI}\, \frac{L}{2} - 1\right). \qquad (9.2)$$

This reveals what we mentioned earlier, that δ is indeed a function of P. Using this value of δ in Eq. d, we finally obtain

$$P = \frac{\sigma_{max}A}{1 + \dfrac{ec}{k^2} \sec \sqrt{P/EI}\, \dfrac{L}{2}}, \tag{9.3a}$$

or

$$\frac{P}{A} = \frac{\sigma_{max}}{1 + \dfrac{ec}{k^2} \sec \sqrt{P/EI}\, \dfrac{L}{2}} = \frac{\sigma_{max}}{1 + \dfrac{ec}{k^2} \sec \left(\dfrac{1}{2} \dfrac{L}{k} \sqrt{P/EA} \right)}.$$

$$\tag{9.3b}$$

Equation 9.3, known as the *secant formula*, gives a true measure of the elastic strength (or the strength per unit of cross-sectional area) of a slender member under eccentric loading, if for σ_{max} is used the proportional-limit stress σ_e. Unfortunately, because of the transcendental form of the equation, it is not possible to solve explicitly for P or P/A, so that if these values are needed from given data, a trial-and-error or other comparable solution becomes unavoidable.

The analysis equation derived from Eq. 9.3a, namely

$$\sigma_{max} = \frac{P}{A} \left(1 + \frac{ec}{k^2} \sec \sqrt{P/EI}\, \frac{L}{2} \right) \tag{9.3c}$$

requires no cut-and-try solution; that is, given P, E, A, I, L, c, and e, the maximum compressive stress can be found directly, provided it is not greater than the proportional-limit stress. Beyond that point, Eq. 9.3 is not valid.

Equation 9.3c clearly shows that the stress σ_{max} is not proportional to P. An increase in P of, say, 10 percent could increase σ_{max} by as much as 100 or more percent, depending on the initial P and other data. Thus, *although the material may obey Hooke's law, the member itself will not*, in the sense that neither the stress nor the deformation is proportional to the load. Consequently, *for slender members in compression, the principle of superposition is not applicable*.

PROBLEMS

9.5. Using the secant formula, Eq. 9.3c, calculate the maximum compressive stress in the eccentrically loaded bar of Prob. 9.1. Compare this with the maximum stress value previously obtained.

9.6. Do the above for the bar of Prob. 9.2.

9.7. A 1-in. round steel member 100 in. long bears a 1200-lb compressive load at an eccentricity of 0.2 in. What is the maximum compressive stress in the member? If the load were increased to 1320 lb, what would be the maximum compressive stress? Compare the percentage increases in the stress and in the load. Use $E = 30 \times 10^6$ psi.

9.8. How large a compressive load may be carried by a 50-in. long bar, 1 in. in diameter, if the eccentricity is 0.25 in. and the maximum compressive stress is not to exceed 20,000 psi? Use $E = 10.5 \times 10^6$ psi. (*Note:* This is a trial-and-error solution. A first trial value for P may be obtained if desired by solving the quadratic that results when Eq. i is substituted in Eq. c of the preceding article.)

9.9. At what maximum eccentricity may a compressive load of 1000 lb be applied on a 1-in. round aluminum alloy member, 80 in. long, without the compressive stress exceeding 30,000 psi? Use $E = 10.5 \times 10^6$ psi.

9.3   Column Behavior. To understand adequately the behavior of a column, it is necessary to appreciate first the influence of the parameters e and L/k, the first one on the transverse deflection δ, and the two together on the elastic strength of the slender member. We can develop this appreciation quickest by analyzing the graphs of Eqs. 9.2 and 9.3.

Figure 9.4 shows a semidimensionless plot of Eq. 9.2 for various values of the eccentricity e. It is evident from this figure that all the curves in the family tend to approach the horizontal line

$$\frac{(L/2)\sqrt{P/EI}}{\pi/2} = 1 \tag{a}$$

as an asymptote and that as the eccentricity decreases the curves tend to the asymptote sooner. It appears reasonable therefore to consider the vertical line joined by the horizontal line a above as the graph of Eq. 9.2 when e is zero. The upper limit of P, denoted as the critical P,* is found from Eq. a to be

$$P_{cr} = \frac{\pi^2 EI}{L^2}. \tag{b}$$

---

* Solution of Eq. e of the preceding article when the exact rather than the approximate expression for curvature is used shows that the asymptote to the family of curves in Fig. 9.4 is not quite a horizontal line (although it has a horizontal slope at $\delta = 0$) and that P_{cr} is not the highest P possible. The exact solution for δ is closely approximated by

$$\delta = \frac{2\sqrt{2}}{\pi}\sqrt{P/P_{cr} - 1}\,[1 - \tfrac{1}{8}(P/P_{cr} - 1)].$$

See S. Timoshenko, *Theory of Elastic Stability*, pp. 73–74, McGraw-Hill Book Company, New York, 1936.

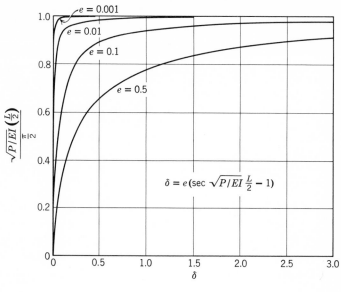

Fɪɢ. 9.4

Thus so long as the *material* obeys Hooke's law, the load-carrying capacity of a slender member in compression (as governed by the transverse deflection) tends to approach an upper limit P_{cr}, as the transverse deflection increases, and this tendency becomes more pronounced as the eccentricity of P decreases. Furthermore, in the limiting case when $e = 0$, the column will remain perfectly straight until P becomes P_{cr}. At this instant the state of equilibrium becomes unstable and the slightest disturbance will cause the member to develop suddenly a sidewise deflection. This phenomenon is known as *buckling*. Immediately after the column has buckled, its state of equilibrium becomes neutral or indifferent. That this is consistent mathematically follows from Eq. 9.2 when the right-hand side reduces to the form $0(\infty)$, which is indeterminate.

Let us now consider the role of L/k. Dividing both sides of Eq. b by A, we derive the relation

$$\frac{P_{cr}}{A} = \frac{\pi^2 E}{(L/k)^2},\qquad (c)$$

where the dimensionless ratio L/k gives an idea of the member's slenderness. We will call it the *physical slenderness*. In Eq. c, let P_{cr}/A

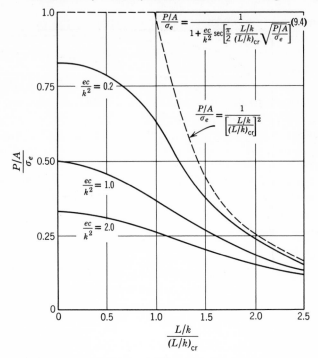

$$\frac{P/A}{\sigma_e} = \frac{1}{1 + \frac{ec}{k^2}\sec\left[\frac{\pi}{2}\frac{L/k}{(L/k)_{\text{cr}}}\sqrt{\frac{P/A}{\sigma_e}}\right]} \quad (9.4)$$

$$\frac{P/A}{\sigma_e} = \frac{1}{\left[\frac{L/k}{(L/k)_{\text{cr}}}\right]^2}$$

$\frac{ec}{k^2} = 0.2$

$\frac{ec}{k^2} = 1.0$

$\frac{ec}{k^2} = 2.0$

$\frac{P/A}{\sigma_e}$

$\frac{L/k}{(L/k)_{\text{cr}}}$

FIG. 9.5

equal σ_e and let the corresponding L/k be $(L/k)_{\text{cr}}$; then

$$\left(\frac{L}{k}\right)_{\text{cr}} = \sqrt{(\pi^2 E)/\sigma_e} = \pi\sqrt{E/\sigma_e}. \quad (d)$$

Setting $\sigma_{\max}$ equal to σ_e in Eq. 9.3b, dividing through by σ_e, and substituting $E = \sigma_e(L/k)_{\text{cr}}^2/\pi^2$ from Eq. d, we obtain the dimensionless form of the secant formula

$$\frac{P/A}{\sigma_e} = \frac{1}{1 + \frac{ec}{k^2}\sec\left[\frac{\pi}{2}\frac{L/k}{(L/k)_{\text{cr}}}\sqrt{(P/A)/\sigma_e}\right]}. \quad (9.4)$$

Let us call $(P/A)/\sigma_e$ the *strength ratio* and $(L/k)/(L/k)_{\text{cr}}$ the *slenderness ratio*. If the strength ratio is plotted against the slenderness ratio for various values of the dimensionless parameter ec/k^2, the result will be a family of curves, some of which are shown in Fig. 9.5. Careful study of these curves reveals the following:

(1) For a given eccentricity, the elastic strength of a column increases as its slenderness decreases.

(2) For a given slenderness, the elastic strength of a column increases as the load eccentricity decreases.

(3) For *extremely large* slenderness values, the elastic strength of a column tends to approach the value $P_{cr} = \pi^2 EI/L^2$, the smaller the eccentricity the closer being this approach.

(4) For *very small* eccentricities, the elastic strength of a column tends to approach either $P_e = \sigma_e A$ for slenderness ratios less than unity or $P_{cr} = \pi^2 EI/L^2$ for slenderness ratios greater than unity.

(5) For a given eccentricity, the *percentage difference* between either of the upper limits ($P_e = \sigma_e A$ or $P_{cr} = \pi^2 EI/L^2$) and the elastic strength of a column *decreases* as the slenderness becomes *very small* or *very large*, *the maximum difference occurring at the slenderness ratio of unity.*

In view of the preceding, it appears proper to consider the dashed-line curve, consisting of a horizontal-line segment joined by what appears to be part of a rectangular hyperbola, as the plot of Eq. 9.4 when the eccentricity e is zero. The straight-line part is the graph of the equation

$$\frac{P/A}{\sigma_e} = 1, \qquad (e)$$

whereas the curved part is the plot of the equation

$$\frac{P/A}{\sigma_e} = \frac{1}{\left[\dfrac{L/k}{(L/k)_{cr}} \right]^2}. \qquad (f)$$

9.4 The Euler Column. The expression for the strength of a perfectly straight uniform slender member under *central* compression was first derived by Leonhard Euler in 1757.* In its modern form, this is written

$$P_{cr} = \frac{\pi^2 EI}{l^2}. \qquad (9.5)$$

Observe that this is practically the same as Eq. *b* of the preceding article. The condition of zero eccentricity of load is here emphasized, and in order forcefully to call attention to this fact we reserve the symbol l to denote this particular column length. Furthermore, to minimize con-

---

* J. A. Van den Broek, "On the Strength of Columns," *American Journal of Physics*, Vol. 15, No. 4 (July, 1947).

fusion we will refer to l as the *Euler column length* in contradistinction to the ordinary *physical length L*. The I that appears in Eq. 9.5 should be the smallest one; that is, the axis about which bending will take place is that principal centroidal axis with respect to which the second moment of area (hence the bending stiffness) is smallest.

Equation 9.5 stands uniquely in the entire domain of strength theory. In a very real sense it is the *only* formula of strength in that it has no symbol for either allowable stress or permissible deformation as the governing criterion. On the other hand, owing to the presence of the material constant E, we now observe the interesting conclusion that among several centrally loaded columns of identical dimensions, the stiffer the material (the higher the modulus E) the stronger the column. Note that this is in marked contrast to the notion of strength in simple tension, torsion, or bending.

In the preceding article, P_{cr} as given by Eq. b was considered the limiting strength of a column as the eccentricity of load approached zero. Very strictly speaking (see footnote on p. 264) this P_{cr} should be interpreted as the largest centrally applied compressive load a slender column can carry *without* buckling, or it is the largest load under which the column can remain elastically stable. Nevertheless, the more useful, although approximate, practical interpretation is that this P_{cr} is the central load under which the column can sustain an indeterminate transverse deflection, or that it is the load which allows the state of equilibrium of the column to change from a stable to a neutral one, *becoming momentarily unstable in transition*.

The truly remarkable and somewhat paradoxical disappearance of the elastic-limit stess σ_e from the strength Eq. 9.5 is the one outstanding consideration that militates against an easy understanding of column behavior. Rearranging Eq. 9.5 so that it now reads

$$\frac{P_{cr}}{A} = \frac{\pi^2 E}{(l/k)^2} \tag{9.5a}$$

and plotting it on cartesian axes, we obtain the curve of Fig. 9.6, which we may then refer to as the *Euler curve*. As noted earlier, this curve is similar to one branch of a rectangular hyperbola, and like that curve it is asymptotic to both the vertical and horizontal axes. That the strength per unit area of a column should diminish to low values for increasingly large column slenderness l/k is easy to accept; but the conclusion that this strength should increase without limit as the slenderness decreases is unacceptable because it is unrealistic. Assuming that the column remained straight under P_{cr}, we recognize P_{cr}/A as the compressive stress

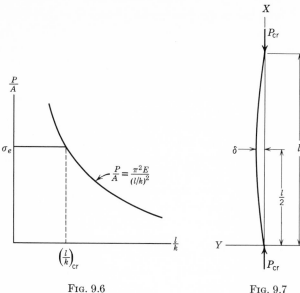

FIG. 9.6   FIG. 9.7

in the column uniformly distributed throughout every cross section; in order to preclude inelastic action, we must accordingly limit the value of P_{cr}/A to σ_e. It is therefore customary to lop off the upper portion of the Euler hyperbola above the level $P_{cr}/A = \sigma_e$ and indeed to consider the composite plot consisting of the straight horizontal-line segment joined to the lower part of the original Euler hyperbola, as a *modified Euler curve*. Although this appears entirely reasonable, nevertheless the rather arbitrary way of arriving at the two values of P/A leaves something to be desired: it seems to suggest that the two are unrelated. That these are indeed intimately related because they spring from one and the same equation we will now demonstrate.

Figure 9.7 shows a slightly buckled centrally loaded column. For very small δ the elastic curve may be assumed sinusoidal, that is, the center line of the column may be taken as one full arch of a sine wave (or one-half of one wavelength). This is the only simple form that would be consistent with the Bernoulli-Euler equation, $1/\rho = M/EI$, since the curvature of a sine curve varies as the offset from its axis, which, in turn, determines the bending moment in the column. Referred to the axes shown, the equation of the elastic curve is

$$y = \delta \sin \frac{\pi x}{l}, \tag{a}$$

whence $$\frac{dy}{dx} = \frac{\pi}{l} \delta \cos \frac{\pi x}{l}$$

and $$\frac{d^2 y}{dx^2} = -\left(\frac{\pi}{l}\right)^2 \delta \sin \frac{\pi x}{l}.$$

From $$\frac{1}{\rho} = \frac{d^2 y/dx^2}{[1 + (dy/dx)^2]^{3/2}}$$

we find at $x = l/2$ that $1/\rho = -\pi^2 \delta/l^2$. Also, since

$$\frac{1}{\rho} = \frac{M}{EI} = -\frac{\sigma_b I}{c}\left(\frac{1}{EI}\right) = -\frac{\sigma_b}{Ec},$$

we obtain $$\frac{\pi^2 \delta}{l^2} = \frac{\sigma_b}{Ec},$$

from which $$\delta = \frac{\sigma_b l^2}{\pi^2 Ec}, \tag{b}$$

where σ_b is the bending stress. At the midsection of the bent member the maximum compressive stress occurs in the concave side and is equal to the sum of the direct compression stress σ_P and the bending stress σ_b, thus:

$$\sigma_{\max} = \sigma_P + \sigma_b$$

$$= \frac{P_{cr}}{A} + \frac{P_{cr}\delta c}{I} = \frac{P_{cr}}{A} + \frac{P_{cr}\delta c}{Ak^2}$$

$$= \frac{P_{cr}}{A}\left(1 + \frac{\delta c}{k^2}\right). \tag{c}$$

Solving for P_{cr}/A, we get

$$\frac{P_{cr}}{A} = \frac{\sigma_{\max}}{1 + \delta c/k^2}. \tag{d}$$

Substituting σ_e for $\sigma_{\max}$ and the value of δ from Eq. b, we obtain

$$\frac{P_{cr}}{A} = \frac{\sigma_e}{1 + \dfrac{\sigma_b(l/k)^2}{\pi^2 E}}. \tag{e}$$

But $\sigma_b = \sigma_e - P_{cr}/A$, by Eq. c. Hence

$$\frac{P_{cr}}{A} = \frac{\sigma_e}{1 + \dfrac{(l/k)^2}{\pi^2 E}\left(\sigma_e - \dfrac{P_{cr}}{A}\right)}. \tag{f}$$

Simplified, this becomes

$$\left(\frac{P_{\rm cr}}{A}\right)^2 - \frac{\pi^2 E}{(l/k)^2}\left[1 + \frac{\sigma_e(l/k)^2}{\pi^2 E}\right]\frac{P_{\rm cr}}{A} + \frac{\sigma_e \pi^2 E}{(l/k)^2} = 0, \qquad (g)$$

which is quadratic in $P_{\rm cr}/A$. The two roots of Eq. g are

$$\frac{P_{\rm cr}}{A} = \frac{1}{2}\left\{\left[\frac{\pi^2 E}{(l/k)^2} + \sigma_e\right] \pm \sqrt{[\pi^2 E/(l/k)^2 - \sigma_e]^2}\right\}; \qquad (9.6)$$

that is,

$$\frac{P_{\rm cr}}{A} = \frac{\pi^2 E}{(l/k)^2} \qquad (h)$$

and

$$\frac{P_{\rm cr}}{A} = \sigma_e. \qquad (i)$$

These results show that lopping off the Euler hyperbola above the level $P_{\rm cr}/A = \sigma_e$ has in fact a rational basis.*

The ratio l/k is called the *column slenderness*, not to be confused with the physical slenderness; the distinction between them is discussed in Article 9.7. In its strictest sense, the column slenderness has meaning only for values larger than the critical, which is defined by (see Eq. d of the preceding article)

$$\left(\frac{l}{k}\right)_{\rm cr} = \pi\sqrt{E/\sigma_e}, \qquad (9.7)$$

corresponding to which $P_{\rm cr}/A$ becomes σ_e. Expressed differently, this means simply that a centrally compressed member will act as a column only when its slenderness exceeds $(l/k)_{\rm cr}$, and that for smaller values of slenderness it is to be considered a short post. This strict usage, however, would find little favor among practicing engineers for reasons we shall presently attempt to explain. For these and other considerations to be discussed in Chapter 14, and in keeping with accepted usage, we unbend and consider the $(l/k)_{\rm cr}$ value as delineating the boundary between *long columns* on the one hand and *short columns* on the other.

The single most important characteristic of column behavior is to be gleaned from item (5) of the preceding article. Eccentricity of load may be looked on as an error over which we have little control except in laboratory experiments. Likewise, initial crookedness or "wow" may be considered an error whose influence on the strength of the slender

---

* J. A. Van den Broek, "Rational Column Analysis," *J. Eng. Inst. Canada*, December 1941. Also, J. A. Van den Broek, *Theory of Limit Design*, pp. 73–77, John Wiley and Sons, New York, 1948.

member is similar to that of eccentricity.* A decrease in the elastic strength of the column is the immediate consequence of one error or another, and this decrease is most pronounced in the vicinity of the critical slenderness. Thus *a column's strength is most sensitive to errors or defects when its slenderness is near critical, becoming less so as the slenderness increases or decreases from the critical.* For example, from Fig. 9.5, corresponding to an eccentricity parameter of $ec/k^2 = 0.2$, the drop in the elastic strength is 17% for a slenderness ratio of 0, 38% for a ratio of 1, and only 6% for a ratio of 2.4. This explains the remarkable fidelity of column test results to Euler values in the long column range and the considerable scatter in the "intermediate" range. We are therefore surest of a column's behavior in the very long column range, somewhat less certain in the very short column range, and most uncertain in the critical region.

The important conclusion to be drawn from this discussion is that the safety factor, which is in reality a factor of ignorance or uncertainty, should be small for very slender columns, somewhat larger for very short columns, and quite generous for intermediate ones. It cannot be overemphasized that this factor should be applied on the load rather than on the stress.

PROBLEMS

9.10. Classify the following centrally loaded pivot-ended compression members as either long or short columns:

(a) A steel rod 2 in. in diameter and 60 in. long for which $E = 30 \times 10^6$ psi and $\sigma_e = 40,000$ psi;

(b) An aluminum alloy bar with a square cross section, 1 in. by 1 in., and 50 in. long, for which $E = 10.5 \times 10^6$ psi and $\sigma_e = 45,000$ psi;

(c) A 50-in. long magnesium alloy bar with a 2 in. by 1 in. rectangular cross section for which $E = 6.5 \times 10^6$ psi and $\sigma_e = 25,000$ psi.

9.11. Compare the elastic compressive strengths of the following pivot-ended centrally loaded members:

(a) Two 2-in. diameter steel rods, one 60 in. long and the other 90 in. long, with the same material properties as in Prob. 9.10a.

(b) Two 100-in. long steel rods, each 1 sq. in. in cross-sectional area, one round, the other square.

(c) The bars of Prob. 9.10b and c.

9.12. (a) Calculate the compressive strength of a centrally loaded 1-in. round steel rod 100 in. long.

(b) If the load on the above member has an eccentricity of 0.02 in., to what value should its length be changed so that its elastic compressive strength will remain the same? Use $E = 30 \times 10^6$ psi and $\sigma_e = 40,000$ psi.

* J. A. Van den Broek, *op. cit.* on p. 271.

9.5 Elastic Deformation. So long as a column remains straight, its axial deformation is governed by the relationship

$$\Delta l_1 = \frac{Pl}{AE}. \qquad (a)$$

In its buckled state the column develops an additional axial deformation consistent with the fact that a chord is always shorter than its arc. For an assumed deflection curve in the form of one full arch of a sine wave, it can be shown that this additional axial deformation Δl_2 is related to the transverse deflection δ approximately thus:

$$\Delta l_2 = \frac{\pi^2 \delta^2}{4l}. \qquad (b)$$

The maximum value of this transverse deflection δ in turn depends on the elastic-limit stress and on the column dimensions as shown by the following.

The maximum fiber stress, occurring in the concave side of the bent member, has the magnitude (see Eq. c of the preceding article)

$$\sigma_{max} = \frac{P_{cr}}{A} + \frac{P_{cr}\delta c}{I}, \qquad (c)$$

from which $$\frac{P_{cr}\delta c}{I} = \sigma_{max} - \frac{P_{cr}}{A}.$$

Setting σ_{max} equal to σ_e and solving for δ, we find

$$\delta = \frac{I}{P_{cr}c}\left(\sigma_e - \frac{P_{cr}}{A}\right). \qquad (d)$$

Substituting the Euler value for P_{cr} and simplifying, we get

$$\delta = \frac{l^2}{\pi^2 Ec}\left[\sigma_e - \frac{\pi^2 E}{(l/k)^2}\right]. \qquad (e)$$

Using this in Eq. b, we finally obtain

$$(\Delta l_2)_{max} = \frac{l^3}{4\pi^2 E^2 c^2}\left[\sigma_e - \frac{\pi^2 E}{(l/k)^2}\right]^2. \qquad (f)$$

The quantity inside the brackets increases with increasing column slenderness. Hence the more slender a column the greater the range of deformation over which it can maintain its load-carrying capacity at the maximum (Euler) level. This also means that the rate at which the

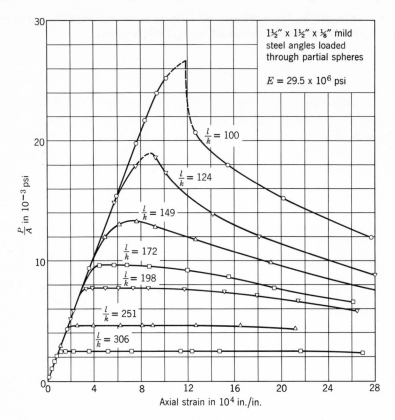

FIG. 9.8   Load-deformation characteristics of centrally loaded long columns.   (By permission of The Engineering Institute of Canada.)

column's postbuckling strength tapers off varies inversely as the slenderness.   Conversely, the less slender a column the more rapidly its postbuckling strength tapers off; a column with critical slenderness manifests on buckling a precipitous drop in this strength.

Figure 9.8 presents experimental evidence of the foregoing observations.   The figure is an adaptation of an original plot of Van den Broek's test data.*   For ease of comparison, all curves have been drawn from a common origin.   Note the marked shrinking of the horizontal part of each curve as the column slenderness decreases to near critical (about 100).   The absence of data, represented by the dotted lines, bespeaks the difficulty of recording instantaneous static values due primarily to the

* *Op. cit.* on p. 271.

inherent sensitivity to errors of columns with near critical slenderness. For each of those curves with an appreciable flat portion, the deformation beyond that portion is partly inelastic.

PROBLEMS

9.13. A centrally loaded slender member 48 in. long, with a $\frac{1}{2}$-in. by $\frac{1}{2}$-in. square cross section, deflects transversely a maxmum amount of 1 in. What minimum elastic-limit stress must the material have in order that the member may be unloaded without permanent set? Use $E = 30 \times 10^6$ psi and assume the elastic curve to be one full arch of a sine wave.

9.14. Determine how much axial deformation may be sustained by a centrally loaded 1-in. diameter hinged-end column without any permanent set (*a*) if its length is 50 in.; (*b*) if its length is 100 in. Use $E = 29 \times 10^6$ psi and $\sigma_e = 36,000$ psi.

9.6   Independent and Dependent Variables.   Another major source of difficulty in understanding column action is the lack of appreciation of the relative roles played by the variables, specifically load and deformation.   If the load that a column is expected to resist is a direct so-called dead weight, then the load is the independent variable and the ensuing deformation the dependent one.   In such a situation buckling means collapse because the increasing bending moment (of a constant force with an increasing lever arm) can no longer be balanced by the internal forces after the elastic limit of the material is overstepped. On the other hand, when a column is tested in a conventional straining machine, the deformation is the independent variable and the load (caused by the member's elasticity) the dependent variable.   In such a case, buckling does not mean collapse because the column's buckled length can be held to any desired value and the actual strength is merely a measure of the column's ability to push back against the heads of the testing machine.

An actual column's behavior is more nearly like what it does in a testing machine in that the deformation is the independent and the load the dependent variable.   The practical column hardly ever stands alone by itself, dissociated from other members, but instead is always part of a structure composed of many components.   Consequently, the ends of such a column are "position fixed," especially so in highly redundant structures, thus virtually insuring the independent role played by the column's axial deformation.

9.7   End Conditions.   The *effective* or *equivalent* column length is the distance between points or sections of zero bending moment in the slightly buckled member. These points correspond to the nodes in a sinusoidal curve. In an Euler column, which may be described as a "hinged-end" or a "pin-ended" column, the effective column length l is identical to the physical length L. If the end conditions are such that restraining or bending moments develop, then the effective column length will no longer be the same as the physical length.

When the end moments tend to bend the column so that they aggravate the deflection due to buckling, the effective column length is *greater* than the physical length. This is illustrated in Fig. 9.9a. In such a case, the end moments are properly considered as *weakening* moments, since the strength of a column varies inversely as its equivalent length squared. On the other hand, if the end moments tend to restrain the column so that they relieve the deflection due to buckling, then the effective column length is *less* than the physical length, and the end moments are properly considered as *strengthening* moments. This is illustrated in Fig. 9.9b.

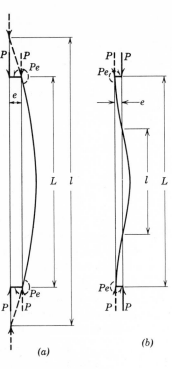

FIG. 9.9

An end moment may be thought of as one of the two components of a force system that is statically equivalent to an eccentrically applied force. These are indicated in Figs. 9.9a and b. An upsetting or weakening end moment may thus be associated with a weakening eccentricity, and a restraining or strengthening end moment with a strengthening eccentricity.

Hence all three concepts—end moment, eccentricity of load, equivalent or effective length—have similar connotation. Of the three, the one that it is easiest to develop a feel for is the effective column length.

Figure 9.10 shows four distinct and easily discernible types of end conditions, which are among an infinite number of possibilities. All columns have the same physical length L and all the elastic curves of the buckled columns are assumed sinusoidal. Sketch a represents a column

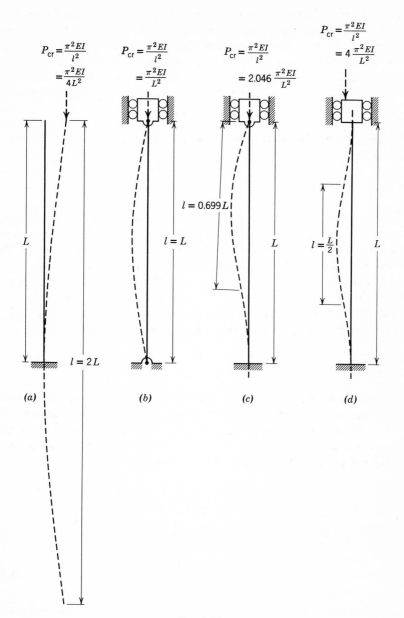

$$P_{cr} = \frac{\pi^2 EI}{l^2} = \frac{\pi^2 EI}{4L^2}$$

$$P_{cr} = \frac{\pi^2 EI}{l^2} = \frac{\pi^2 EI}{L^2}$$

$$P_{cr} = \frac{\pi^2 EI}{l^2} = 2.046 \frac{\pi^2 EI}{L^2}$$

$$P_{cr} = \frac{\pi^2 EI}{l^2} = 4 \frac{\pi^2 EI}{L^2}$$

$l = 0.699 L$

$l = L$

L

L

$l = \frac{L}{2}$

L

L

$l = 2L$

(a)   *(b)*   *(c)*   *(d)*

Fɪɢ. 9.10

fixed at one end and free at the other. The free end remains a point of zero bending moment, whereas the fixed end, where the tangent does not rotate, is the point of maximum moment. The length L then represents one-half of one full arch of a sine wave, or $l = 2L$. Hence for this column

$$P_{cr} = \frac{\pi^2 EI}{l^2} = \frac{\pi^2 EI}{(2L)^2} = \frac{\pi^2 EI}{4L^2}. \qquad (a)$$

Figure 9.10b shows the familiar hinged-end column, for which $l = L$ and hence

$$P_{cr} = \frac{\pi^2 EI}{l^2} = \frac{\pi^2 EI}{L^2}. \qquad (b)$$

Sketch c is for a column fixed at one end and hinged at the other. Since the hinge prevents sidesway but not rotation, there is induced in the buckled column a small horizontal (transverse) component in the hinge reaction, and this combines with the vertical (longitudinal) force to produce a slightly inclined total end load that differs only slightly from the vertical component. The action line of the slightly inclined load then cuts the elastic curve at the node, a distance of $l = 0.699L$ * below the hinge; the critical load for the column becomes

$$P_{cr} = \frac{\pi^2 EI}{l^2} = \frac{\pi^2 EI}{(0.699L)^2} = 2.046 \frac{\pi^2 EI}{L^2}. \qquad (c)$$

Figure 9.10d represents the extreme case of complete restraint at both ends against sidesway as well as rotation. In the buckled column, the two ends must be points of maximum moment, and the midpoint must necessarily be one also. The simplest curve gives $l = 0.5L$. Hence, for this extreme case, the strength of the column is

$$P_{cr} = \frac{\pi^2 EI}{l^2} = \frac{\pi^2 EI}{(0.5L)^2} = 4 \frac{\pi^2 EI}{L^2}. \qquad (d)$$

These results and the earlier remarks suggest that, in general, we may write

$$P_{cr} = \frac{\pi^2 EI}{l^2} = \frac{\pi^2 EI}{(nL)^2} = C \frac{\pi^2 EI}{L^2}. \qquad (9.8)$$

The factor C is called the *end-fixity coefficient;* it can have any value between 0 and 4. The constant n is the ratio of the Euler length l to the physical length L: $n = l/L$; it can have any value larger than 0.5. These

---

* This follows from a solution of the equation, $\tan \sqrt{P/EI}L = \sqrt{P/EI}L$.

two are tied together by the relationship

$$Cn^2 = 1. \tag{e}$$

It is interesting to note that, whereas the Euler column can be considered a special (limiting) case of an eccentrically loaded slender member, it is equally valid to consider an eccentrically loaded column as a special case of the Euler column.

For any actual end conditions such that the effective length is less than the physical length, the *realizable* value of C may be smaller than its theoretical magnitude (or the minimum realizable n may be larger than the theoretical) for the reason that the P_{cr} per unit area may not exceed σ_e. For example, suppose that the critical column slenderness is 80 and the physical slenderness is 140. Then, even if both ends of the column were perfectly fixed, the minimum realizable n would be $n = 80/140 = 0.571$, which is larger than 0.5; hence the maximum realizable C is only $1/(0.571)^2 = 3.06$ rather than 4. In other words, any measures taken in the hope of strengthening a column beyond practical realizable limits could represent nothing more than wishful thinking and hence would be wasteful.

As mentioned earlier in Article 9.3, the second-moment of area I that enters into the Euler formula is the minimum one. This is correct when the end conditions are identical for bending about either of the principal axes of the cross section. It may happen that the end conditions for bending about one axis will differ from those for bending about the other axis. In such a situation one must be careful to match the proper C (or n) with the corresponding I. This is illustrated in the following.

Illustrative Example 2. A column 6 ft long has a 1-in. by 3-in. rectangular cross section. Its ends are free to rotate about rigid smooth hinges whose axes are perpendicular to the 3-in. faces. The ends may be assumed completely restrained against rotating about axes normal to those of the hinges. If the column is made of an aluminum alloy for which $E = 10.7 \times 10^6$ psi and $\sigma_e = 40{,}000$ psi, determine the elastic strength of the column.

SOLUTION. The critical slenderness for columns of this material is

$$\left(\frac{l}{k}\right)_{cr} = \pi\sqrt{\frac{E}{\sigma_e}} = \pi\sqrt{\frac{10{,}700{,}000}{40{,}000}} = 51.4.$$

The principal second-moments of area are: $1(3)^3/12 = 2.25$ in.^{4} and $3(1)^3/12 = 0.25$ in.^{4} The radii of gyration of area are therefore $3/\sqrt{12} = 0.866$ in. and $1/\sqrt{12} = 0.2885$ in.

For bending about the major principal axis, the effective length is 72 in.; hence the slenderness is

$$\frac{l}{k} = \frac{72}{0.866} = 83.1.$$

For bending about the minor principal axis, the equivalent length is $(0.5)72 = 36$ in.; therefore the column slenderness is

$$\frac{l}{k} = \frac{36}{0.2885} = 124.8.$$

Since both l/k values exceed the critical, the member could buckle as an Euler column about either axis. Clearly, it will buckle where it is weakest, and in this instance it is about the minor principal axis because the matching slenderness value is larger. Therefore the elastic strength of the column is

$$P_{\mathrm{cr}} = A \frac{\pi^2 E}{(l/k)^2} = (3) \frac{\pi^2 (10.7) 10^6}{(124.8)^2} = 20{,}350 \text{ lb.} \qquad Ans.$$

PROBLEMS

9.15. Where should P be applied for optimum conditions? The rigid bar B is prevented from moving sidewise by bars like M. For member C, $E = 30 \times 10^6$ psi and $\sigma_e = 36{,}000$ psi; for member D, $E = 10.5 \times 10^6$ psi and $\sigma_e = 40{,}000$ psi. Both C and D are 1 in. in diameter.

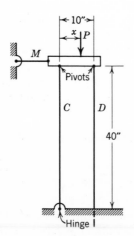

Fig. P9.15

9.16. A solid 1-in. round steel rod 30 in. long is loaded in compression. One end is completely restrained against any movement (fixed), whereas the other end is hinged. If $E = 30 \times 10^6$ psi and $\sigma_e = 30,000$ psi (a) what is the maximum elastic strength of the rod and (b) what is the effective end-fixity coefficient for it?

9.17. Find the compressive strength of a 10-ft long hollow tube with an outside diameter of 2 in. and a wall thickness of $\frac{1}{8}$ in. if both its ends are built in. Use $E = 10.5 \times 10^6$ psi and $\sigma_e = 40,000$ psi.

9.18. Solve the preceding problem if one of the ends is hinged instead of built in.

9.19. Slender members B and C are identical as to length (50 in.), cross section (1 in. by 1 in. square), and material ($E = 30 \times 10^6$ psi and $\sigma_e = 36,000$ psi). The lower end of B is hinged, whereas that of C is built in. Their tops are hinged together and are prevented from sidesway by short bars schematically represented by D. How should the load P be inclined (in the plane of B and C) in order that it can be a maximum, and how large is this maximum P?

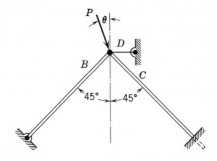

FIG. P9.19

9.20. A 5I14.75 steel shape 12 ft long is used as a column. The manner in which the member is supported is such that the effective end-fixity coefficients are 2.0 for bending about the minor principal axis (least second-moment of area) and 1.0 for bending about the major principal axis. What ultimate load may be carried by the member? Use $E = 30 \times 10^6$ psi and $\sigma_e = 40,000$ psi. See the Appendix tables for the cross-sectional characteristics of the steel shape.

9.8   The Problem of Column Design.   *A long column fails because it buckles; a short column buckles because it fails.*   This is the quintessence of column behavior.   The word "failure" here means overstepping of the proportional limit in the material and therefore development of permanent set.   A long column is incapable of developing a strength higher than its Euler value; a short column, on the other hand, can develop a higher strength than $P_e = \sigma_e A$ through inelastic action.   We will discuss this in Chapter 14.

Except for minor structural detailing, the problem of designing a column centers on the establishment of the correct n or C. This is never easy and is always attended by uncertainty. The magnitude of either coefficient which matters is that obtaining at the instant just before failure. The initial value may or may not have any bearing on the true strength of the column.* As stated earlier in this chapter, it is only in the laboratory where control can be exercised over the eccentricity, hence over n or C, *throughout* the duration of a test. For an actual column as a component of a structure, it is possible for the final value of the end-fixity coefficient to differ materially from its initial value. This difficulty occasioned by the indeterminateness surrounding n or C in practice is compounded by the inherent sensitivity to error and defects of a column with near critical slenderness. Thus a value judgment could place a column in the long column range when it might actually be acting as a short column; since this would be an error on the safe side, it would not be objectionable. The reverse, however, could be disastrous.

Recognizing this uncertainty, the engineering profession has had to rely on empirical formulas for design purposes. These formulas, which really represent attempts to fit curves to scattered experimental points, are of three basic types: (1) the Burr straight-line formula, (2) the Johnson parabolic formula, and (3) the Gordon-Rankine formula.

The straight-line formula, first proposed by W. H. Burr in 1882, is of the general form

$$\frac{P}{A} = a - b\left(\frac{l}{k}\right). \tag{9.9}$$

To lend this formula a semblance of rationality, we should set a equal to σ_e and then determine b so that the straight line will be tangent to the Euler hyperbola (Fig. 9.11a). It would then give upper limits to unit column strength. In practice, a and b are so chosen as to take some safety factor into account (dashed line in Fig. 9.11a). One well-known example is this formula from the Chicago Building Code:

$$\left(\frac{P}{A}\right)_w = 16{,}000 - 70\left(\frac{l}{k}\right). \tag{a}$$

It gives *working* values for the strength per unit area of steel columns in the slenderness range $30 < l/k < 120$.

The parabolic formula, first proposed by J. B. Johnson in 1893, is of the general form

$$\frac{P}{A} = a - b\left(\frac{l}{k}\right)^2. \tag{9.10}$$

---

* J. A. Van den Broek, *op. cit.* on p. 271.

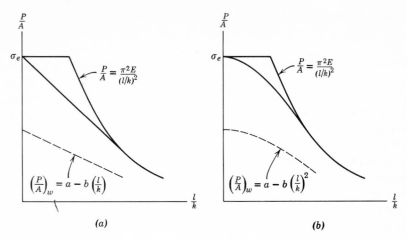

$$\left(\frac{P}{A}\right)_w = a - b\left(\frac{l}{k}\right)$$

(a)

$$\left(\frac{P}{A}\right)_w = a - b\left(\frac{l}{k}\right)^2$$

(b)

FIG. 9.11

Again, to preserve a modicum of rationality, we should equate a to σ_e, which locates the vertex of the parabola; then b should be such as to make the parabola tangent to the Euler curve (Fig. 9.11b). One example of this formula which gives working values for steel columns is the following from the American Institute of Steel Construction:

$$\left(\frac{P}{A}\right)_w = 17{,}000 - 0.485 \left(\frac{l}{k}\right)^2. \qquad (b)$$

It is for l/k values not greater than 120.

Observe from Figs. 9.11a and b that both the straight line and the parabola accomplish the same objective after a fashion—to take into account the variable uncertainty of column strength that is most pronounced in the vicinity of the critical slenderness. The Gordon-Rankine formula also achieves this objective; it is of the general form

$$\frac{P}{A} = \frac{a}{1 + b(l/k)^2}, \qquad (9.11)$$

where for limit values a should be σ_e and b so selected as to make the curve fair through as many experimental points as possible. With b so selected, however, the curve would intersect the Euler hyperbola and for large l/k would give higher values than P_{cr}/A. It is therefore necessary to delimit the slenderness range over which the formula may be used. A typical equation of this form that gives working values for steel columns in the slenderness range from 120 to 200 is

$$\left(\frac{P}{A}\right)_w = \frac{18,000}{1 + \dfrac{1}{18,000}\left(\dfrac{l}{k}\right)^2}. \tag{c}$$

Of these empirical formulas, only the Gordon-Rankine one can lay claim to any rationality, at least on the basis on which it is derived. It appears to have been proposed originally by Tredgold in 1822, revised by Gordon at an undetermined date and by Rankine in 1866.* After the pattern of Eq. 9.1, we may write

$$\frac{P}{A} = \frac{\sigma_e}{1 + \delta c/k^2}, \tag{d}$$

in which δ is the offset of P from the centroid of the cross section where the bending moment is greatest. If the approximation is now made that δ is proportional to the square of l (which is tantamount to assuming the deflection curve to be parabolic), and if the product of the proportionality factor and the dimension c is replaced by a single *constant*, then Eq. 9.11 will be the outcome. With the assumption that δ is proportional to l^2, however, ends the rationality of the formula, for, although the deflection may always be written in the form $\delta = \alpha l^2$, it is not difficult to see that the coefficient α will not necessarily remain constant for varying l.

PROBLEMS

9.21. Derive an empirical formula of the straight-line type that may be used in calculating maximum compressive strengths of hinged-end columns of a material for which $E = 10.5 \times 10^6$ psi and $\sigma_e = 40,000$ psi.

9.22. Derive an empirical formula of the parabolic type that may be used in calculating maximum compressive strengths of the columns in the preceding problem.

9.23. Using the Chicago straight-line formula, Eq. *a*, select a WF-section for a column that will carry a working load of 100,000 lb. The length of the column is to be 15 ft. Assume both ends pivoted. (*Note:* This involves trial and error.)

9.24. Solve the preceding problem, using the A.I.S.C. formula, Eq. *b*.

9.25. Select an equal-leg angle shape for a column 12 ft long, both of whose ends are built in, that will safely carry a centric compressive load of 25,000 lb. Use Eq. *c*.

* E. H. Salmon, *Columns*, p. 132, Oxford Technical Publications, Henry Frowde and Hodder & Stoughton, London, 1921.

VARIATION OF STRESS
AT A POINT

10.1 Introduction. In the analysis of elementary structural members considered so far, we have determined the spatial variation of stress; in so doing, we have confined our attention to special families of planes, usually transverse and longitudinal. The slender forms of the members have virtually dictated which planes are convenient to deal with. Having derived an approximate law governing this variation in each typical member, we then proceeded to evaluate the maximum values attained by the stress and have implied that these represent critical magnitudes. It may happen that the greatest possible normal or shear stress at a point will not be on either a transverse or a longitudinal plane; since the response of a material to stress must obviously depend on the magnitude of such stress, we should be equipped to determine the value of this maximum and the orientation of the plane on which it acts.

The maximum and minimum values of stress are aspects of its over-all variation. Before we make this variation clear, we should first demonstrate quantitatively the statement made in Chapter 2, that six distinct cartesian components of stress are sufficient for a complete specification of the state of stress at a point.

10.2 State of Stress at a Point. Let us begin by assuming that the six components of the stress tensor are given: σ_x, σ_y, σ_z, τ_{xy}, τ_{yz}, and τ_{zx}. The state of stress is completely specified if the stress components on a plane of whatever aspect, containing the point in question, can be

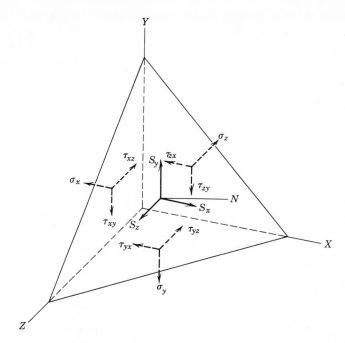

FIG. 10.1

uniquely determined in terms of the given quantities. Figure 10.1 shows a tetrahedron of differential dimensions, enclosing point p. On the three cartesian planes are indicated the given stress components, assumed positive according to the sign convention previously explained in Chapter 2. The generic plane, inclined to all three cartesian planes, is defined by its outward normal N whose direction cosines are: $l = \cos \theta_x$, $m = \cos \theta_y$, and $n = \cos \theta_z$. The stress on the generic plane is represented by its three cartesian components: S_x, S_y, and S_z.

If the area of the inclined face is ΔA, then the areas of the three mutually perpendicular faces are $l(\Delta A)$, $m(\Delta A)$, and $n(\Delta A)$, which are equal to the projections of ΔA on the y-z, z-x, and x-y planes. Keeping in mind that the small tetrahedron is understood to shrink to the point p in the limit and that therefore we need not bring in body forces, we now apply the conditions of equilibrium. Thus, from the summation of *forces* in the X direction,

$$\Sigma F_x = 0 = S_x(\Delta A) - \sigma_x l(\Delta A) - \tau_{yx} m(\Delta A) - \tau_{zx} n(\Delta A),$$

we obtain
$$S_x = l\sigma_x + m\tau_{yx} + n\tau_{zx}. \tag{10.1a}$$

Summations of forces in the Y and Z directions give the two other components of S

$$S_y = m\sigma_y + n\tau_{zy} + l\tau_{xy}, \tag{10.1b}$$

and

$$S_z = n\sigma_z + l\tau_{xz} + m\tau_{yz}. \tag{10.1c}$$

Using the well-known corollary of the parallelogram law, that the orthographic projection of a vector in any direction equals the algebraic sum of the orthographic projections of its components in this same direction, we now derive the expression for the normal component of stress on the generic plane

$$\sigma = lS_x + mS_y + nS_z$$

$$= l^2\sigma_x + m^2\sigma_y + n^2\sigma_z + 2(lm\tau_{xy} + mn\tau_{yz} + nl\tau_{zx}), \tag{10.2}$$

where we have used the equalities $\tau_{xy} = \tau_{yx}$, $\tau_{yz} = \tau_{zy}$, and $\tau_{zx} = \tau_{xz}$. With σ known, τ follows directly as the vector difference between S and σ, thus:

$$\tau = \sqrt{S^2 - \sigma^2}, \tag{10.3}$$

whose expansion in terms of the given stress components we have not written out because it is long and unwieldy, although by no means difficult.

We have thus shown that, for any aspect of plane, both σ and τ are uniquely defined in terms of the given stress components. Therefore the state of stress at p is completely specified.

10.3 Variation of Stress. We see from Eqs. 10.2 and 10.3 that for any given cartesian components both σ and τ are functions of the direction cosines of the normal N. Since the analysis of the variation of σ and τ for the general case involves considerable and formidable algebra, we will now discuss this variation from the standpoint of three special cases; later we shall show that any case can always be reduced to one of these three.

CASE 1. UNIAXIAL STRESS. For our first case let us suppose that all the stress components except σ_x are zero. This state is *uniaxial stress*. From Eqs. 10.1 we find $S_x = l\sigma_x$, and $S_y = S_z = 0$. Equation 10.2 now gives

$$\sigma = l^2\sigma_x = \sigma_x \cos^2 \theta_x$$

$$= \frac{\sigma_x}{2}(1 + \cos 2\theta_x), \tag{10.4}$$

where the double angle has been introduced for later convenience. Substituting this in Eq. 10.3, we get

$$\tau = \sqrt{l^2 \sigma_x^2 - l^4 \sigma_x^2} = l\sigma_x \sqrt{1 - l^2}$$

$$= -\sigma_x \cos \theta_x \sin \theta_x = -\frac{\sigma_x}{2} \sin 2\theta_x, \qquad (10.5)$$

where the choice of the minus rather than the plus sign will be clarified later.

Although the maximum and minimum values attained by σ and τ are obvious by inspection, it is nevertheless instructive to bring in the calculus. Let us differentiate σ with respect to θ_x, thus:

$$\frac{d\sigma}{d\theta_x} = -2\left(\frac{\sigma_x}{2} \sin 2\theta_x\right) = 2\tau, \qquad (10.6)$$

by virtue of Eq. 10.5. Equation 10.6 shows that, when σ is stationary, τ is zero; these stationary values are

$$\sigma_{\max} = \sigma_x, \qquad \text{on the plane whose } \theta_x = 0,$$

and $\qquad \sigma_{\min} = 0, \qquad$ on the plane whose $\theta_x = \dfrac{\pi}{2}.$

Every such plane, on which the normal stress is stationary, and on which, by Eq. 10.6, the shear stress is zero, is known as a *principal plane;* the normal stress on it is then a *principal stress.* Since σ is independent of both m and n (Eq. 10.4), *there is an infinite number of principal planes in uniaxial stress.* These planes have the following characteristics: one of them, the only distinct one, is the given y-z plane on which σ_x acts; all the others are perpendicular to it.

Let us now look into the variation of τ. Differentiating τ in Eq. 10.5 with respect to θ_x, we obtain

$$\frac{d\tau}{d\theta_x} = -2\left(\frac{\sigma_x}{2} \cos 2\theta_x\right) = -2\left(\sigma - \frac{\sigma_x}{2}\right), \qquad (10.7)$$

where we have used Eq. 10.4. In contrast to the behavior of σ, τ when stationary is accompanied by a nonzero normal stress, $\sigma_x/2$. The shear stress is stationary at $\theta_x = \pm \pi/4$, with the magnitudes $\mp\sigma_x/2$. Deciding which one of these two values to designate the algebraic maximum depends on the sign convention chosen (see Eq. 10.5). Henceforth, in reference to τ, we shall understand the maximum to mean the *numerically* greatest values; these are always on perpendicular planes. Thus, for uniaxial stress,

$$\tau_{\max} = \frac{\sigma_x}{2}, \qquad \text{on planes whose } \theta_x = \pm\frac{\pi}{4}.$$

At this point, the thoughtful and observant reader is probably confused, as well he might be. The fact that the shear stress on the plane $\theta_x = \pi/4$ has the same magnitude as that on the plane $\theta_x = -\pi/4$ is consistent with the fundamental fact first brought out in Chapter 2, that cross shears on perpendicular planes are equal; apparently, however, one shear stress now bears a sign opposite to that of the other. How come? Is there here a contradiction in signs? To minimize confusion, it is necessary that, *when considering the variation of σ and τ relative to aspect of plane*, we do *not* interpret the signs plus and minus as positive and negative, but must now employ instead other words that are more meaningful in the present context.

First, note that the nondependence of both σ and τ on θ_y and θ_z allows us to say without loss of generality that we need consider only those planes whose $\theta_z = \pi/2$. Let us project on the x-y plane the small prism which has now replaced the small tetrahedron, Fig. 10.2a; this is the view from the positive end of the Z axis. Here is the interpretation that we must attach to the plus and minus signs of σ and τ:

To an observer standing within the enclosed area and looking in the sense of the outward normal to the plane in question, a plus normal stress is directed away from him, and is described as tensile; a plus shear stress is directed to his left, and is described as counterclockwise.

Reference to Fig. 10.2b makes the second part of the preceding clear: if the point is surrounded by a small rectangle, the four shear stress components will appear as two couples, one pair having a counterclockwise

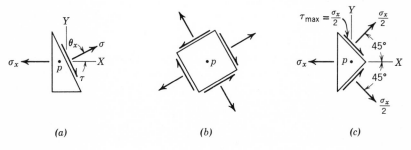

(a)   *(b)*   *(c)*

Fɪɢ. 10.2

sense, the other a clockwise sense. Therefore, in Eq. 10.5, whenever τ comes out plus it is counterclockwise, and when minus it is clockwise.

Fortunately, so far as normal stress is concerned, no inconsistency is involved, since this new description is still in harmony with the original one; in regard to shear stress, what has been introduced is not so much an inconsistency as it is an *additional* association. It certainly is not inconsistent to describe a positive τ_{xy} as being counterclockwise and a positive τ_{yx} as clockwise. Later (see Eq. 10.25), a positive τ_{xy} will actually come out plus, hence counterclockwise, whereas a positive τ_{yx} will actually come out minus, hence clockwise.

We cannot overemphasize the observation made in Article 2.11, that *a fixed interpretation of the signs of directed quantities will, in general, work out without apparent inconsistencies only when applied to their cartesian components.* Owing to the fact that for a generic plane both σ and τ are inclined to all three given cartesian axes, the definitions of signs reserved for the cartesian components should not necessarily be extended to σ and τ.* This should be no cause for uneasiness because after all signs by themselves are not important; what matters is the interpretation one can attach to them.

Returning now to the variation of σ and τ, we graph Eqs. 10.4 and 10.5 (Fig. 10.3). Visually obvious are aspects previously explained as well as others not explicitly mentioned: (1) where σ is stationary, τ is zero; (2) where τ is stationary, $\sigma = \sigma_x/2$; (3) the planes of maximum shear stress are inclined 45 deg to the principal planes; (4) the rate of change of σ relative to θ_x is proportional to τ; (5) the rate of change of τ relative to θ_x is proportional to σ diminished by some constant.

Finally, we observe that in uniaxial stress just as there are numberless principal planes so there are numberless pairs of perpendicular planes that bear the maximum shear stress, on each of which a normal stress

---

* We hasten to remark that it is, of course, possible to consider the generic σ and τ as cartesian components referred to a *new* cartesian frame which is inclined to the original one; then the introduction of the additional descriptions, clockwise and counterclockwise, would become altogether unnecessary. To do so, and make a thorough job of it, would lead us to the interesting subject of cartesian tensors, of which, as we pointed out in Chapter 2, stress is an example. Since, however, our interest here is less on the elegant transformations, which are at the heart of tensors, and more on the significant magnitudes attained by the stress components as they vary, we forego the esoteric pleasure of tensor manipulation and cling instead to the more pragmatic system of associations that we have described. The interested reader is referred to H. Jeffreys, *Cartesian Tensors*, Cambridge University Press, Cambridge, England, 1952, and to R. R. Long, *Mechanics of Solids and Fluids*, Prentice-Hall, Englewood Cliffs, New Jersey, 1961.

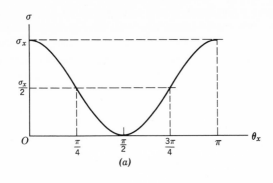

(a)

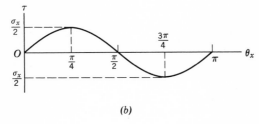

(b)

FIG. 10.3

$\sigma_x/2$ accompanies the shear stress. Figure 10.2c shows a pair of these perpendicular planes for any arbitrarily chosen Z direction.

Similar remarks hold when σ_x is compressive. In such a situation, $\sigma_{\max} = 0$ and $\sigma_{\min} = \sigma_x$; all arrows in Fig. 10.2 should be reversed, and the curves in Fig. 10.3 revolved 180 deg about the θ_x axis.

There is ample experimental evidence that the maximum shear stresses in uniaxial stress do indeed occur on 45-deg planes. A ductile material will yield in simple tension or compression by developing slip planes in 45-deg directions. Thus, when a bar of mild steel that is covered with mill scale (an oxide of iron that forms on rolled and extruded stock while on the cooling beds) yields in simple tension, the brittle scale flakes off in a more or less regular pattern of criss-crossing 45-deg lines, suggesting that the planes, of which these lines are the traces, slide ever so slightly under the maximum shear stresses. These lines are sometimes called *Lüders's lines*. In sheet metal, these slip lines (also called *stretcher strains* or *flow figures*) are identified by little depressions in pieces subjected to tension or by little elevations in pieces subjected to compression.

CASE 2. BIAXIAL STRESS. The next case we will consider is when all stress components except two of the normal ones, say σ_x and σ_y, are zero;

this is *biaxial stress*. Equations 10.1 then give $S_x = l\sigma_x$, $S_y = m\sigma_y$, and $S_z = 0$; and, by Eq. 10.2, we find

$$\sigma = l^2\sigma_x + m^2\sigma_y, \qquad (a)$$

whereas by Eq. 10.3 we have

$$\tau = \sqrt{S^2 - \sigma^2} = \sqrt{(S_x^2 + S_y^2 + S_z^2) - \sigma^2}$$

$$= \sqrt{l^2\sigma_x^2(1 - l^2) + m^2\sigma_y^2(1 - m^2) - 2l^2m^2\sigma_x\sigma_y}. \qquad (b)$$

We know from analytic geometry that the three direction cosines are related thus:

$$l^2 + m^2 + n^2 = 1, \qquad (c)$$

which shows that any two of the three may be considered the independent variables and the third then the dependent one. The following differential relations may therefore be established between them:

$$\frac{\partial n}{\partial l} = -\frac{l}{n} \quad \text{and} \quad \frac{\partial n}{\partial m} = -\frac{m}{n}, \qquad (d)$$

when n is the dependent variable.

Differentiating σ in Eq. *a* relative to n, assuming that l and m are the independent variables, we obtain

$$\frac{\partial \sigma}{\partial n} = 2l\left(-\frac{n}{l}\right)\sigma_x = -2n\sigma_x,$$

from which it is clear that the normal stress is stationary relative to n when $n = 0$. Setting $n = 0$, we obtain from Eq. *c*: $m^2 = 1 - l^2$, which when substituted in Eq. *a* gives us

$$\sigma = l^2\sigma_x + (1 - l^2)\sigma_y = \sigma_x \cos^2\theta_x + \sigma_y \sin^2\theta_x$$

$$= \frac{\sigma_x + \sigma_y}{2} + \frac{\sigma_x - \sigma_y}{2}\cos 2\theta_x, \qquad (10.8)$$

which is valid for all those planes whose $\theta_z = \pi/2$. This shows that $\sigma = \sigma_{\max} = \sigma_x$ when $\theta_x = 0$, and $\sigma = \sigma_{\min} = \sigma_y$ when $\theta_x = \pi/2$, it being assumed that $\sigma_x > \sigma_y$.

Differentiating σ in Eq. *a* relative to l, we obtain

$$\frac{\partial \sigma}{\partial l} = 2l\sigma_x.$$

Thus σ is stationary with respect to l when $l = 0$. Hence, setting $l = 0$, we obtain, from Eq. *a*,

$$\sigma = m^2 \sigma_y = \sigma_y \cos^2 \theta_y = \frac{\sigma_y}{2} (1 + \cos 2\theta_y), \qquad (10.9)$$

which is valid for all planes whose $\theta_x = \pi/2$. We find from the preceding that $\sigma = \sigma_{max} = \sigma_y$ when $\theta_y = 0$, and $\sigma = \sigma_{min} = 0$ when $\theta_y = \pi/2$.

Finally, differentiating σ in Eq. *a* with respect to m, we get

$$\frac{\partial \sigma}{\partial m} = 2m\sigma_y,$$

which shows that σ is stationary relative to m when $m = 0$. Using this value of m and the relation $l^2 = 1 - n^2$ in Eq. *a*, we obtain

$$\sigma = l^2 \sigma_x = (1 - n^2)\sigma_x$$

$$= \sigma_x(1 - \cos^2 \theta_z) = \frac{\sigma_x}{2} (1 - \cos 2\theta_z), \qquad (10.10)$$

which is valid for all planes whose $\theta_y = \pi/2$. We note that $\sigma = \sigma_{max} = \sigma_x$ when $\theta_z = \pi/2$, and $\sigma = \sigma_{min} = 0$ when $\theta_z = 0$.

Summarizing the preceding results regarding the variation of σ in biaxial stress, we have the following:

If $\sigma_x > \sigma_y > 0$,

 $\sigma_{max} = \sigma_x$, on the plane whose $\theta_x = 0$, $\theta_y = \theta_z = \pi/2$;

 $\sigma_{minimax} = \sigma_y$, on the plane whose $\theta_y = 0$, $\theta_x = \theta_z = \pi/2$;

 $\sigma_{min} = 0$, on the plane whose $\theta_z = 0$, $\theta_x = \theta_y = \pi/2$.

If $\sigma_x > 0$ and $\sigma_y < 0$,

 $\sigma_{max} = \sigma_x$, on the same plane as the first one above;

 $\sigma_{minimax} = 0$, on the same plane as the third one above;

 $\sigma_{min} = \sigma_y$, on the same plane as the second one above.

Other combinations are obvious. The designation $\sigma_{minimax}$ will be made clear in the general case, to be discussed in the next article, and in the explanation of Mohr's circle, Article 10.7.

That the preceding are principal stresses should be self-evident; if formal proof is desired that the shear stress τ is indeed zero on the planes indicated, it can be obtained readily by substituting the proper direction cosines in Eq. *b*.

In exactly the same fashion, we investigate the variation of τ, differentiating it in Eq. *b* relative to n, l, and m, in turn, and substituting back in Eq. *b* the proper value of each direction cosine which makes τ stationary. The following are the final results.

$$\tau = -(\sigma_x - \sigma_y) \cos \theta_x \sin \theta_x = -\frac{\sigma_x - \sigma_y}{2} \sin 2\theta_x, \qquad (10.11)$$

which is valid for all planes whose $\theta_z = \pi/2$. This gives $\tau = \tau_{\max} = (\sigma_x - \sigma_y)/2$, when $\theta_x = \pm\pi/4$; it is accompanied by $\sigma = (\sigma_x + \sigma_y)/2$, by Eq. 10.8.

$$\tau = -\sigma_y \cos\theta_y \sin\theta_y = -\frac{\sigma_y}{2}\sin 2\theta_y, \qquad (10.12)$$

which is valid for all planes whose $\theta_x = \pi/2$. This shows that $\tau = \tau_{\max} = \sigma_y/2$, when $\theta_y = \pm\pi/4$; it is accompanied by $\sigma = \sigma_y/2$, by Eq. 10.9.

$$\tau = \sigma_x \cos\theta_z \sin\theta_z = \frac{\sigma_x}{2}\sin 2\theta_z, \qquad (10.13)$$

which is valid for all planes whose $\theta_y = \pi/2$. It is clear that $\tau = \tau_{\max} = \sigma_x/2$ when $\theta_z = \pm\pi/4$; the accompanying normal stress is $\sigma = \sigma_x/2$, by Eq. 10.10.

We summarize the preceding results regarding the stationary values of τ as follows:

If $\sigma_x = \sigma_{\max}$, $\sigma_y = \sigma_{\text{minimax}}$, and $\sigma_{\min} = 0$,
$\tau_{\max} = \sigma_x/2 = \sigma_{\max}/2$, on the plane whose $\theta_y = \pi/2$,
$\theta_x = \theta_z = \pm\pi/4$; it is accompanied by $\sigma = \sigma_x/2 = \sigma_{\max}/2$.
If $\sigma_y = \sigma_{\max}$, $\sigma_x = \sigma_{\text{minimax}}$, and $\sigma_{\min} = 0$,
$\tau_{\max} = \sigma_y/2 = \sigma_{\max}/2$, on the plane whose $\theta_x = \pi/2$,
$\theta_y = \theta_z = \pm\pi/4$; it is accompanied by $\sigma = \sigma_y/2 = \sigma_{\max}/2$.
If $\sigma_x = \sigma_{\max}$, $\sigma_{\text{minimax}} = 0$, and $\sigma_{\min} = \sigma_y$,
$\tau_{\max} = (\sigma_x - \sigma_y)/2 = (\sigma_{\max} - \sigma_{\min})/2$, on the plane whose $\theta_z = \pi/2$, $\theta_x = \theta_y = \pm\pi/4$; it is accompanied by $\sigma = (\sigma_x + \sigma_y)/2 = (\sigma_{\max} + \sigma_{\min})/2$.

Figures 10.4a, b, and c display important facts of biaxial stress. Other situations (for example, when both nonzero principal stresses are compressive) can be easily sketched and filled in.

CASE 3.   TRIAXIAL STRESS.   As the name suggests, this is when all shear cartesian components are zero and the normal ones are all different from zero. Equations 10.1 then give $S_x = l\sigma_x$, $S_y = m\sigma_y$, and $S_z = n\sigma_z$. From Eq. 10.2 we obtain

$$\sigma = l^2\sigma_x + m^2\sigma_y + n^2\sigma_z, \qquad (e)$$

and from Eq. 10.3,

$$\tau = [l^2\sigma_x{}^2(1 - l^2) + m^2\sigma_y{}^2(1 - m^2) + n^2\sigma_z{}^2(1 - n^2)$$
$$- 2(l^2m^2\sigma_x\sigma_y + l^2n^2\sigma_x\sigma_z + m^2n^2\sigma_y\sigma_z)]^{1/2}. \qquad (f)$$

Since the analysis follows the same lines as that of Case 2, we will omit the details and give only the final pertinent equations.

For all planes whose $\theta_z = \pi/2$,

$$\sigma = \frac{\sigma_x + \sigma_y}{2} + \frac{\sigma_x - \sigma_y}{2} \cos 2\theta_x \qquad (10.14)$$

and

$$\tau = -\frac{\sigma_x - \sigma_y}{2} \sin 2\theta_x. \qquad (10.15)$$

When $\theta_x = 0$, $\sigma = \sigma_{\max} = \sigma_x$, and when $\theta_x = \pi/2$, $\sigma = \sigma_{\min} = \sigma_y$, it be-

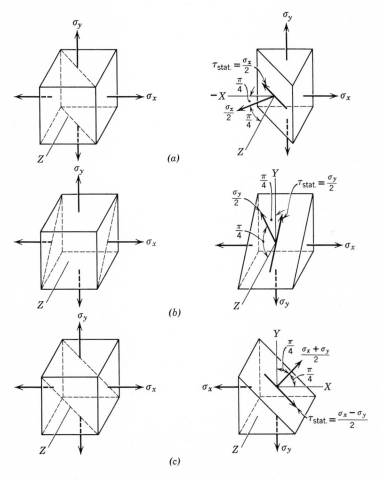

FIG. 10.4   Showing planes of stationary τ in biaxial stress.

ing assumed that $\sigma_x > \sigma_y$. When $\theta_x = \pm \pi/4$, $\tau = \tau_{max} = (\sigma_x - \sigma_y)/2$ $= (\sigma_{max} - \sigma_{min})/2$, and $\sigma = (\sigma_x + \sigma_y)/2 = (\sigma_{max} + \sigma_{min})/2$.
For all planes whose $\theta_x = \pi/2$,

$$\sigma = \frac{\sigma_y + \sigma_z}{2} + \frac{\sigma_y - \sigma_z}{2} \cos 2\theta_y \qquad (10.16)$$

and
$$\tau = -\frac{\sigma_y - \sigma_z}{2} \sin 2\theta_y. \qquad (10.17)$$

When $\theta_y = 0$, $\sigma = \sigma_{max} = \sigma_y$, and when $\theta_y = \pi/2$, $\sigma = \sigma_{min} = \sigma_z$, it being assumed that $\sigma_y > \sigma_z$. When $\theta_y = \pm\pi/4$, $\tau = \tau_{max} = (\sigma_y - \sigma_z)/2 = (\sigma_{max} - \sigma_{min})/2$, and $\sigma = (\sigma_y + \sigma_z)/2 = (\sigma_{max} + \sigma_{min})/2$.
For all planes whose $\theta_y = \pi/2$,

$$\sigma = \frac{\sigma_z + \sigma_x}{2} + \frac{\sigma_z - \sigma_x}{2} \cos 2\theta_z \qquad (10.18)$$

and
$$\tau = -\frac{\sigma_z - \sigma_x}{2} \sin 2\theta_z. \qquad (10.19)$$

Assuming that $\sigma_x > \sigma_z$, we find that $\sigma = \sigma_{max} = \sigma_x$, when $\theta_z = \pi/2$, and $\sigma = \sigma_{min} = \sigma_z$, when $\theta_z = 0$. When $\theta_z = \pm\pi/4$, $\tau = \tau_{max} = (\sigma_x - \sigma_z)/2 = (\sigma_{max} - \sigma_{min})/2$, and $\sigma = (\sigma_z + \sigma_x)/2 = (\sigma_{max} + \sigma_{min})/2$.

Following is a summary of the significant results regarding the stationary values of σ and τ in triaxial stress:

If $\sigma_x > \sigma_y > \sigma_z > 0$, and $\tau_{xy} = \tau_{yz} = \tau_{zx} = 0$,
$\sigma_{max} = \sigma_x$, on the plane whose $\theta_x = 0$, $\theta_y = \theta_z = \pi/2$;
$\sigma_{minimax} = \sigma_y$, on the plane whose $\theta_y = 0$, $\theta_x = \theta_z = \pi/2$;
$\sigma_{min} = \sigma_z$, on the plane whose $\theta_z = 0$, $\theta_x = \theta_y = \pi/2$;
$\tau_{max} = (\sigma_x - \sigma_z)/2 = (\sigma_{max} - \sigma_{min})/2$, on the plane whose $\theta_y = \pi/2$, $\theta_x = \theta_z = \pm\pi/4$; it is accompanied by $\sigma = (\sigma_x + \sigma_z)/2 = (\sigma_{max} + \sigma_{min})/2$. The other two stationary values of τ, $(\sigma_x - \sigma_y)/2$ and $(\sigma_y - \sigma_z)/2$, are not true maxima.

These facts are depicted in Fig. 10.5. Other combinations can be easily written out and sketched.

It should be clear from the discussion up to this point that uniaxial stress is but a special case of biaxial stress, which, in turn, is a special case of triaxial stress. (Note for just one example that Eq. 10.19 reduces to Eq. 10.13 when σ_z is set equal to zero.) The main difference is this: In uniaxial stress, there is an infinity of principal planes, only one

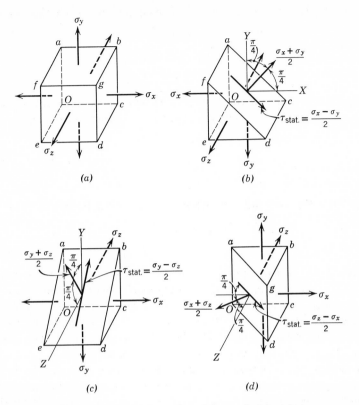

FIG. 10.5   Showing planes of stationary τ in triaxial stress.

of which is distinct, and numberless pairs of perpendicular planes bearing the maximum shear stress, none of which is distinct; on the other hand, in biaxial and triaxial stress, so long as $\sigma_{\max} \neq \sigma_{\min\max} \neq \sigma_{\min}$, there are always only three principal planes, all distinct, and only one pair of perpendicular planes bearing the maximum shear stress.

10.4   General Three-Dimensional Stress.   In the general case, when all cartesian components of stress at a point are not zero, the following can be shown with the aid of Eqs. 10.1 and the relations between the direction cosines as contained in Eqs. c and d of the preceding article:

(1) That when σ is stationary, the shear component τ is zero, that is,

$$\frac{S_x}{l} = \frac{S_y}{m} = \frac{S_z}{n} = S = \sigma. \qquad (10.20)$$

(2) That the direction cosines of a principal plane satisfy the equations

$$l(\sigma_x - \sigma) + m\tau_{xy} + n\tau_{xz} = 0,$$

$$l\tau_{xy} + m(\sigma_y - \sigma) + n\tau_{yz} = 0, \qquad (10.21)$$

and $\qquad l\tau_{xz} + m\tau_{yz} + n(\sigma_z - \sigma) = 0.$

(3) That in order for the homogeneous equations 10.21 to be solvable for l, m, and n, the determinant of their coefficients must vanish, thus:

$$\begin{vmatrix} (\sigma_x - \sigma) & \tau_{xy} & \tau_{xz} \\ \tau_{xy} & (\sigma_y - \sigma) & \tau_{yz} \\ \tau_{xz} & \tau_{yz} & (\sigma_z - \sigma) \end{vmatrix} = 0. \qquad (10.22)$$

(4) That this determinant, when expanded, results in the cubic

$$\sigma^3 - (\sigma_x + \sigma_y + \sigma_z)\sigma^2 + (\sigma_x\sigma_y + \sigma_y\sigma_z + \sigma_z\sigma_x - \tau_{xy}^2 - \tau_{yz}^2 - \tau_{zz}^2)\sigma$$

$$- (\sigma_x\sigma_y\sigma_z + 2\tau_{xy}\tau_{yz}\tau_{zx} - \sigma_x\tau_{yz}^2 - \sigma_y\tau_{zx}^2 - \sigma_z\tau_{xy}^2) = 0. \quad (10.23)$$

Thus there are three principal stresses whose values are the roots of Eq. 10.23; when arranged in descending algebraic order, they are called σ_{max}, $\sigma_{minimax}$, and σ_{min}. The principal planes, whose direction cosines are determined from Eq. 10.21 and Eq. c of Article 10.3, can be shown to be mutually perpendicular. We shall refer to them as the *major*, the *intermediate*, and the *minor principal planes*.

In view of the discussion of Case 3 in the preceding article, we say that the state of stress in the general case can always be specified in terms of the equivalent triaxial stress: σ_{max}, $\sigma_{minimax}$, σ_{min}. If all three principal stresses are distinct, then there are only three (distinct) principal planes and only one pair of perpendicular planes which bear the maximum shear stress, $\tau_{max} = (\sigma_{max} - \sigma_{min})/2$. On the other hand, if, say $\sigma_{minimax} = \sigma_{min} \neq \sigma_{max}$, then there is an unlimited number of principal planes, only one of which is distinct—the major principal plane; furthermore, there are then also numberless pairs of perpendicular planes that bear the maximum shear stress, all inclined 45 deg to the major principal plane.

Worthy of special mention is the situation when $\sigma_{max} = \sigma_{minimax} = \sigma_{min}$; this is referred to as "hydrostatic" stress, tensile or compressive, as the case may be. Then all planes through the point are principal planes, since none of them is subject to shear stress. This is called an *isotropic point.*

Illustrative Example 1. For three-dimensional pure shear, that is, when $\tau_{xy} = \tau_{yz} = \tau_{zx} \neq 0$ and $\sigma_x = \sigma_y = \sigma_z = 0$, determine the principal stresses and hence the maximum shear stress.

SOLUTION. Making the proper substitutions in Eq. 10.23, we find

$$\sigma^3 - 3\tau_{xy}^2\sigma - 2\tau_{xy}^3 = 0. \qquad (a)$$

This can be written in the factored form

$$(\sigma - 2\tau_{xy})(\sigma + \tau_{xy})^2 = 0.$$

Therefore the roots of Eq. a are: $2\tau_{xy}$, $-\tau_{xy}$, and $-\tau_{xy}$. Hence $\sigma_{\max} = 2\tau_{xy}$, $\sigma_{\text{minimax}} = \sigma_{\min} = -\tau_{xy}$; and from the results of Case 3, the maximum shear stress is $\tau_{\max} = (\sigma_{\max} - \sigma_{\min})/2 = 1.5\tau_{xy}$, and it is accompanied by $\sigma = (\sigma_{\max} + \sigma_{\min})/2 = 0.5\tau_{xy}$.   *Ans.*

It can be shown that the major principal plane is defined by $\theta_x = \theta_y = \theta_z = \cos^{-1}(1/\sqrt{3})$, and that the other two principal planes have direction cosines which satisfy the two equations

$$l^2 + m^2 + n^2 = 1$$

$$(b)$$

and $$l + m + n = 0.$$

Since there are only these two equations which the three direction cosines must satisfy, the intermediate and minor principal planes are not distinct—all planes perpendicular to the major principal plane are also principal planes.

Figure 10.6a represents the given state of stress, where for clarity the components on only the three visible cartesian planes are indicated. Relative to the cartesian axes, the principal planes are shown in Fig. 10.6b.

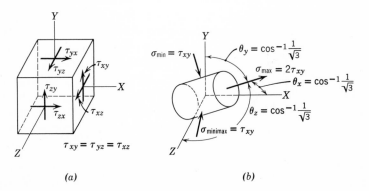

(a)   (b)

FIG. 10.6

10.5   Plane Stress.   There are many important applications, among which are some of the elementary structural elements we have discussed, where the state of stress at each of various points in the body is such that some one family of planes is either completely free of stress or stressed so slightly as to be considered practically stress-free.   Such a state of stress is described as *two-dimensional* or *plane stress*.   We now show that the state of stress at a point in a body subject to plane stress is always equivalent to biaxial stress, which is Case 2 discussed previously.   Let this set of components be given: $\sigma_z = \tau_{zx} = \tau_{zy} = 0$, and $\sigma_x \neq \sigma_y \neq \tau_{xy} \neq 0$.

If our prime interest is merely in the values of the principal stresses, we can solve for these directly from Eq. 10.23 after the proper substitutions (see Prob. 10.3).   If, however, we are interested as well in other aspects of plane stress, we can go back further to Eqs. 10.1 through 10.3.   For a change, we are not going to follow either procedure; we will instead start from the barest fundamentals of equilibrium.

Since all planes whose $\theta_z = 0$ are free of stress (and hence are principal planes), it will suffice to investigate only those planes for which $\theta_z = \pi/2$.   If we can prove that among them there are two perpendicular ones which are free of shear stress, then our task of showing that the general case of plane stress is reducible to biaxial stress can be considered accomplished.   Accordingly, let us isolate the point p by cutting out a right triangular prism.   This is done by passing five planes in the immediate vicinity of the point: two cartesian planes with normals in the X and Y directions and the generic plane, all three being perpendicular to two parallel stress-free planes.   The projection on the x-y plane is shown in Fig. 10.7a, in which the given stress components σ_x, σ_y, and τ_{xy} are indicated with positive senses according to previous convention.   The generic components are assumed as follows: σ is tensile and τ is

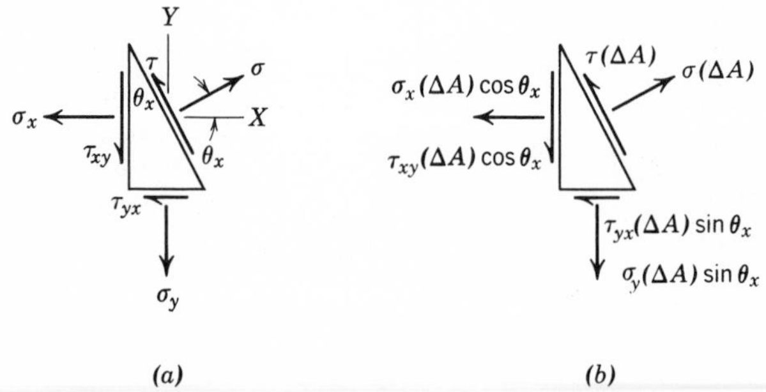

(a)   (b)

Fig. 10.7

counterclockwise. The aspect of the generic plane is specified by θ_x, considered positive in the counterclockwise sense from $+X$.

The surface forces on the little free body are represented in Fig. 10.7b; ΔA stands for the area of the face in the generic plane. Summing forces along the normal to the inclined face, we write

$$\Sigma F_n = 0 = \sigma(\Delta A) - \sigma_x(\Delta A)\cos^2\theta_x - \sigma_y(\Delta A)\sin^2\theta_x$$
$$- \tau_{xy}(\Delta A)\cos\theta_x\sin\theta_x - \tau_{yx}(\Delta A)\sin\theta_x\cos\theta_x.$$

Dividing through by ΔA and solving for σ, noting that $\tau_{xy} = \tau_{yx}$, we obtain

$$\sigma = \sigma_x\cos^2\theta_x + \sigma_y\sin^2\theta_x + 2\tau_{xy}\sin\theta_x\cos\theta_x. \qquad (a)$$

Introducing the double angle $2\theta_x$ and making the necessary simplifications, we arrive at the result

$$\sigma = \frac{\sigma_x + \sigma_y}{2} + \frac{\sigma_x - \sigma_y}{2}\cos 2\theta_x + \tau_{xy}\sin 2\theta_x. \qquad (10.24)$$

Summing forces along the tangent to the plane, we get

$$\Sigma F_t = 0 = \tau(\Delta A) + \sigma_x(\Delta A)\cos\theta_x\sin\theta_x - \sigma_y(\Delta A)\sin\theta_x\cos\theta_x$$
$$- \tau_{xy}(\Delta A)\cos^2\theta_x + \tau_{yx}(\Delta A)\sin^2\theta_x,$$

from which follows:

$$\tau = -\sigma_x\cos\theta_x\sin\theta_x + \sigma_y\sin\theta_x\cos\theta_x + \tau_{xy}(\cos^2\theta_x - \sin^2\theta_x). \quad (b)$$

Again, introducing the double angle $2\theta_x$, we finally obtain

$$\tau = -\frac{\sigma_x - \sigma_y}{2}\sin 2\theta_x + \tau_{xy}\cos 2\theta_x. \qquad (10.25)$$

It should be clear that both σ and τ, being harmonic, go through maximum and minimum values. Let us establish these with the aid of the calculus. Differentiating σ in Eq. 10.24 with respect to θ_x, we get

$$\frac{d\sigma}{d\theta_x} = -2\frac{\sigma_x - \sigma_y}{2}\sin 2\theta_x + 2\tau_{xy}\cos 2\theta_x, \qquad (c)$$

which by virtue of Eq. 10.25 becomes

$$\frac{d\sigma}{d\theta_x} = 2\tau. \qquad (10.26)$$

Equating $d\sigma/d\theta_x$ to zero and solving for $\tan 2\theta_x$, we find from Eq. c,

$$\tan 2\theta_{xP} = \frac{2\tau_{xy}}{\sigma_x - \sigma_y}. \qquad (10.27)$$

Note that there are two values less than 2π of the double angle $2\theta_{xP}$, 180 deg apart, whose tangent functions have the same sign; therefore there are two values of θ_{xP}, 90 deg apart, for which, according to Eq. 10.27, the normal stress σ is stationary. Since of two angles that differ by $\pi/2$, one always has its sine and cosine functions of the same sign, whereas the other has them of opposite signs, we conclude by Eq. a that one of these angles gives a maximum for σ, whereas the other gives a minimum. Or, equivalently, substituting $2\theta_{xP}$ from Eq. 10.27 in Eq. 10.24 and keeping both values of the radical, we obtain the sought for stationary values of σ, thus:

$$\left.\begin{array}{c}\sigma_{max}\\ \sigma_{min}\end{array}\right\} = \frac{\sigma_x + \sigma_y}{2} \pm \sqrt{[(\sigma_x - \sigma_y)/2]^2 + \tau_{xy}{}^2}. \tag{10.28}$$

It is obvious from Eq. 10.26 that on planes where σ is stationary the shear stress τ is zero. We have thus shown that normal to the stress-free plane $\theta_z = 0$, there are two perpendicular planes which are free of shear stress and on which the normal stress is stationary; but these are precisely the conditions of biaxial stress, which is Case 2 in the preceding article. Hence the state of stress at any point in a body subject to plane stress can always be specified by the equivalent biaxial system: (1) σ_{max}, $\sigma_{minimax}$, $\sigma_{min} = 0$ when the two nonzero principal stresses are both tensile; or (2) σ_{max}, $\sigma_{minimax} = 0$, σ_{min} when the two nonzero principal stresses have opposite senses; or (3) $\sigma_{max} = 0$, $\sigma_{minimax}$, σ_{min} when both nonzero principal stresses are compressive.

Turning now to the variation of τ, we differentiate this relative to θ_x in Eq. 10.25 and obtain

$$\frac{d\tau}{d\theta_x} = -2\frac{\sigma_x - \sigma_y}{2}\cos 2\theta_x - 2\tau_{xy}\sin 2\theta_x, \tag{d}$$

which because of Eq. 10.24 becomes

$$\frac{d\tau}{d\theta_x} = -2\left(\sigma - \frac{\sigma_x + \sigma_y}{2}\right). \tag{10.29}$$

Equating the first derivative to zero and solving for $\tan 2\theta_x$ from Eq. d, we get

$$\tan 2\theta'_{xP} = -\frac{\sigma_x - \sigma_y}{2\tau_{xy}}. \tag{10.30}$$

Substituting this in Eq. 10.27, we obtain the stationary value of τ:

$$\tau_{max} = \sqrt{[(\sigma_x - \sigma_y)/2]^2 + \tau_{xy}{}^2}. \tag{10.31}$$

We observe from Eq. 10.29 that the planes of maximum shear stress are not free of normal stress; τ_{max} is accompanied by $\sigma = (\sigma_x + \sigma_y)/2$.

It is noted that $\tan 2\theta'_{xP}$ (Eq. 10.30) is the negative reciprocal of $\tan 2\theta_{xP}$ (Eq. 10.27). Therefore $2\theta'_{xP}$ differs from $2\theta_{xP}$ by 90 deg and consequently θ'_{xP} differs from θ_{xP} by 45 deg. This then is a repeat of a previous conclusion: planes of maximum shear stress are inclined 45 deg to the principal planes.

Figure 10.8a represents the given state of stress: σ_x, σ_y, τ_{xy}; sketch b shows the principal planes and the principal stresses, where it has been assumed that $\sigma_x > \sigma_y > 0$ and $(\sigma_x + \sigma_y)/2 > \sqrt{[(\sigma_x - \sigma_y)/2]^2 + \tau_{xy}{}^2}$. The given stress-free plane is, of course, itself a principal plane. Figure 10.8c shows the relative orientation of the plane where τ is a maximum: this is perpendicular to the intermediate principal plane and is inclined 45 deg to both the major and minor principal planes. Sketch d

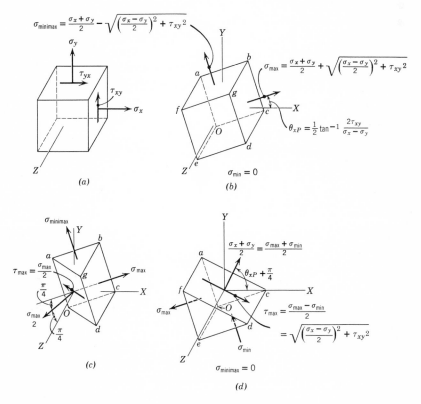

FIG. 10.8   Showing planes of stationary σ and stationary τ in two-dimensional stress.

shows the plane of maximum τ when $\sigma_{\max}$ is tensile and $\sigma_{\min}$ is compressive, which happens when $\sqrt{[(\sigma_x - \sigma_y)/2]^2 + \tau_{xy}^2} > (\sigma_x + \sigma_y)/2$; then this plane is perpendicular to the intermediate principal (stress-free) plane, and its normal is inclined to the X axis an angle of $\pi/4 + \theta_{xP}$.

Illustrative Example 2. At a point p in a plane-stressed body, the state of stress is known in terms of the total stress S_1 on plane 1 and the shear stress τ_2 on plane 2, as shown in Fig. 10.9a. Determine the principal stresses and show them on properly oriented planes. Determine the maximum shear stress.

SOLUTION. Since the X and Y axes are not specified, and since the choice of their inclination is purely arbitrary, let us take the Y axis in the direction of N_2. This is equivalent to saying that the following are known: $\tau_{yx} = -500$ psi, hence $\tau_{xy} = -500$ psi; on the plane $\theta_x = 30$ deg, $\sigma = 2400$ psi, tension, and $\tau = 1000$ psi, clockwise; and that the following are unknown: σ_x and σ_y.

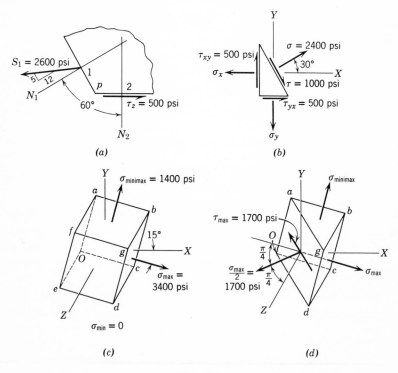

(a)

(b)

(c)

(d)

FIG. 10.9

The most direct solution for σ_x and σ_y is accomplished by applying equilibrium conditions to the small element of Fig. 10.9b. Thus, denoting by ΔA the area of the inclined face of the prism, we write

$$\Sigma F_x = 0 = -\sigma_x(\Delta A \cos 30°) + 500(\Delta A \sin 30°)$$
$$+ 2400(\Delta A) \cos 30° + 1000(\Delta A) \sin 30°,$$

which gives us $\sigma_x = \dfrac{1}{\sqrt{3}} (500 + 1000 + 2400\sqrt{3})$

$$= 866 + 2400 = 3266 \text{ psi},$$

assumed sense correct: σ_x is tensile as shown in Fig. 10.9b. From

$$\Sigma F_y = 0 = -\sigma_y(\Delta A \sin 30°) + 500(\Delta A \cos 30°)$$
$$+ 2400(\Delta A) \sin 30° - 1000(\Delta A) \cos 30°,$$

we find $\sigma_y = (500 - 1000)\sqrt{3} + 2400$

$$= 2400 - 866 = 1534 \text{ psi},$$

tensile, as assumed.

By Eq. 10.28, we now find the stationary values of σ to be

$$\frac{3266 + 1534}{2} \pm \sqrt{[(3266 - 1534)/2]^2 + 500^2} = 2400 \pm 1000$$

or 3400 psi and 1400 psi, both tensile. Since these have the same sense, it follows that

$$\sigma_{\max} = 3400 \text{ psi}, \quad \sigma_{\text{minimax}} = 1400 \text{ psi}, \quad \text{and} \quad \sigma_{\min} = 0. \quad \textit{Ans.}$$

The principal planes are now located with the aid of Eq. 10.27, thus:

$$\tan 2\theta_{xP} = \frac{2(-500)}{3266 - 1534} = -0.577,$$

which gives $2\theta_{xP} = -30$ deg and 150 deg. Hence $\theta_{xP} = -15$ deg and 75 deg. Figure 10.9c shows the relative orientation of the principal planes.

Finally, from the discussion of biaxial stress, we conclude that

$$\tau_{\max} = \frac{\sigma_{\max}}{2} = \frac{3400}{2} = 1700 \text{ psi}. \quad \textit{Ans.}$$

This is accompanied by a normal stress $\sigma = \sigma_{\max}/2 = 1700$ psi, tensile. The plane of maximum shear stress is perpendicular to the intermediate principal plane and inclined 45 deg to the other two principal planes; Fig. 10.9d shows its relative orientation.

An alternative but less direct and hence longer solution for σ_x and σ_y may be pursued with the aid of Eqs. 10.24 and 10.25, which after proper substitutions will give two independent equations in the two unknowns. These must then be solved simultaneously. The beginner is cautioned most especially regarding the observance of proper signs in numerical problems when solved this second way. The cartesian components of stress are always governed by the sign convention explained in Article 2.10; components not parallel to the cartesian axes are governed by the rule: *tensile σ and counterclockwise τ bear the plus sign, whereas compressive σ and clockwise τ bear the minus sign.* The consistency of these signs may be shown by the observation that if $\theta_x = 0$ is substituted in Eq. 10.25, the result $\tau = +\tau_{xy}$ shows that the positive cartesian component τ_{xy} appears counterclockwise to a properly oriented observer; on the other hand, when $\theta_x = \pi/2$, the result $\tau = -\tau_{xy} = -\tau_{yx}$ indicates that the positive cartesian component τ_{yx} appears clockwise.

PROBLEMS

10.1. Show that this state of plane stress reduces to uniaxial stress. Specify its direction relative to the given reference frame.

10.2. Derive Eqs. 10.24 and 10.25 directly from Eqs. 10.2 and 10.3, setting $n = 0$.

10.3. Derive the values of the principal stresses as contained in Eq. 10.28 directly from Eq. 10.23, setting $\sigma_z = \tau_{zx} = \tau_{zy} = 0$.

10.4. Show by means of the calculus that, of the two angles θ_{xP} given by Eq. 10.27, one corresponds to a maximum and the other to a minimum σ.

10.5. Verify the values of σ_x and σ_y in Example 2 by solving Eqs. 10.24 and 10.25 for them, assuming as in the example that the Y direction coincides with N_2.

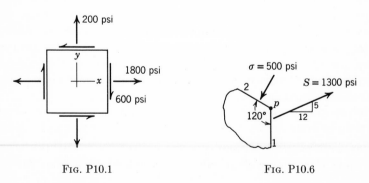

FIG. P10.1   FIG. P10.6

10.6. The state of stress at a point p in a plane-stressed body is known to the following extent: on plane 1 the total stress is 1300 psi, inclined 5 on 12 to the normal; on plane 2 only the normal stress of 500 psi, compression, is given. Both planes 1 and 2 are perpendicular to the stress-free planes. Determine the principal stresses and their planes. Determine the maximum shear stress and accompanying normal stress. Show all results on properly oriented sketches.

10.7. At a point in a plane-stressed body, only the normal stresses on the three planes shown are known. Determine the principal stresses and their planes. Determine the maximum shear stress and accompanying normal stress and the corresponding planes. Show results on properly oriented sketches.

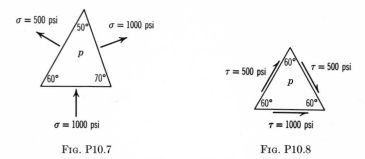

FIG. P10.7   FIG. P10.8

10.8. If only the shear stresses shown are given, is the state of stress (plane stress) at the point uniquely defined?

10.6   Pure Shear in Plane Stress. This state of stress is important enough to deserve a separate article. Pure shear in plane stress occurs when, say, $\tau_{xy} \neq 0$ and $\sigma_x = \sigma_y = \sigma_z = \tau_{yz} = \tau_{zx} = 0$. That this, being as much plane stress as the general case discussed, must reduce to biaxial stress we should now anticipate. Making the proper substitutions in Eqs. 10.28 and 10.31, we find that $\sigma_{\max} = +\tau_{xy}$, $\sigma_{\min} = -\tau_{xy}$, and $\tau_{\max} = \tau_{xy}$. Thus the nonzero principal stresses have equal magnitudes but opposite senses; furthermore, the maximum shear stress is not accompanied by normal stress. The existence of planes free of normal stress is typical of biaxial stress whenever the two nonzero principal stresses are opposite in sense (or of triaxial stress whenever one of the principal stresses has a sense opposite to that of the other two). It is also true, of course, that the planes of maximum shear bisect the right angles formed by the principal planes. The important facts of pure shear in plane stress are depicted in Fig. 10.10.

The occurrence of so-called diagonal tension as a concomitant of pure shear can be dramatically demonstrated in a simple experiment. A right circular cylinder subjected to torsion has all points at its periphery in a state of pure shear. If the cylinder is of a brittle material, one whose

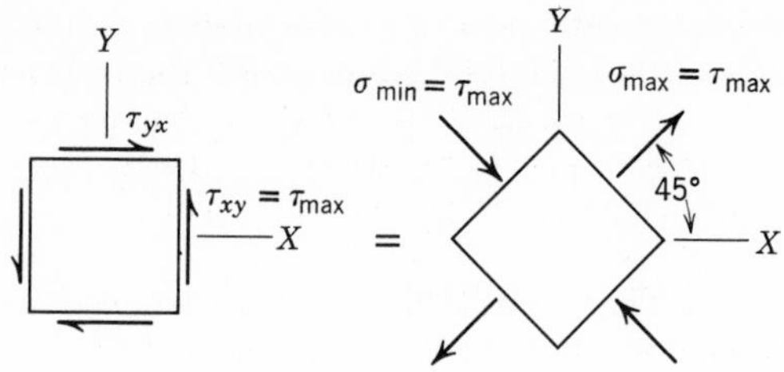

FIG. 10.10

tensile strength is very small compared to its compressive strength, the separation crack at the instant of failure should start at the periphery (where the shear stresses are greatest) in a direction perpendicular to the diagonal tension. If the material of the cylinder is homogeneous, there is, of course, no telling where the crack will start; we should expect that the crack probably will not start at any one point but rather will occur simultaneously at a multitude of points forming an envelope in the shape of a 45-deg helix. This is precisely what happens when a piece of ordinary chalk is twisted until it fractures; the fracture surface intersects the outer surface in what is obviously part of a 45-deg helix, Fig. 10.11.

PROBLEM

10.9. Derive the expression for the nonzero principal stresses for the state of pure shear in plane stress by solving Eq. 10.23.

10.7 Mohr's Circle for Stress. The variation of the stress components on a family of planes perpendicular to a fixed direction can be depicted graphically, resulting in a useful visual aid. We have already

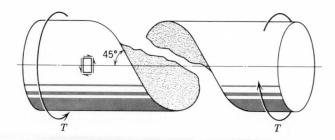

Fig. 10.11 Showing evidence of diagonal tension as a concomitant of pure shear.

utilized one picture of this variation, the harmonic curves of Fig. 10.3. The student will recall that, in his study of the sine and cosine functions, the understanding of their behavior came easily with the aid of that device, the unit circle. The circle is likewise a favorite crutch for explaining the simple harmonic motion of a particle. It is a simple matter to prove that the equations governing the variation of σ and τ with the aspect coordinate θ reduce to that of a circle in the coordinates σ and τ. Rather than do this (which we are relegating to one of the exercises), we shall adopt a direct heuristic approach, discussing the graphical representation of stress for each of the three cases in Article 10.3, and later showing its application to the general case of plane stress.

CASE 1. UNIAXIAL STRESS. Let us set up the rectangular axes σ and τ, on which σ values to the right of the origin are to be considered tensile, those to the left compressive, and τ values above the origin are clockwise, those below counterclockwise. On these axes we construct a circle whose center is at $\sigma = \sigma_x/2$, $\tau = 0$, and whose radius is $\sigma_x/2$, Fig. 10.12. Locate a point on the circle by the position coordinate or central angle $2\theta_x$, measured counterclockwise from point A, whose coordinates are $\sigma = \sigma_x$ and $\tau = 0$. Then the coordinates of this generic point are

$$\sigma = \frac{\sigma_x}{2} (1 + \cos 2\theta_x) \qquad (a)$$

and
$$\tau = -\frac{\sigma_x}{2} \sin 2\theta_x. \qquad (b)$$

But these are the very same Eqs. 10.4 and 10.5. Hence we may say that every point on this circle "corresponds" to some one plane in a family

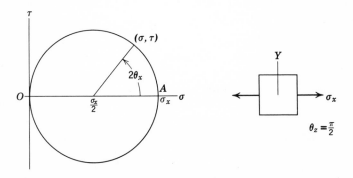

FIG. 10.12   Mohr's circle for uniaxial stress.

for which, in this instance, $\theta_z = \pi/2$; this correspondence consists of the fact that the two coordinates of the point on the circle are precisely the two stress components on the plane whose aspect is defined by θ_x.

Such a graph is known as *Mohr's circle for stress*, named in honor of Otto Mohr.* Many interesting conclusions can be gleaned from an inspection of the circle, among which are the following fairly obvious ones:

(1) When σ is stationary, τ is zero.

(2) When τ is stationary, σ is not zero, except in special cases.

(3) The planes of greatest shear stress are inclined 45 deg to the principal planes.

(4) The shear stresses on perpendicular planes are always equal in magnitude but opposite in sense.

This last one implies that the center of Mohr's circle is always on the σ axis; this will show much clearer in the next article. And since this is so, it follows that the radius of the circle always gives the maximum shear stress on the planes of the family for which the circle is valid.

Thus the circle may be used either to supplement the equations, and thereby help make their meaning clearer, or to supplant them altogether inasmuch as once the circle is constructed the equations may be derived from it, if desired, with no more complex mathematics involved than simple trigonometry.

We note that since counterclockwise τ bears the plus sign and clockwise τ the minus sign, the σ-τ frame appears left handed; it is not quite completely so, however, because the parameter 2θ is considered positive in the counterclockwise rather than in the clockwise sense that is standard for a left-handed system. This slight departure from consistency in the use of the right-handed system, mentioned earlier in Chapter 2, is necessary in order that the signs for strains, to be discussed in the next chapter, will be completely analogous to the signs for stresses in this chapter.

CASE 2. BIAXIAL STRESS.   It is assumed that $\sigma_x > \sigma_y > 0$ and $\sigma_z = \tau_{xy} = \tau_{yz} = \tau_{zx} = 0$. There are three significant circles, one for each of the families: $\theta_z = \pi/2$, $\theta_x = \pi/2$, and $\theta_y = \pi/2$.

The first one for the family of planes whose $\theta_z = \pi/2$ is shown in Fig. 10.13a; its center is at $\sigma = (\sigma_x + \sigma_y)/2$, $\tau = 0$, and its radius is $(\sigma_x - \sigma_y)/2$. The generic point is located by the central angle $2\theta_x$, counterclockwise from point A, which corresponds to the plane whose normal is the X axis. The coordinates of the generic point are

---

* See S. Timoshenko, *History of Strength of Materials*, pp. 285–286, McGraw-Hill Book Company, New York, 1953.

$$\sigma = \frac{\sigma_x + \sigma_y}{2} + \frac{\sigma_x - \sigma_y}{2} \cos 2\theta_x \qquad (c)$$

and
$$\tau = -\frac{\sigma_x - \sigma_y}{2} \sin 2\theta_x. \qquad (d)$$

These are identical to Eqs. 10.8 and 10.11, respectively. The circle shows that for this family of planes the maximum τ is of magnitude

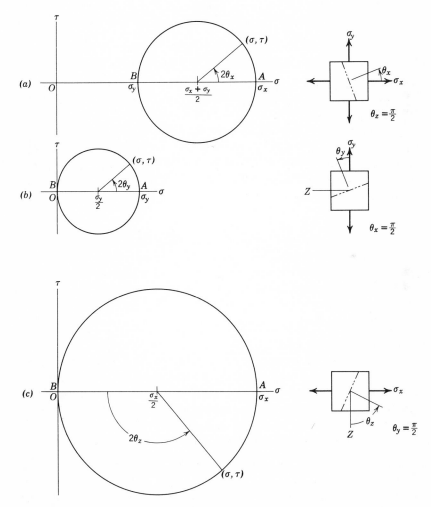

FIG. 10.13   Mohr's circles for biaxial stress.

$(\sigma_x - \sigma_y)/2$ and occurs on the planes $\theta_x = \pm\pi/4$; it is accompanied by the normal stress $(\sigma_x + \sigma_y)/2$.

Figure 10.13b shows the second Mohr's circle for the family of planes whose $\theta_x = \pi/2$; the little block representing the state of stress is shown as seen from $+X$. The center of the circle is at $\sigma = \sigma_y/2$, $\tau = 0$, and its radius is $\sigma_y/2$; the generic point is located by the central angle $2\theta_y$, counterclockwise from A, which corresponds to the plane whose normal is the Y axis. The coordinates of the generic point are

$$\sigma = \frac{\sigma_y}{2}(1 + \cos 2\theta_y) \qquad (e)$$

and
$$\tau = -\frac{\sigma_y}{2}\sin 2\theta_y, \qquad (f)$$

which are the same as Eqs. 10.9 and 10.12. The maximum shear stress, of magnitude $\sigma_y/2$, acts on the planes $\theta_y = \pm\pi/4$ and is accompanied by the normal stress $\sigma_y/2$.

The third circle, for the family of planes whose $\theta_y = \pi/2$, is shown in Fig. 10.13c; the small block is viewed from $+Y$. The center of the circle is at $\sigma_x/2$, $\tau = 0$, and its radius is $\sigma_x/2$. The generic point is located by the central angle $2\theta_z$, counterclockwise from point B, which corresponds to the plane whose normal is the Z axis; its coordinates are

$$\sigma = \frac{\sigma_x}{2}(1 - \cos 2\theta_z) \qquad (g)$$

and
$$\tau = \frac{\sigma_x}{2}\sin 2\theta_z, \qquad (h)$$

which are identical to Eqs. 10.10 and 10.13. The maximum shear stress, of magnitude $\sigma_x/2$, acts on the planes $\theta_z = \pm\pi/4$ and is accompanied by the normal stress $\sigma_x/2$.

The three Mohr's circles, constructed on a common set of axes, are shown in Fig. 10.14. Owing to the fact that the radius of any one circle gives the greatest shear stress on some one member of the particular family of planes for which that circle is valid, it is apparent that the largest circle gives the absolute maximum τ possible, in this case $\sigma_x/2$. This agrees with our previous observation in Article 10.3.

CASE 3. TRIAXIAL STRESS. The three circles are shown in Fig. 10.15; they are for the state $\sigma_x > \sigma_y > \sigma_z > 0$, $\tau_{xy} = \tau_{yz} = \tau_{zx} = 0$. The figure explains, among other things, the use of the designation σ_{minimax}, which usually suggests a saddle point. Observe that on the

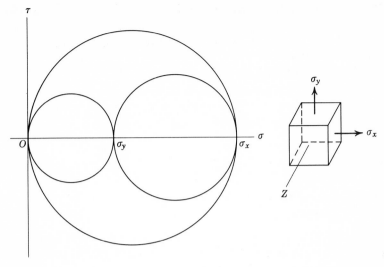

Fig. 10.14

circle marked $\theta_z = \pi/2$ σ_y is a minimum, whereas on the circle marked $\theta_x = \pi/2$ it is a maximum. It is therefore appropriate to call this intermediate principal stress σ_{minimax}.

Notice that the generic point on each circle is located by a central angle which is always measured counterclockwise from that point on the circle corresponding to the plane whose normal is indicated by the subscript of the aspect angle. Thus $2\theta_x$ is reckoned from that point whose

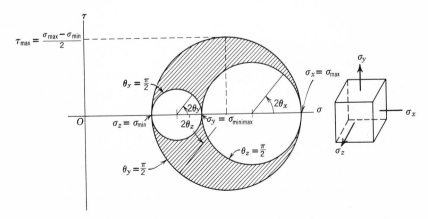

Fig. 10.15   Mohr's circles for triaxial stress.

coordinates are σ_x, 0; $2\theta_y$ from the point σ_y, 0; and $2\theta_z$ from the point σ_z, 0.

The following equations, giving the coordinates of the generic points, can be easily verified:

For the planes whose $\theta_z = \pi/2$,

$$\sigma = \frac{\sigma_x + \sigma_y}{2} + \frac{\sigma_x - \sigma_y}{2} \cos 2\theta_x \qquad (i)$$

and

$$\tau = -\frac{\sigma_x - \sigma_y}{2} \sin 2\theta_x, \qquad (j)$$

which are Eqs. 10.14 and 10.15.

For the planes whose $\theta_x = \pi/2$,

$$\sigma = \frac{\sigma_y + \sigma_z}{2} + \frac{\sigma_y - \sigma_z}{2} \cos 2\theta_y \qquad (k)$$

and

$$\tau = -\frac{\sigma_y - \sigma_z}{2} \sin 2\theta_y, \qquad (l)$$

which are Eqs. 10.16 and 10.17.

Finally, for the planes whose $\theta_y = \pi/2$,

$$\sigma = \frac{\sigma_z + \sigma_x}{2} + \frac{\sigma_z - \sigma_x}{2} \cos 2\theta_z \qquad (m)$$

and

$$\tau = -\frac{\sigma_z - \sigma_x}{2} \sin 2\theta_z, \qquad (n)$$

which are Eqs. 10.18 and 10.19. The observant reader will notice that the preceding three pairs of equations are related to each other through the cyclic permutation of the subscripts: x to y to z.

One of the most important facts brought out by Mohr is that, if the σ and τ coordinates, corresponding to any plane whatever that is inclined to all three principal planes, were plotted on the σ-τ plane, the point so located would always fall within the shaded area of Fig. 10.15: never inside the smaller circles and never outside the largest.* It is for this reason that we need consider only the three families of planes, each family being perpendicular to a principal plane.

---

* For instance, see J. P. Den Hartog, *Advanced Strength of Materials*, pp. 311–314, McGraw-Hill Book Company, New York, 1952.

Illustrative Example 3. At a point in triaxial stress the following are known: $\sigma_{min} > 0$, $\sigma_{minimax} = 2\sigma_{min}$, $\sigma_{max} = 3\sigma_{min}$. Construct the three Mohr's circles and show that the point corresponding to the plane $\theta_x = \theta_y = \theta_z$ plots within the area bounded by the three circles.

SOLUTION. Figure 10.16 shows the three circles. The direction cosines of the plane which intersects all three principal planes at the same angle are: $l = m = n = 1/\sqrt{3}$. Therefore by Eqs. *e* and *f* of Article 10.3, we have

$$\sigma = \tfrac{1}{3}(3\sigma_{min}) + \tfrac{1}{3}(2\sigma_{min}) + \tfrac{1}{3}(\sigma_{min}) = 2\sigma_{min}$$

and $\quad \tau = \{ \tfrac{1}{3}(9\sigma_{min}{}^2)\tfrac{2}{3} + \tfrac{1}{3}(4\sigma_{min}{}^2)\tfrac{2}{3} + \tfrac{1}{3}(\sigma_{min}{}^2)\tfrac{2}{3}$

$$- 2[\tfrac{1}{9}(3\sigma_{min})2\sigma_{min} + \tfrac{1}{9}(3\sigma_{min})\sigma_{min} + \tfrac{1}{9}(2\sigma_{min})\sigma_{min}]\}^{1/2}$$

$$= \frac{\sqrt{6}}{3}(\sigma_{min}) = 0.816\sigma_{min}.$$

The point, $\sigma = 2\sigma_{min}$, $\tau = 0.816\sigma_{min}$, does indeed plot inside the large circle and outside the small circles, as shown in Fig. 10.16. Where to plot the point, above or below the σ axis, is a moot question; we have taken the positive value of $\sqrt{6}$ merely as a matter of convenience. There are actually eight planes, or four pairs of parallel planes, which are similarly inclined to the principal planes. Although intuitively we can safely say that half of these should be represented by the point above the σ axis and the other half by the point below, to explain why this is so

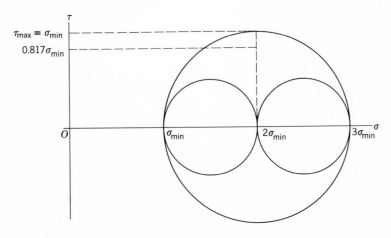

Fig. 10.16

would involve us in pointlessly describing the necessary orientation of the observer in order that, to him, the shear stress τ would appear clockwise or counterclockwise. The sense of the shear stress is, after all, unimportant. Note that, by contrast, the sense of the normal stress σ is always uniquely defined.

10.8   Mohr's Circle for the General Case of Plane Stress.   The question should now naturally arise: Can Mohr's circle be used to evaluate the principal stresses when these are not given? The answer, of course, is that it can be so used; the ease or difficulty or constructing the circle, however, will depend on the given data. In general, this is true: If cartesian components of stress are given from which it is then required to determine, by means of Mohr's circle, the maximum stresses and their orientation, then this can be done without any difficulty. On the other hand, if the components given are not parallel to the cartesian axes, and, especially, if such components are not on perpendicular planes, then constructing the required Mohr's circle directly could be a test of one's geometrical prowess. We shall not dwell on those cases which make for interesting problems in geometrical construction; we hasten to add, however, that such cases can still be easily handled via Mohr's circle if the intermediate step is taken of first calculating the cartesian components as explained in Illustrative Example 2.

Let us now assume that the following are given: $\sigma_x > \sigma_y > 0$, $\tau_{xy} > 0$, $\sigma_z = \tau_{yz} = \tau_{zx} = 0$. We construct Mohr's circle as follows. On the σ-τ plane, plot point A whose coordinates are $\sigma = \sigma_x$ and $\tau = \tau_{xy}$, Fig. 10.17a; plot point B whose coordinates are $\sigma = \sigma_y$ and $\tau = \tau_{yx}$. Observe that, since τ_{xy} is always equal in magnitude but opposite in sense to τ_{yx}, points A and B will always lie on opposite sides of the σ axis at the same distance from it, the point above corresponding to the clockwise τ and that below to the counterclockwise τ. On the line joining A to B as a diameter, construct Mohr's circle; we note that the center necessarily lies on the σ axis. It must be thoroughly understood that this circle is only for that family of planes whose $\theta_z = \pi/2$.

The quantities of immediate interest can now be derived from the construction.

(1) The center C of the circle is at $\sigma = (\sigma_x + \sigma_y)/2$, $\tau = 0$; hence the distance along the σ axis between B and C, as well as between C and A, is $(\sigma_x - \sigma_y)/2$.

(2) The radius of the circle is given by the hypotenuse of the right triangle whose two arms are $(\sigma_x - \sigma_y)/2$ and τ_{xy}; its length is

$$R = \sqrt{[(\sigma_x - \sigma_y)/2]^2 + \tau_{xy}^2}.$$

(3) Therefore the two principal stresses are:

$$\left.\begin{array}{c}\sigma_{max}\\[4pt]\sigma_{min}\end{array}\right\} = \frac{\sigma_x + \sigma_y}{2} \pm \sqrt{[(\sigma_x - \sigma_y)/2]^2 + \tau_{xy}{}^2}. \tag{a}$$

Compare this with Eq. 10.28. If the radius of the circle is larger than $(\sigma_x + \sigma_y)/2$, then the minus sign in Eq. a gives the true minimum σ; if the radius is smaller, as shown in Fig. 10.17a, then the minus sign in Eq. a gives the intermediate principal stress, $\sigma_{minimax}$, with σ_{min} being zero.

(4) Twice the aspect angle θ_{xP} is found as $\underline{/ACE}$, whose tangent is, from the construction,

$$\tan 2\theta_{xP} = \frac{\tau_{xy}}{(\sigma_x - \sigma_y)/2} = \frac{2\tau_{xy}}{\sigma_x - \sigma_y}. \tag{b}$$

Compare this with Eq. 10.27. Since this bears a plus sign, the smallest value less than $\pi/2$ of $2\theta_{xP}$ locates E counterclockwise from A; this corresponds to the major principal plane. The other value of $2\theta_{xP}$ lo-

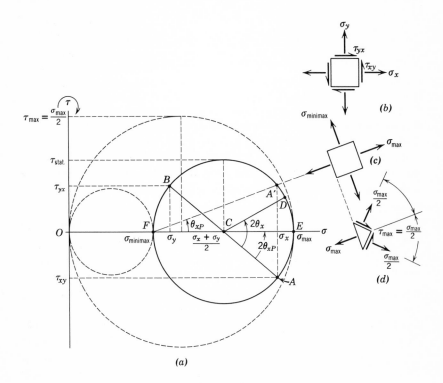

(a)

FIG. 10.17

cates point F, which corresponds to the intermediate principal plane. If A is reflected to A', and if A' is joined to F, the angle $\underline{/EFA'}$ is exactly one-half of the angle $\underline{/ECA'} = \underline{/ECA}$. Therefore $\underline{/EFA'} = \theta_{xP}$, and the line FA' is inclined to the σ axis in exactly the same relative way as that in which the direction of the major principal stress σ_{max} is inclined to σ_x. Figure 10.17c shows the major and intermediate principal planes relative to the given cartesian planes of sketch b.

(5) Since the circle for the planes whose $\theta_z = \pi/2$ lies completely to the right of the origin (which is another way of saying: since the two nonzero principal stresses are both tensile), the maximum shear stress is given by the radius of the large circle shown by dashed lines in Fig. 10.17a; that is, $\tau_{max} = \sigma_{max}/2$. The planes that bear this shear stress are shown in sketch d, which is an auxiliary view projected from sketch c perpendicularly to the intermediate principal plane.

To complete the graphical representation, we have shown the small dashed circle in Fig. 10.17a. It is valid for that family of planes perpendicular to the major principal plane.

As a matter of secondary interest, we remark that the coordinates of the generic point D, located an angle $2\theta_x$ from point A, are precisely those given by Eqs. 10.24 and 10.25. This explains our statement made earlier that Mohr's circle may be used to supplant the significant equations governing the variation of the two stress components. We leave the details as an exercise for the student.

Illustrative Example 4. At a certain point in a plane-stressed body, the following stress components are known: $\sigma_x = -1000$ psi, $\tau_{xy} = 500$ psi, and $\sigma_y = 500$ psi (see Fig. 10.18a). Determine the principal stresses, the maximum shear stress and accompanying normal stress, and locate any planes that are free of normal but not shear stress. Show the results on appropriately oriented sketches.

SOLUTION. Since the stress components given are on perpendicular planes, the direct Mohr-circle approach is indicated. In sketch b of Fig. 10.18, point A is plotted with coordinates $\sigma = 1000$ psi, compression, and $\tau = 500$ psi, counterclockwise. Because point A corresponds to the plane normal to the X axis, it is helpful to indicate beside it the information, $(X, 2\theta_x = 0)$, as a reminder of this association; it serves notice that the position coordinate 2θ of any point on the circle is to be reckoned from A. This is a key point in the construction. Point B is plotted next, with coordinates $\sigma = 500$ psi, tension, and $\tau = 500$ psi, clockwise. The self-explanatory information, $(Y, 2\theta_x = \pi)$, may be noted beside B, if desired. On AB as diameter the circle is then constructed.

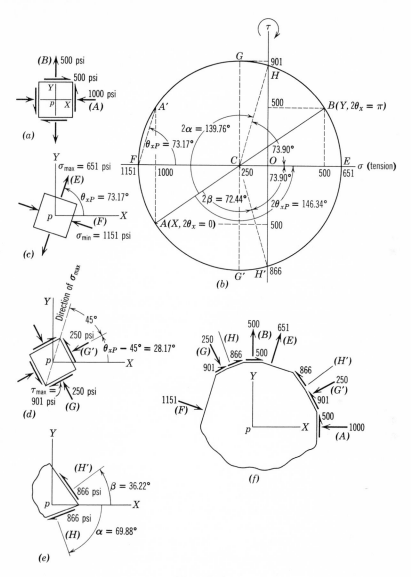

Fig. 10.18

The center C falls at $\sigma = -250$, $\tau = 0$. The radius is of length

$$\sqrt{750^2 + 500^2} = 901.$$

Therefore

$$\sigma_{\max} = 901 - 250 = 651 \text{ psi, tension,} \qquad Ans.$$

and $\qquad \sigma_{\min} = 901 + 250 = 1151$ psi, compression. $Ans.$

The angle $2\theta_{xP}$ to point E is found from $\tan 2\theta_{xP} = -500/750$, which gives $2\theta_{xP} = 146.4$ deg, counterclockwise; hence $\theta_{xP} = 73.2$ deg, also counterclockwise. This locates the major principal plane. It should be clear that the minor principal plane is defined by either $73.2 + 90 = 163.2$ deg, counterclockwise, or $90 - 73.2 = 16.8$ deg, clockwise from $+X$. The angle θ_{xP} may be calculated through the alternative procedure whereby A is first reflected to A' and then the tangent of θ_{xP} evaluated as $500/151$; this gives $\theta_{xP} = 73.2$ deg, as before (see sketch b). Sketch c shows the major and minor principal planes with their stresses; it is understood that the intermediate principal plane is the given stress-free plane.

Referring back to Case 2, biaxial stress, we note that the two nonzero principal stresses have opposite senses; therefore the radius of the circle in sketch b gives the true maximum τ:

$$\tau_{\max} = 901 \text{ psi.} \qquad Ans.$$

The accompanying normal stress is 250 psi, compression. $Ans.$

The perpendicular planes which bear these stresses are displayed in sketch d.

The planes that are free of normal but not shear stress correspond to points H and H' on the circle. The angle $\underline{/ECH} = \underline{/ECH'}$ is found from the arc cosine of $250/901$ to be 73.9 deg. Hence H is located an angle $2\alpha_x = 360 - (146.4 + 73.9) = 139.7$ deg, clockwise from A, and H' an angle $2\beta_x = 146.4 - 73.9 = 72.5$ deg, counterclockwise from A. Sketch e shows the two normal stress-free planes identified by the appropriate letter in parentheses and whose aspects are $\alpha_x = 69.9$ deg, clockwise, and $\beta_x = 36.2$ deg, counterclockwise from $+X$; the shear stresses on them are of magnitude $\sqrt{901^2 - 250^2} = 866$ psi. $Ans.$

Figure 10.18f presents a summary of the preceding results in pictorial form, where the letters in parentheses serve to associate the various planes with their corresponding points on Mohr's circle.

In closing, we observe that the two circles for the other principal families of planes are both smaller than that of Fig. 10.18b, both being contained in this largest of the three circles.

PROBLEMS

10.10. With the aid of Mohr's circle (*a*) show that, if only the shear stresses are known on three distinct planes through a point in plane stress, all perpendicular to the stress-free direction, the state of stress is not uniquely defined; (*b*) show further that not just any shear stress values on three arbitrarily defined plane will constitute a possible set.

10.11. Show that elimination of θ_x from Eqs. 10.24 and 10.25 results in the equation of a circle.

10.12. From Fig. 10.17*a*, evaluate the coordinates of a generic point D located an angle $2\theta_x$ counterclockwise from point A. Show that they reduce to the values given by Eqs. 10.24 and 10.25.

10.13. Sketch Mohr's circle for uniaxial compressive stress.

For each of the following plane-stress problems, determine with the aid of Mohr's circle the principal stresses and their planes as well as the maximum shear stresses and their accompanying normal stresses. Also locate any planes that are free of normal but not shear stress and evaluate the shear stress on each such plane. Show all results on properly oriented sketches. All given stress values are in psi.

10.14. $\sigma_x = +1000$, $\tau_{xy} = -500$, $\sigma_y = 0$.
10.15. $\sigma_x = -500$, $\tau_{xy} = +500$, $\sigma_y = +1000$.
10.16. $\sigma_x = 0$, $\tau_{xy} = +1000$, $\sigma_y = -1000$.
10.17. $\sigma_x = -1000$, $\tau_{xy} = -500$, $\sigma_y = -2000$.
10.18. $\sigma_x = +10{,}000$, $\tau_{xy} = +5000$, $\sigma_y = +10{,}000$.
10.19. $\sigma_x = +10{,}000$, $\tau_{xy} = 0$, $\sigma_y = +10{,}000$.
10.20. See sketch.

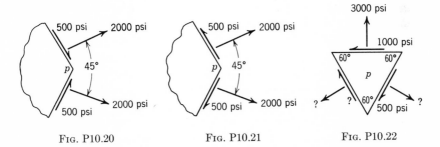

FIG. P10.20   FIG. P10.21   FIG. P10.22

10.21. See sketch.
10.22. See sketch.
10.23. Sketch Mohr's circles for this state of stress: $\sigma_x = +5000$ psi, $\sigma_y = +2000$ psi, $\sigma_z = -3000$ psi, $\tau_{xy} = \tau_{yz} = \tau_{zx} = 0$. Determine the maximum shear stress and accompanying normal stress. Show results on a suitable oriented pictorial sketch.

10.24. For the state of stress in Prob. 10.23, calculate the normal and shear stress components on a plane whose normal has the direction cosines $1/\sqrt{3}$, $1/\sqrt{5}$, $\sqrt{\frac{7}{15}}$. Plot the point defined by these stress components on the sketch of the three circles.

The state of stress at a point may come about as the result of two or more systems of stresses being superposed. The superposition can be accomplished very simply by vector addition, provided the several systems are transformed first to equivalent sets of components acting on a common family of planes. Keeping this in mind, determine for each of the following situations the principal stresses. Show the results on properly oriented sketches. All numerical values shown are in psi. (*Note:* Mohr's circle can be a great help in effecting the transformations.)

10.25. See sketches.

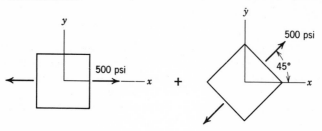

FIG. P10.25

10.26. See sketches.

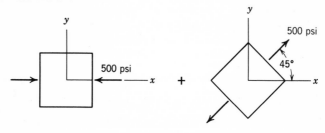

FIG. P10.26

10.27. See sketches

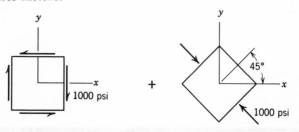

FIG. P10.27

10.28. See Sketches.

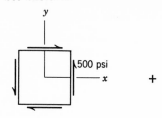

10.29. See sketches.

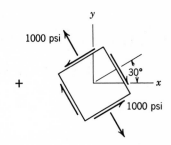

Fig. P10.29

10.30. See sketches.

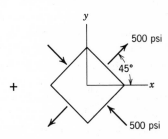

Fig. P10.30

11

VARIATION OF STRAIN
AT A POINT

11.1 Introduction. Strain is a more difficult concept to grasp and to depict than stress. This is strange indeed in view of the fact that deformation, a strictly geometrical quantity, is certainly observable, whereas force is not. No doubt, this is due in no small measure to the prominence in our thinking which the notion of force occupies, in contrast to the insignificant position which geometry does. In the following discussion, we shall pursue a procedure somewhat similar to that in the preceding chapter: From simple cases we shall synthesize, in terms of the cartesian components defined in Chapter 2, the general expressions governing the variation of strain at a point. In the process we shall lean more on geometry than on direct mathematical manipulation of the equations defining the six cartesian components of strain, Eqs. 2.5.

It is tacitly assumed throughout this chapter that the strains are so small as to allow ignoring their powers higher than one. Primarily because of this, the following hold in the immediate vicinity of the point in question: (1) *straight lines remain straight* and (2) *parallel lines remain parallel;* consequently, (3) *planes carry over into planes.**

11.2 Plane Strain. This is that state of deformation in which it is possible to so orient the cartesian axes that the strain components bearing

* See A. J. Durelli, E. A. Phillips, C. H. Tsao, *Introduction to the Theoretical and Experimental Analysis of Stress and Strain*, pp. 38–43, McGraw-Hill Book Company, New York, 1958.

one of the subscripts are either nil or negligibly small. Let $\epsilon_z = \gamma_{zx} = \gamma_{zy} = 0$. We shall now derive the expressions governing the variation of ϵ and γ, analogous to those governing σ and τ, by considering separately the following special cases.

CASE A. UNIAXIAL STRAIN IN THE X DIRECTION. It is assumed that only ϵ_x is different from zero. We seek the influence of ϵ_x on (1) the linear strain ϵ and (2) the shear strain γ in a plane containing the X axis, both these components being in a direction defined by the angle θ_x. Figure 11.1 represents this state of strain, the solid lines showing the undeformed shape of a small rectangle of differential dimensions Δx by Δy, whose diagonal pb is inclined an angle θ_x to the X axis, and the dashed lines its deformed shape. Keeping in mind the assumption of small quantities, we have from the sketch $\epsilon \, \Delta L = (\epsilon_x \, \Delta x) \cos \theta_x$.

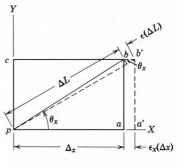

FIG. 11.1

Solving for ϵ, noting that $\Delta x / \Delta L = \cos \theta_x$, we obtain

$$\epsilon = \frac{\Delta x}{\Delta L} \epsilon_x \cos \theta_x = \epsilon_x \cos^2 \theta_x, \tag{a}$$

which, after introduction of the double angle, becomes

$$\epsilon = \frac{\epsilon_x}{2} (1 + \cos 2\theta_x). \tag{11.1}$$

Compare this with Eq. 10.4
To evaluate the shear strain in the directions θ_x, $\theta_x + \pi/2$, we need the final value of the original right angle between line pb in Fig. 11.1 and a line perpendicular to it in the plane of the figure. Accordingly, we first find the final inclinations of these two lines. The direction cosines of pb', the deformed position of pb, are l_1' and m_1'. From the figure,

$$l_1' = \frac{\Delta x (1 + \epsilon_x)}{\Delta L (1 + \epsilon)} = \cos \theta_x (1 + \epsilon_x)(1 - \epsilon),$$

where $(1 - \epsilon)$ is the series expansion of $(1 + \epsilon)^{-1}$, with powers of ϵ higher than one being ignored. Remembering that the ϵ's are very small quantities, we reduce the preceding to the form

$$l_1' = \cos\theta_x(1 + \epsilon_x - \epsilon) = (1 + \epsilon_x \sin^2\theta_x)\cos\theta_x, \qquad (b)$$

by virtue of Eq. a. Also,

$$m_1' = \frac{\Delta y}{\Delta L(1 + \epsilon)} = \sin\theta_x(1 - \epsilon)$$

$$= (1 - \epsilon_x \cos^2\theta_x)\sin\theta_x. \qquad (c)$$

In its deformed position, the line originally perpendicular to pb has the direction cosines l_2' and m_2'. Their values are obtained from Eqs. b and c when for θ_x the value $\theta_x + \pi/2$ is substituted, thus:

$$l_2' = \left[1 + \epsilon_x \sin^2\left(\theta_x + \frac{\pi}{2}\right)\right]\cos\left(\theta_x + \frac{\pi}{2}\right)$$

$$= -(1 + \epsilon_x \cos^2\theta_x)\sin\theta_x, \qquad (d)$$

and $$m_2' = \left[1 - \epsilon_x \cos^2\left(\theta_x + \frac{\pi}{2}\right)\right]\sin\left(\theta_x + \frac{\pi}{2}\right)$$

$$= (1 - \epsilon_x \sin^2\theta_x)\cos\theta_x. \qquad (e)$$

Assuming the shear strain γ to be positive, we write the final value of the original right angle as $\pi/2 - \gamma$ (see Article 2.3). Now the angle between two lines on a plane is a function of the direction cosines of the lines as stated in the relation

$$\cos\alpha = l_1 l_2 + m_1 m_2.$$

Substituting $\pi/2 - \gamma$ for α and the preceding values of the four direction cosines in this relation, we get

$$\cos\left(\frac{\pi}{2} - \gamma\right) = [(1 + \epsilon_x \sin^2\theta_x)\cos\theta_x][-(1 + \epsilon_x \cos^2\theta_x)\sin\theta_x]$$

$$+ [(1 - \epsilon_x \cos^2\theta_x)\sin\theta_x][(1 - \epsilon_x \sin^2\theta_x)\cos\theta_x],$$

from which, after simplification, retaining only the first powers of ϵ_x and using the approximation, $\sin\gamma = \gamma$ for small angles, we obtain

$$\gamma = -2\epsilon_x \cos\theta_x \sin\theta_x = -\epsilon_x \sin 2\theta_x. \qquad (f)$$

When both sides of Eq. f are divided by 2, there follows:

$$\frac{\gamma}{2} = -\frac{\epsilon_x}{2}\sin 2\theta_x. \qquad (11.2)$$

Note the similarity between this and Eq. 10.5.

Concerning the maximum values of ϵ and γ the same observations may now be made as those relating to the maximum values of σ and τ in uniaxial stress; for instance, that when ϵ is stationary, γ is zero; or that the direction of maximum γ is inclined 45 degrees to that of maximum ϵ. We observe particularly that linear strain in one direction has no effect on linear and shear strains in all perpendicular directions; this is essential for future applications.

CASE B. UNIAXIAL STRAIN IN THE Y DIRECTION. Linear strain in the Y direction only is represented in Fig. 11.2. Proceeding in exactly the same manner as previously, we establish the following:

$$\epsilon = \epsilon_y \sin^2 \theta_x = \frac{\epsilon_y}{2}(1 - \cos 2\theta_x), \qquad (11.3)$$

and
$$\frac{\gamma}{2} = \frac{\epsilon_y}{2} \cos \theta_x \sin \theta_x = \frac{\epsilon_y}{2} \sin 2\theta_x. \qquad (11.4)$$

Superposing the results of these two cases, which is permissible because (1) the strains are small and (2) the generic and the given cartesian components are related linearly, we obtain the equations for biaxial strain, *valid whenever $\theta_z = \pi/2$*:

$$\epsilon = \frac{\epsilon_x + \epsilon_y}{2} + \frac{\epsilon_x - \epsilon_y}{2} \cos 2\theta_x, \qquad (11.5)$$

and
$$\frac{\gamma}{2} = -\frac{\epsilon_x - \epsilon_y}{2} \sin 2\theta_x. \qquad (11.6)$$

These are analogous to Eqs. 10.8 and 10.11 for biaxial stress. Therefore conclusions may be drawn from the preceding equations which are analogous to those which were drawn from the stress equations; for example,

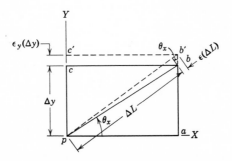

FIG. 11.2

when $\epsilon_x > \epsilon_y > 0$, $\gamma_{\max} = \epsilon_x$; on the other hand, when $\epsilon_x > 0$ and $\epsilon_y <$ 0, $\gamma_{\max} = \epsilon_x - \epsilon_y$; and so on.

CASE C. PURE SHEAR STRAIN. Figure 11.3a depicts a state of pure shear strain in the x-y plane, in which γ_{xy} is shown positive—a decrease in the original right angle in the first quadrant. Although, in analogy to shear stress, we say that $\gamma_{xy} = \gamma_{yx}$, both quantities representing a decrease in the right angle, with the aid of the sketch we may now distinguish between the senses of the two by the following additional description:

The positive shear strain γ_{xy} has a counterclockwise sense because, as the right angle decreases, the X axis moves counterclockwise relative to the Y axis; the positive γ_{yx} has a clockwise sense because, as the right angle decreases, the Y axis moves clockwise relative to the X axis.

This means that, whenever the generic shear strain γ comes out plus, it is counterclockwise, when minus it is clockwise.

The influence of γ_{xy} on the generic ϵ and γ can be established in exactly the same way as in cases A and B, with the following results:

$$\epsilon = \gamma_{xy} \sin \theta_x \cos \theta_x = \frac{\gamma_{xy}}{2} \sin 2\theta_x \qquad (11.7)$$

and $\qquad \dfrac{\gamma}{2} = \dfrac{\gamma_{xy}}{2} (\cos^2 \theta_x - \sin^2 \theta_x) = \dfrac{\gamma_{xy}}{2} \cos 2\theta_x. \qquad (11.8)$

(Notice from Eq. 11.8 that when $\theta_x = 0$, $\gamma = +\gamma_{xy}$, counterclockwise, and when $\theta_x = \pi/2$, $\gamma = -\gamma_{xy} = -\gamma_{yx}$, clockwise.) These equations

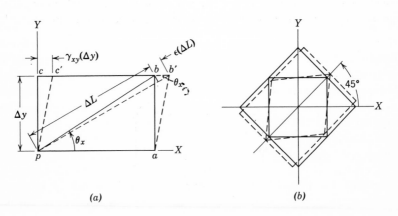

(a)   (b)

FIG. 11.3

show that pure shear strain on a plane is equivalent to biaxial strain, $\epsilon_{max} = +\gamma_{xy}/2$, $\epsilon_{min} = -\gamma_{xy}/2$, along directions inclined 45 deg to the axes of pure shear; this is depicted in Fig. 11.3b. Compare this with pure shear in plane stress.

Superposition of the preceding three cases results in the general equations for ϵ and γ in plane strain, *valid for all directions whose* $\theta_z = \pi/2$:

$$\epsilon = \frac{\epsilon_x + \epsilon_y}{2} + \frac{\epsilon_x - \epsilon_y}{2} \cos 2\theta_x + \frac{\gamma_{xy}}{2} \sin 2\theta_x \qquad (11.9)$$

and $$\frac{\gamma}{2} = -\frac{\epsilon_x - \epsilon_y}{2} \sin 2\theta_x + \frac{\gamma_{xy}}{2} \cos 2\theta_x. \qquad (11.10)$$

Once again we note the complete similarity in the structure of the preceding equations with that of Eqs. 10.24 and 10.25 for plane stress. Apparently, we may move from the equations for plane stress to those for plane strain, and vice versa, if we observe the following "dictionary" of correspondence:

$$\epsilon_x \leftrightarrow \sigma_x$$

$$\epsilon_y \leftrightarrow \sigma_y$$

$$\frac{\gamma_{xy}}{2} \leftrightarrow \tau_{xy}$$

$$\epsilon \leftrightarrow \sigma$$

$$\frac{\gamma}{2} \leftrightarrow \tau$$

$$\theta \leftrightarrow \theta.$$

This interesting and remarkable one-to-one correspondence between the components of strain and those of stress suggests the basic characteristic of tensors: that when referred to other axes, obtained from an original set by some process (in this elementary treatment, this has been one of rotation), tensor quantities transform in a certain special manner, which is determined by the relation between the new and the original axes. The equations derived in Chapter 10, up to Eq. 11.10 in this chapter, are merely special cases of the general transformation relations that govern *both* the stress tensor and the strain tensor. We may now explain why, in writing the strain tensor in its symbolic matrix D (Eq. 2.6), we introduced the factor $1/2$ seemingly out of nowhere. Without this factor, strain is not a tensor quantity, that is, it will not satisfy certain criteria that identify a tensor.

With the use of the preceding dictionary, we may now establish the stationary values of ϵ and γ for plane strain, thus:

$$\left.\begin{array}{c}\epsilon_{\max}\\ \epsilon_{\min}\end{array}\right\} = \frac{\epsilon_x + \epsilon_y}{2} \pm \sqrt{[(\epsilon_x - \epsilon_y)/2]^2 + (\gamma_{xy}/2)^2}. \qquad (11.11)$$

This is based on Eq. 10.28. If the radical is larger than $(\epsilon_x + \epsilon_y)/2$, then the minus sign gives the true minimum; otherwise it gives the intermediate principal strain. The principal directions are found from the relation

$$\tan 2\theta_{xP} = \frac{\gamma_{xy}}{\epsilon_x - \epsilon_y}, \qquad (11.12)$$

which is based on Eq. 10.27. The stationary values of γ are

$$\gamma_{\text{stat}} = 2\sqrt{[(\epsilon_x - \epsilon_y)/2]^2 + (\gamma_{xy}/2)^2} \qquad (11.13)$$

on planes whose aspects are given by

$$\tan 2\theta'_{xP} = -\frac{\epsilon_x - \epsilon_y}{\gamma_{xy}}. \qquad (11.14)$$

These follow from Eqs. 10.31 and 10.30. If the γ_{stat} of Eq. 11.13 is larger than $(\epsilon_x + \epsilon_y)$, then it is also $\gamma_{\max}$; otherwise the maximum shear strain is simply $\gamma_{\max} = \epsilon_{\max}$.

PROBLEMS

11.1. Supply the missing algebra in the derivation of Eqs. 11.3 and 11.4.

11.2. Supply the missing algebra in the derivation of Eqs. 11.7 and 11.8.

11.3   Principal Strains in the Three-Dimensional Case.   Preparatory to extending the analogy to three dimensions, we now complete the dictionary. The missing terms are, obviously,

$$\epsilon_z \leftrightarrow \sigma_z$$

$$\frac{\gamma_{yz}}{2} \leftrightarrow \tau_{yz}$$

$$\frac{\gamma_{zx}}{2} \leftrightarrow \tau_{zx}.$$

With Eq. 10.23 as a pattern, we write the equation embodying the three principal strains, as follows:

$$\epsilon^3 - (\epsilon_x + \epsilon_y + \epsilon_z)\epsilon^2 + \left(\epsilon_x \epsilon_y + \epsilon_y \epsilon_z + \epsilon_z \epsilon_x - \frac{\gamma_{xy}^2}{4} - \frac{\gamma_{yz}^2}{4} - \frac{\gamma_{zx}^2}{4} \right)\epsilon$$

$$- \left(\epsilon_x \epsilon_y \epsilon_z + \frac{\gamma_{xy}\gamma_{yz}\gamma_{zx}}{4} - \frac{\epsilon_x \gamma_{yz}^2}{4} - \frac{\epsilon_y \gamma_{zx}^2}{4} - \frac{\epsilon_z \gamma_{xy}^2}{4} \right) = 0. \quad (11.15)$$

The three roots of this cubic, when distinct, are ϵ_{max}, $\epsilon_{minimax}$, and ϵ_{min}; their directions, which are mutually perpendicular, are referred to as the major principal, the intermediate principal, and the minor principal axes of strain. The direction cosines are found from equations analogous to Eqs. 10.21.

There are three stationary values of the shear strain, each pair being in directions that bisect the angles formed by the principal axes. Of these the largest is $\gamma_{max} = \epsilon_{max} - \epsilon_{min}$; it is accompanied by the linear strain $(\epsilon_{max} + \epsilon_{min})/2$.

11.4 Mohr's Circle for Strain. Based on the identity in the variations of stress and strain deduced in the foregoing, Mohr's circle for strain may now be constructed and interpreted for any conveniently defined data, assumed or known. This is demonstrated in the following.

Illustrative Example 1. At a point in a body under plane strain, the following strain components are known: $\epsilon_x = 750 \times 10^{-6}$, $\epsilon_y = 250 \times 10^{-6}$, and $\gamma_{xy} = -500 \times 10^{-6}$. Determine the principal strains and their directions, as well as the maximum shear strain with its accompanying linear strain.

SOLUTION. First we represent the state of strain by means of a unit square element, Fig. 11.4a. The positive linear strains are shown as extensions. The negative shear strain, $-\gamma_{xy} = -\gamma_{yx}$, appears as an increase in the original right angle of the first quadrant. Observe that, as this right angle increases, the X axis moves clockwise relative to the Y axis, or, equivalently, the Y axis moves counterclockwise relative to the X axis. An alternate way of presenting the given state of strain is depicted in Fig. 11.4b, where vectors are used in lieu of the geometrical quantities: extensions being represented by outward vectors and shear strains by couples, a clockwise couple for γ_{xy} and a counterclockwise couple for γ_{yx}. We emphasize that these do NOT stand for stresses.

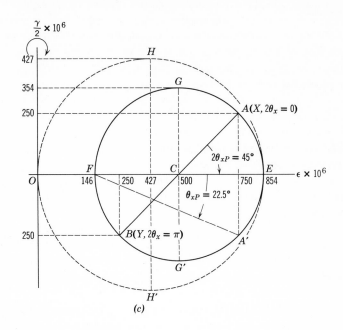

(c)

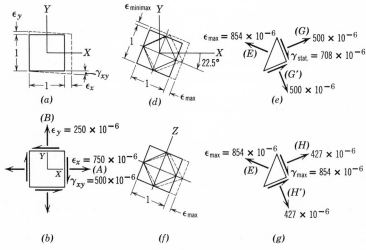

(a)   (d)   (e)

(b)   (f)   (g)

FIG. 11.4

Mohr's circle for strain is laid out in exactly the same manner as that for stress. On the ϵ axis extensions are plotted to the right of the origin, contractions to the left of the origin; on the $\gamma/2$ axis clockwise half-shear strains are plotted above the origin, counterclockwise below the origin. In Fig. 11.4c point A is laid off with the coordinates: $\epsilon = 750$ units ($= 10^6\epsilon_x$) to the right, $\gamma/2 = 250$ units ($= 10^6\gamma_{xy}/2$) upward; it is identified further by $(X, 2\theta_x = 0)$. As in Mohr's circle for stress, A is a key point in the construction. Point B is plotted next with the coordinates: $\epsilon = 250$ to the right, $\gamma/2 = 250$ downward. On AB as diameter the circle is then scribed. In Fig. 11.4c all strains indicated are 10^6 times as large as their actual values. This circle is valid for all directions whose $\theta_z = \pi/2$.

From the construction, the significant quantities may now be directly evaluated. Thus the linear strain $(\epsilon_x + \epsilon_y)/2 = 500$ locates the center C of the circle. The radius, which gives the stationary value of $\gamma/2$, is

$$\sqrt{[(\epsilon_x - \epsilon_y)/2]^2 + (\gamma_{xy}/2)^2} = \sqrt{[(750 - 250)/2]^2 + 250^2} = 354.$$

Hence the principal strains, corresponding to points E and F, are

$$(500 + 354)10^{-6} = 854 \times 10^{-6}, \qquad \text{extension} = \epsilon_{\max}$$

and $(500 - 354)10^{-6} = 146 \times 10^{-6}, \qquad \text{extension} = \epsilon_{\text{minimax}}. \qquad Ans.$

The direction of the major principal axis of strain is defined by θ_{xP}; this is obtained either as one-half of the central angle from A to E, which is obviously 45 deg, or as the arc tangent of $/EFA'$, where A' is the reflection of A (see Fig. 11.4c). Either way, θ_{xP} is found to be 22.5 deg, clockwise.

The state of strain in terms of the principal strains is depicted in Fig. 11.4d, which also shows the directions of maximum shear strain in the x-y plane. Sketch e shows the alternative representation, where the stationary value of γ is given by the diameter of the circle, that is, $\gamma_{\text{stat}} = 708 \times 10^{-6}$; the associated linear strain is 500×10^{-6}.

Because the two nonzero principal strains have the same sense, both extensions, reflected by the circle lying completely to the right of the origin, the true maximum shear strain is indicated by the diameter of the circle shown by dashed lines in sketch c; that is, $\gamma_{\max} = 854 \times 10^{-6}$; the associated linear strain is $\epsilon_{\max}/2 = 427 \times 10^{-6}$. $\qquad Ans.$

This result is presented in Fig. 11.4f, which is an auxiliary projection of the little block in sketch d, taken perpendicularly to the major principal axis of strain and showing the strain-free planes in edge view. The directions of maximum shear strain lie in the plane of this figure and are inclined 45 deg to both the principal axis of strain and the strain-free planes. An equivalent representation is shown in sketch g.

PROBLEMS

11.3. Sketch Mohr's circle for each of the following states of strain: (a) uniaxial extension; (b) uniaxial contraction; (c) pure shear strain (plane strain).

For the following states of plane strain, determine the principal strains and the maximum shear strains with their accompanying normal strains. In every case, for each result sketch the axes involved at their proper orientation and indicate the undeformed and the deformed shapes of a small element.

11.4. $\epsilon_x = +1000 \times 10^{-6}$, $\epsilon_y = +200 \times 10^{-6}$, $\gamma_{xy} = -100 \times 10^{-6}$.

11.5. $\epsilon_x = 0$, $\epsilon_y = -500 \times 10^{-6}$, $\gamma_{xy} = +1000 \times 10^{-6}$.

11.6. $\epsilon_x = -1000 \times 10^{-6}$, $\epsilon_y = +1000 \times 10^{-6}$, $\gamma_{xy} = +2000 \times 10^{-6}$.

11.7. $\epsilon_x = 0$, $\epsilon_y = 0$, $\gamma_{xy} = +2000 \times 10^{-6}$.

11.8. $\epsilon_x = +5000 \times 10^{-6}$, $\epsilon_y = +2000 \times 10^{-6}$, $\gamma_{xy} = +2000 \times 10^{-6}$.

Two or more states of strain may be combined to give a resultant state of strain. As with stress, the superposition can be accomplished through simple vector addition, provided the different states of strain are first transformed so that their components are in a common set of directions. With this in mind, for each of the following determine the principal strains and then sketch the principal axes at their proper orientation relative to the given reference frame. Indicate on each sketch the undeformed and the deformed shapes of a small element. All given numerical values are 10^6 times the actual magnitudes. (*Note:* Mohr's circle may be used to effect quick transformations.)

11.9   See sketches.

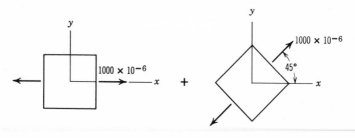

FIG. P11.9

11.10. See sketches.

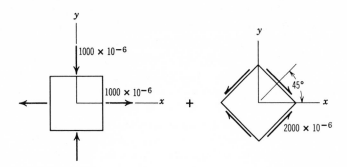

Fɪɢ. P11.10

11.11. See sketches.

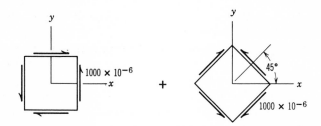

Fɪɢ. P11.11

11.12. See sketches.

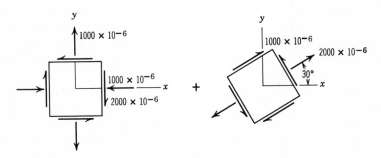

Fɪɢ. P11.12

11.5   Strain Gage Rosettes.   The equations developed in the fore-going, and especially Mohr's circle for strain, find their chief use in connection with the experimental determination of principal strains at various points on the exposed surface of a body, where these strains are often maximal.   With the exception of photoelastic and similar tech-niques, strain gages are capable of indicating only average linear strain values over finite gage lengths; the shorter the gage length the better the approximation to the strain value at the point in the direction of the gage axis.

Since, as brought out earlier in this chapter, the state of strain at any point in a body subject to plane strain may always be represented by the equivalent biaxial strain, no more than two gages are really necessary for a complete experimental determination of the strain components—provided, of course, that the directions of the principal axes of strain on the surface are known.   Unfortunately, however, these principal direc-tions are not known beforehand (although there are techniques that can make them visibly stand out, such as the use of brittle lacquers); there-fore at least three *linear* strain gages are needed for a complete solution of the problem because no gage has as yet been developed which will indicate *shear* strain at a point.

That three linear strain values in nonparallel directions on a plane enable one to find the principal strains in that plane becomes clear when we consider Eq. 11.9.   Assuming the X axis to be in the direction of one of the three gages, we then automatically have ϵ_x; if we now substitute in Eq. 11.9, first, one of the two remaining strain readings together with its direction angle θ_x, and then the third reading together with its direc-tion angle, we obtain two independent equations in the two unknowns ϵ_y and γ_{xy}.   After these equations have been solved for the unknowns, the principal strains can be easily evaluated and their directions estab-lished from the now known cartesian components; this can be accom-plished by using the formulas or with the aid of Mohr's circle.

Strain gages, usually with electric wire or foil elements of extremely short gage lengths, arranged in clusters of two, three, or more units, are called *strain gage rosettes.*   Of the several arrangements in use, one of the most popular is the 60-deg three-gage rosette illustrated in the following.

Illustrative Example 2.   A 60-deg rosette is attached to the surface of a body in the vicinity of a point of interest.   Its three gages, a, b, and c, whose axes are oriented counterclockwise in that order relative to one another, as indicated in Fig. 11.5a, give the following readings: $\epsilon_a = 800 \times 10^{-6}$, $\epsilon_b = 400 \times 10^{-6}$, and $\epsilon_c = -300 \times 10^{-6}$.   Determine the principal strains and locate the principal axes of strain.

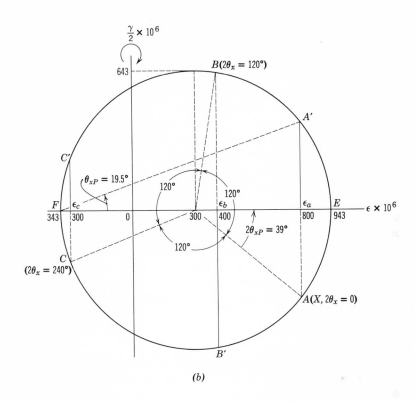

(b)

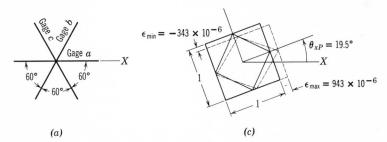

(a)   (c)

FIG. 11.5

SOLUTION. Taking $\epsilon_x = \epsilon_a$, we obtain from Eq. 11.9 the following two equations:

$$\epsilon_b = \epsilon_{60°} = \frac{\epsilon_a + \epsilon_y}{2} + \frac{\epsilon_a - \epsilon_y}{2}\left(-\frac{1}{2}\right) + \frac{\gamma_{xy}}{2}\left(\frac{\sqrt{3}}{2}\right)$$

$$= \frac{\epsilon_a}{4} + \frac{3\epsilon_y}{4} + \frac{\sqrt{3}\gamma_{xy}}{4}, \tag{a}$$

and $\quad \epsilon_c = \epsilon_{120°} = \dfrac{\epsilon_a + \epsilon_y}{2} + \dfrac{\epsilon_a - \epsilon_y}{2}\left(-\dfrac{1}{2}\right) + \dfrac{\gamma_{xy}}{2}\left(-\dfrac{\sqrt{3}}{2}\right)$

$$= \frac{\epsilon_a}{4} + \frac{3\epsilon_y}{4} - \frac{\sqrt{3}\gamma_{xy}}{4}. \tag{b}$$

Solving for ϵ_y and γ_{xy}, we obtain

$$\epsilon_y = \frac{2(\epsilon_b + \epsilon_c) - \epsilon_a}{3} \tag{c}$$

and $$\gamma_{xy} = \frac{2(\epsilon_b - \epsilon_c)}{\sqrt{3}}. \tag{d}$$

If we choose to complete the solution with the aid of Mohr's circle, we must next locate its center by evaluating the "mean" linear strain, thus:

$$\epsilon_{\text{mean}} = \frac{\epsilon_x + \epsilon_y}{2} = \frac{\epsilon_a + \epsilon_b + \epsilon_c}{3}, \tag{e}$$

and then determine its radius:

$$\frac{\gamma_{\text{stat}}}{2} = \sqrt{[(\epsilon_x - \epsilon_y)/2]^2 + (\gamma_{xy}/2)^2}$$

$$= \frac{\sqrt{2}}{3}\sqrt{(\epsilon_a - \epsilon_b)^2 + (\epsilon_b - \epsilon_c)^2 + (\epsilon_c - \epsilon_a)^2}. \tag{f}$$

The principal strains then follow:

$$\left.\begin{array}{c}\epsilon_{\max}\\[4pt]\epsilon_{\min}\end{array}\right\} = \epsilon_{\text{mean}} \pm \frac{\gamma_{\text{stat}}}{2}. \tag{g}$$

Equation 11.12 gives the principal directions, thus:

$$\tan 2\theta_{xP} = \frac{\gamma_{xy}}{\epsilon_x - \epsilon_y} = \frac{\epsilon_b - \epsilon_c}{\sqrt{3}(\epsilon_a - \epsilon_{\text{mean}})}. \tag{h}$$

Substituting the numerical data, we obtain the following:

From Eq. e, $\qquad \epsilon_{\text{mean}} = 300 \times 10^{-6}$.

From Eq. f, $\qquad \dfrac{\gamma_{\text{stat}}}{2} = 643 \times 10^{-6} = \dfrac{\gamma_{\max}}{2}$,

since, obviously, the circle is going to straddle the $\gamma/2$ axis, because of the fact that one of the given linear strains has a sign opposite to that of the other two. Therefore

$$\gamma_{\max} = 1286 \times 10^{-6}.$$

From Eq. g, $\qquad \epsilon_{\max} = (300 + 643)10^{-6} = 943 \times 10^{-6}$, $\qquad$ *Ans.*

and $\qquad \epsilon_{\min} = (300 - 643)10^{-6} = -343 \times 10^{-6}$; $\qquad$ *Ans.*

From Eq. h, $\quad 2\theta_{xP} = \tan^{-1} \dfrac{7\sqrt{3}}{15} = 39$ deg, 219 deg;

hence $\qquad \theta_{xP} = 19.5$ deg, 109.5 deg (or -70.5 deg). $\qquad$ *Ans.*

The preceding means that the major principal axis of strain is inclined 19.5 deg counterclockwise from the gage a axis. That this is so can be verified from Mohr's circle, shown in Fig. 11.5b. This is constructed by first locating the center C at the point $\epsilon = 300$, $\gamma/2 = 0$, and then scribing a circle with a radius of 643. Observe that when the three linear strain values, ϵ_a, ϵ_b, and ϵ_c, are laid off by the three lines parallel to the $\gamma/2$ axis, the six points of intersection with the circle form two triads, A-B-C and A'-B'-C', whose members are located 120 degrees from each other. Inasmuch as the relative orientation of points on the circle must agree with the relative orientation of their corresponding axes at the point in the body, the unprimed triad A-B-C must be the correct set. Therefore point A must now correspond to the X axis, and from A to E is $2\theta_{xP} = 39$ deg, counterclockwise, from which it follows that $\theta_{xP} = 19.5$ deg, counterclockwise from X (or gage a). As explained previously, the angle $\underline{/EFA'}$ may also be utilized to give θ_{xP} directly.

The state of strain in terms of the principal strains is depicted in Fig. 11.5c. Lying in the plane of the figure and inclined 45 deg to both major and minor principal directions are the directions of maximum shear strain.

PROBLEMS

11.13. A 60-deg three-gage rosette, similar to that of Example 2, gave the following strain values:

$$\epsilon_a = +1000 \times 10^{-6}, \qquad \epsilon_b = +500 \times 10^{-6}, \qquad \epsilon_c = -800 \times 10^{-6}.$$

Determine the corresponding principal strains and specify their directions relative to the axis of gage a.

11.14. After the manner of Example 2, derive the equations for a 45-deg three-gage rosette analogous to Eqs. *e*, *f*, and *h*.

FIG. P11.14

11.15. Either using the results of Prob. 11.14 or substituting directly into Eq. 11.9, calculate the principal strains from the following strain values obtained from a 45-deg three-gage rosette:

$$\epsilon_a = +2000 \times 10^{-6}, \qquad \epsilon_b = +500 \times 10^{-6}, \qquad \epsilon_c = -1500 \times 10^{-6}.$$

Locate the axis of $\epsilon_{\max}$ relative to the axis of gage *a*.

11.16. Substituting directly into Eq. 11.9, determine the principal strains from the following strain values:

$$\theta_x = 0, \qquad \epsilon = -500 \times 10^{-6};$$
$$\theta_x = 30°, \qquad \epsilon = 0;$$
$$\theta_x = 60°, \qquad \epsilon = +1500 \times 10^{-6}.$$

Give the principal directions relative to the X axis.

11.6 Stress and Strain. Hooke's Law. A body under stress necessarily strains because no substance is perfectly rigid; conversely, a body that undergoes strain, not as a result of temperature changes, is necessarily subject to stress. Whenever stress and strain are proportional to each other, their relation is expressed by Hooke's law, which, in its most general form, is embodied in six equations of the type

$$\epsilon_x = \alpha_{11}\sigma_x + \alpha_{12}\sigma_y + \alpha_{13}\sigma_z + \alpha_{14}\tau_{xy} + \alpha_{15}\tau_{yz} + \alpha_{16}\tau_{zx}, \quad (11.16)$$

or six of the type

$$\sigma_x = \beta_{11}\epsilon_x + \beta_{12}\epsilon_y + \beta_{13}\epsilon_z + \beta_{14}\gamma_{xy} + \beta_{15}\gamma_{yz} + \beta_{16}\gamma_{zx}. \quad (11.17)$$

The 36 coefficients α_{ij} or β_{ij}, called the elastic constants of the material, may not all be distinct, depending on its nature. For homogeneous isotropic substances, it can be proved that the number of constants reduces to 2.* The two constants E and ν in Eqs. 2.8 of Chapter 2 are sometimes called the engineering constants in Hooke's law.

* For instance, see C. T. Wang, *Applied Elasticity*, pp. 26–27, McGraw-Hill Book Company, New York, 1953.

An essential concomitant of the proof alluded to is the conclusion that the principal axes of strain coincide with the directions of the principal stresses; intuitively we sense that this must be so in an isotropic material. Since the orientation of the cartesian axes in the body is purely arbitrary, there is no reason why they may not be chosen in the principal directions. Assuming this has been done, and using the symbols σ_1, σ_2, σ_3 and τ_1, τ_2, τ_3 for the stationary stress values, and ϵ_1, ϵ_2, ϵ_3 and γ_1, γ_2, γ_3 for the stationary strain values, we may rewrite the equations of Hooke's law in the equivalent forms

$$\epsilon_1 = \frac{1}{E}[\sigma_1 - \nu(\sigma_2 + \sigma_3)]$$

$$\epsilon_2 = \frac{1}{E}[\sigma_2 - \nu(\sigma_3 + \sigma_1)]$$

$$\epsilon_3 = \frac{1}{E}[\sigma_3 - \nu(\sigma_1 + \sigma_2)]$$

(11.18a)

$$\gamma_1 = \frac{2(1 + \nu)}{E}\tau_1$$

$$\gamma_2 = \frac{2(1 + \nu)}{E}\tau_2$$

$$\gamma_3 = \frac{2(1 + \nu)}{E}\tau_3,$$

where the strains are explicit functions of the stresses; or

$$\sigma_1 = \frac{E}{(1 + \nu)(1 - 2\nu)}[(1 - \nu)\epsilon_1 + \nu(\epsilon_2 + \epsilon_3)]$$

$$\sigma_2 = \frac{E}{(1 + \nu)(1 - 2\nu)}[(1 - \nu)\epsilon_2 + \nu(\epsilon_3 + \epsilon_1)]$$

$$\sigma_3 = \frac{E}{(1 + \nu)(1 - 2\nu)}[(1 - \nu)\epsilon_3 + \nu(\epsilon_1 + \epsilon_2)]$$

(11.18b)

$$\tau_1 = \frac{E}{2(1 + \nu)}\gamma_1$$

$$\tau_2 = \frac{E}{2(1 + \nu)}\gamma_2$$

$$\tau_3 = \frac{E}{2(1 + \nu)}\gamma_3,$$

where the stresses are explicit functions of the strains. Substitution of the proper zero terms in the preceding gives the equations for special cases. Thus, for *plane stress*, setting $\sigma_3 = 0$, we obtain

$$\epsilon_1 = \frac{1}{E}(\sigma_1 - \nu\sigma_2)$$

$$\epsilon_2 = \frac{1}{E}(\sigma_2 - \nu\sigma_1)$$

$$\epsilon_3 = -\frac{\nu}{E}(\sigma_1 + \sigma_2)$$

$$\sigma_1 = \frac{E}{1 - \nu^2}(\epsilon_1 + \nu\epsilon_2)$$

$$\sigma_2 = \frac{E}{1 - \nu^2}(\epsilon_2 + \nu\epsilon_1), \qquad (11.18c)$$

with the equations connecting shear strain to shear stress remaining unchanged. For *plane strain*, putting $\epsilon_3 = 0$, we get

$$\sigma_1 = \frac{E}{(1 + \nu)(1 - 2\nu)}[(1 - \nu)\epsilon_1 + \nu\epsilon_2]$$

$$\sigma_2 = \frac{E}{(1 + \nu)(1 - 2\nu)}[(1 - \nu)\epsilon_2 + \nu\epsilon_1]$$

$$\sigma_3 = \frac{\nu E}{(1 + \nu)(1 - 2\nu)}(\epsilon_1 + \epsilon_2) \qquad (11.18d)$$

$$\epsilon_1 = \frac{1 + \nu}{E}[(1 - \nu)\sigma_1 - \nu\sigma_2]$$

$$\epsilon_2 = \frac{1 + \nu}{E}[(1 - \nu)\sigma_2 - \nu\sigma_1].$$

For *uniaxial stress*, with $\sigma_2 = \sigma_3 = 0$, we find

$$\epsilon_1 = \frac{\sigma_1}{E}$$

$$\epsilon_2 = \epsilon_3 = -\frac{\nu\sigma_1}{E}$$

$$\sigma_1 = E\epsilon_1. \qquad (11.18e)$$

And for *uniaxial strain*, with $\epsilon_2 = \epsilon_3 = 0$, we have

$$\sigma_1 = \frac{E(1 - \nu)\epsilon_1}{(1 + \nu)(1 - 2\nu)}$$

$$\sigma_2 = \sigma_3 = \frac{\nu E\epsilon_1}{(1 + \nu)(1 - 2\nu)}$$

$$\epsilon_1 = \frac{(1 + \nu)(1 - 2\nu)\sigma_1}{E(1 - \nu)}. \qquad (11.18f)$$

Illustrative Example 3. For the material of Example 2, the following are given: $E = 30 \times 10^6$ psi and $\nu = 0.3$. Determine, for the point previously investigated, the principal stresses and the maximum shear stress on each of the following bases: (1) that ϵ_z is free to develop; (2) that ϵ_z is completely suppressed.

SOLUTION. (1) If ϵ_z is free to develop, this should be considered plane stress. Using Eqs. 11.18c, we find

$$\sigma_{max} = \frac{30(10)^6}{1 - 0.09} [943 + 0.3(-343)]10^{-6}$$

$$= 27{,}700 \text{ psi, tensile} \qquad\qquad Ans.$$

and
$$\sigma_{min} = \frac{30}{0.91} [-343 + 0.3(943)]$$

$$= -1980 \text{ psi, compressive.} \qquad\qquad Ans.$$

Since the two nonzero principal stresses have opposite signs, the maximum shear stress equals one-half of their difference, thus:

$$\tau_{max} = \frac{27{,}700 - (-1980)}{2} = 14{,}840 \text{ psi.} \qquad\qquad Ans.$$

(2) If ϵ_z is completely suppressed, then the equations for plane strain should be used. Accordingly, from Eqs. 11.18d, we find

$$\sigma_1 = \frac{30(10)^6}{(1 + 0.3)(1 - 0.6)} [0.7(943) + 0.3(-343)]10^{-6}$$

$$= 32{,}150 \text{ psi, tensile} = \sigma_{max} \qquad\qquad Ans.$$

$$\sigma_2 = \frac{30}{0.52} [0.7(-343) + 0.3(943)]$$

$$= 2470 \text{ psi, tensile} = \sigma_{min} \qquad\qquad Ans.$$

$$\sigma_3 = \frac{30}{0.52} (0.3)(943 - 343)$$

$$= 10{,}380 \text{ psi, tensile} = \sigma_{minimax} \qquad\qquad Ans.$$

Thus suppression of ϵ_z necessitates triaxiality in the state of stress. The maximum shear stress is now found as one-half of the difference between the maximum and minimum principal stresses:

$$\tau_{max} = \frac{32,150 - 2470}{2} = 14,840 \text{ psi.} \qquad Ans.$$

PROBLEMS

11.17. The two principal strains at a certain spot on the surface of a stressed body were found to be

$$\epsilon_1 = 1670 \times 10^{-6} \qquad and \qquad \epsilon_2 = -330 \times 10^{-6}.$$

Determine the maximum shear stress, assuming plane stress and using $E = 30 \times 10^6$ psi and $\nu = 0.28$.

11.18. Using the data of Prob. 11.4 and $E = 10.5 \times 10^6$ psi and $\nu = 0.32$, assuming plane stress, calculate the principal stresses and the maximum shear stress

(a) by first determining σ_x, σ_y, and τ_{xy};

(b) by first determining the principal strains.

Compare the results.

11.19. Do the preceding problem for the data of Prob. 11.6 and $E = 16 \times 10^6$ psi and $\nu = 0.34$.

11.7 Relations between Mohr's Two Circles in Plane Stress. The circle for stress in plane stress can be related quite simply to the corresponding circle for strain if their scale factors are adjusted relative to each other. Of the many ways this can be done, two are significant because they lead to practical results. In one, the two circles are concentric and are referred to a common origin; in the other, the two circles are identical but are referred to different origins.

Figure 11.6 shows the two concentric circles set in the same reference frame. To establish the relation between the scale factors, r for the stress circle and s for the strain circle, we observe that

$$\frac{\sigma_1 + \sigma_2}{2r} = \frac{\epsilon_1 + \epsilon_2}{2s}. \qquad (a)$$

Substituting in the preceding the first two equations of 11.18c, we obtain

$$\frac{\sigma_1 + \sigma_2}{2r} = \frac{(\sigma_1 + \sigma_2)(1 - \nu)}{2Es}, \qquad (b)$$

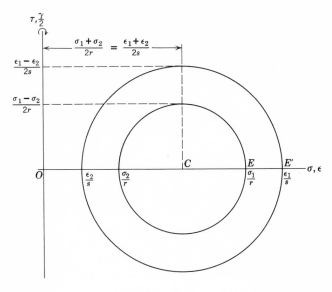

FIG. 11.6

from which it follows that

$$\frac{s}{r} = \frac{1 - \nu}{E}.$$ (11.19)

The relative sizes of the two circles may now be found in the ratio of their radii, thus:

$$\frac{CE'}{CE} = \frac{(\epsilon_1 - \epsilon_2)/2s}{(\sigma_1 - \sigma_2)/2r} = \left(\frac{r}{s}\right)\frac{(\sigma_1 - \sigma_2)(1 + \nu)}{(\sigma_1 - \sigma_2)E},$$ (c)

which, by virtue of Eq. 11.19, becomes

$$\frac{CE'}{CE} = \frac{1 + \nu}{1 - \nu}.$$ (11.20)

Figure 11.7 displays the common circle set in two different reference frames. For the two circles to be identical, the following must be true:

$$\frac{\sigma_1 - \sigma_2}{r} = \frac{\epsilon_1 - \epsilon_2}{s},$$ (d)

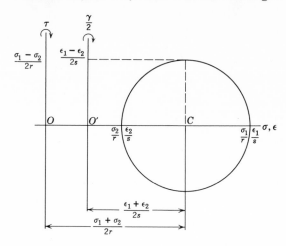

FIG. 11.7

which, again because of Eqs. 11.18c, becomes

$$\frac{s}{r} = \frac{1 + \nu}{E}.$$

(11.21)

The relative distances of the origins from the center of the common circle are expressed in the ratio

$$\frac{OC}{O'C} = \frac{(\sigma_1 + \sigma_2)/2r}{\cdot\,(\epsilon_1 + \epsilon_2)/2s} = \left(\frac{s}{r}\right)\frac{(\sigma_1 + \sigma_2)E}{(\sigma_1 + \sigma_2)(1 - \nu)}.$$

(e)

Substituting Eq. 11.21 in the preceding, we finally obtain

$$\frac{OC}{O'C} = \frac{1 + \nu}{1 - \nu}.$$

(11.22)

We observe from the foregoing that (1) when the two circles are concentric, the strain circle must be the larger one, and (2) when the two circles are identical, the strain circle must be nearer to its origin.

Illustrative Example 4.   On the same set of axes, show Mohr's circle for uniaxial tensile stress and the corresponding Mohr's circle for strain.

SOLUTION.   Figure 11.8 shows the stress circle lying completely to the right of the τ axis, touching it tangentially; the concentric strain circle has a radius $(1 + \nu)/(1 - \nu)$ times as large.   It is obvious that the latter circle must straddle the $\gamma/2$ axis, showing that uniaxial stress results

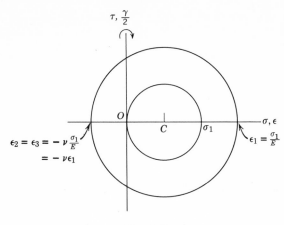

FIG. 11.8

in triaxial strain. We leave to the student as an exercise the details of demonstrating that the intermediate and minor principal strains, which are not distinct, are exactly $-\nu$ times the major principal strain, as required by the second of Eqs. 11.18e.

PROBLEMS

11.20. Referring to Fig. 11.8, show that the intermediate and minor principal strains in uniaxial tension are $-\nu$ times as large as the major principal strain.

11.21. Sketch Mohr's circle for strain for the data of Prob. 11.5; then, assuming the data valid for plane stress, sketch the concentric Mohr's circle for stress, taking $\nu = 0.3$.

11.22. Do the preceding problem for the data of Prob. 11.8.

11.23. Derive the relation between the scale factors and the radii of Mohr's circles for strain and for stress when they are concentric and referred to the same origin for the case of plane strain.

11.24. Using the results of the preceding problem, sketch the two Mohr's circles for uniaxial extension. Assume $\nu = 0.3$.

11.25. Repeat the above for pure shear strain.

12

THEORIES OF FAILURE.
COMBINED LOADING

12.1 Introduction. The elementary expressions for the strengths of structural elements are predicated on a theory which is based largely on the behavior of a material in simple uniaxial tension or compression. The question now arises: In a general state of stress, what criterion should be used for predicting failure and hence for measuring strength and establishing margins of safety?

In its strictest sense, failure of a material means actual fracture or separation—a destruction of its continuity. Sometimes it is necessary to attach a somewhat looser meaning to the word. For instance, failure may be interpreted to mean overstepping of the proportional limit; or failure may be taken as the beginning of yielding. These two less strict definitions may or may not be identical with the notion of failure. In perfectly brittle materials, overstepping of the proportional limit may be considered synonymous with fracture; in materials that are perfectly plastic beyond the proportional limit, overstepping of this limit is the same as yielding. But this is merely convenient idealization. There are instances (usually temperature-dependent) when a ductile material will fracture as if it were brittle, or when a brittle material will deform as if it were ductile. As Nadai points out, it is more correct to refer to the brittle or the plastic *states* of materials than it is to speak of them simply as brittle or ductile.*

* A. Nadai, *Theory of Flow and Fracture of Solids*, p. 207, McGraw-Hill Book Company, New York, 1950.

Were the material absolutely structureless, homogeneous, and iso-tropic, it should be possible to establish some criterion governing the threshold of failure. This could be expressed as a function of the level attained by, say, the strain or by the stress if the material obeys Hooke's law when separation first becomes detectable. Unfortunately, actual materials are far from structureless, are by no means homogeneous, and may be considered approximately isotropic only because of the random orientation of their constituent particles. Thus, although the concepts of stress and strain at a point are perfectly logical, the quantities as defined are not precisely realizable; any numerical values of them must be considered nothing more than statistical averages. Furthermore, the early detection of failure cracks at points other than those on the free surface of an undisturbed piece entails almost insuperable problems. Accordingly, no proposal to prescribe a criterion of strength in terms of the stresses or strains at a point can ever have the stature of a law; it must remain a theory, or more properly, a tentative hypothesis, be-cause of necessity it is based on phenomenological grounds.

A number of such proposals have been made at various times:

1. The *maximum normal-stress theory*, first proposed by Lamé and later revived by Rankine.

2. The *maximum linear-strain theory*, proposed by Poncelet and Saint-Venant.

3. The *maximum shear-stress theory*, associated with the names of Coulomb, Tresca, Duguet, and Guest.

4. The *"internal-friction"* theory of Mohr, of which the maximum shear-stress theory is a special case.

5. The *maximum strain-energy theory*, due to Beltrami.

6. The *maximum distortion-energy theory*, first proposed by Maxwell but now linked with the names of Huber, von Mises, and Hencky.

All these theories purport to define some aspect of the strength of a ma-terial when it is subjected to a general state of stress, in terms of the stress or strain that governs this aspect in simple tension or compres-sion. In the following we will discuss only three of these theories, one of them due largely to historical interest, the other two because they enjoy a certain respectability conferred by some measure of experimental veri-fication and, consequently, are favored for practical application.

12.2 The Maximum Normal-Stress Theory. As originally pro-posed, this theory assumed that the maximum principal stress in a ma-terial determines failure regardless of what the other principal stresses may be, provided it has the largest numerical value. In view of the fact that the simple tensile strength usually differs from the simple compressive strength, we find it proper to reinterpret this oldest of the strength theories as follows: *The elastic strength of a material is assumed reached when one of the principal stresses attains the level of the corresponding principal stress at the proportional limit in uniaxial stress.* This suggests that, if this principal stress is tensile, the tensile elastic strength is the one involved in the comparison; if it is compressive, then the simple compressive elastic strength serves as the yardstick.

Let σ_1, σ_2, and σ_3 denote the principal stresses, and σ_t and σ_c the tensile and compressive elastic strength in uniaxial stress. The theory assumes that, if $\sigma_1 > \sigma_2 > \sigma_3$ algebraically, then $\sigma_1 \leqq \sigma_t$ and $\sigma_3 \geqq -\sigma_c$; if $\sigma_2 > \sigma_3 > \sigma_1$, then $\sigma_2 \leqq \sigma_t$ and $\sigma_1 \geqq -\sigma_c$; and if $\sigma_3 > \sigma_1 > \sigma_2$, then $\sigma_3 \leqq \sigma_t$ and $\sigma_2 \geqq -\sigma_c$. Thus the relations

$$-\sigma_c \leqq \sigma_1 \leqq \sigma_t,$$

$$-\sigma_c \leqq \sigma_2 \leqq \sigma_t, \tag{12.1}$$

and $\qquad\qquad -\sigma_c \leqq \sigma_3 \leqq \sigma_t$

define what might be termed "safe" stress values. In plane stress, with $\sigma_3 = 0$, the criteria become

$$-\sigma_c \leqq \sigma_1 \leqq \sigma_t$$
$$\tag{12.1a}$$
and $\qquad\qquad -\sigma_c \leqq \sigma_2 \leqq \sigma_t.$

It is convenient to depict the limits of the theory. For purposes of later comparison, let us assume that the elastic strengths in tension and compression are equal in magnitude, that is, $|\sigma_t| = |\sigma_c| = \sigma_e$. Dividing the principal stresses by σ_e and replacing σ_1/σ_e by x, σ_2/σ_e by y, and σ_3/σ_e by z, we obtain from 12.1 the limits

$$x = \pm 1,$$

$$y = \pm 1, \tag{a}$$

and $\qquad\qquad z = \pm 1.$

The yield or failure "surface" may therefore be represented by a cube formed by the planes of Eqs. *a*.

In plane stress, the yield or failure "line" is the square shown in Fig. 12.1. This is the intersection of the cube *a* and the plane $z = 0$. The significance of this figure is as follows. No combination of σ_1 and σ_2, for which the stress ratios x and y are the coordinates of any point P inside the square, will, according to this theory, induce brittle failure or yielding. If through P a line is drawn from the origin intersecting the yield or failure line at P', then the line segment PP' will give all the sets of

σ_1 and σ_2 up to yield or failure for what is called *proportional loading*. The length of PP' itself represents the margin of safety for this kind of loading

The expectations of the theory are not fulfilled in many instances. For example, even materials that are very weak in uniaxial stress can withstand considerable triaxial stresses of equal magnitude, that is, hydrostatic stress. Also, the theory is overly optimistic in crediting a ductile material with too high a yield strength when the principal stresses are of different senses. Nevertheless, for brittle materials subject only to biaxial tensile stresses, experiments give results that are not too far from its predictions. Hence the maxi-

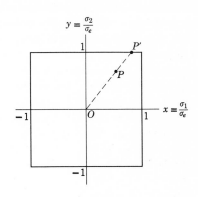

FIG. 12.1

mum normal-stress theory finds some use (1) for predicting fracture in brittle materials and (2) for predicting yield in ductile materials, when such materials are subjected to biaxial tensile stresses.

12.3   The Maximum Shear-Stress Theory.   This theory assumes that *elastic behavior ceases, hence yielding begins, when the maximum shear stress in whatever state of stress becomes equal to the maximum shear stress at yield in the uniaxial case.*   Since the maximum shear stress in the uniaxial case equals one-half of the nonzero principal stress, regardless of sense, *this theory tacitly assumes that the yield strength in simple tension is of the same magnitude as that in simple compression.*   This has been observed to be approximately so in ductile metals; hence there is at least one experimental fact in support of this theory.

The relations that define safe stress values may again be stated as before in terms of the three principal stresses and the elastic-limit stress σ_e, taken equal to the yield stress in the uniaxial case. Noting that the stationary values of the shear stress are each equal to one-half of the difference between a pair of principal stresses (see Fig. 10.15), and eliminating the factor $1/2$ which is common to all terms, we obtain the following criteria for safe stresses:

$$-\sigma_e \leqq \sigma_1 - \sigma_2 \leqq \sigma_e,$$

$$-\sigma_e \leqq \sigma_2 - \sigma_3 \leqq \sigma_e, \tag{12.2}$$

and
$$-\sigma_e \leqq \sigma_3 - \sigma_1 \leqq \sigma_e.$$

Dividing through by σ_e and designating the three stress ratios x, y, and z, we obtain from the above the limits

$$x - y = \pm 1,$$

$$y - z = \pm 1, \qquad\qquad (a)$$

and $\qquad\qquad z - x = \pm 1.$

Therefore the yield surface is represented by a regular hexagonal prism formed by the six planes of Eqs. a; its geometric axis is the line $x = y = z$.

Since there is no point on the yield surface for which $x = y = z$, the maximum shear-stress theory predicts that no yielding can take place in either hydrostatic tension or hydrostatic compression. We noted in Article 10.4 that at an isotropic point no planes are subject to shear stress. The theory is therefore consistent in the assumption that there cannot be any yielding in the absence of shear stress, no matter how large the normal stresses might be.

In plane stress, assuming σ_3 to be zero, we have the following three possibilities for maximum shear stress (see Article 10.5, Case 2): (1) when σ_1 and σ_2 have the same sign and σ_1 is the numerically larger stress, then $\tau_{\max} = \sigma_1/2$; (2) when σ_1 and σ_2 have the same sign and σ_2 is the numerically larger stress, then $\tau_{\max} = \sigma_2/2$; (3) when σ_1 and σ_2 have opposite signs, then $\tau_{\max} = (\sigma_1 - \sigma_2)/2$. Hence the safe stress values are defined by the relations

$$-\sigma_e \leqq \sigma_1 \leqq \sigma_e,$$

$$-\sigma_e \leqq \sigma_2 \leqq \sigma_e, \qquad\qquad (12.2a)$$

and $\qquad\qquad -\sigma_e \leqq \sigma_1 - \sigma_2 \leqq \sigma_e.$

In terms of the dimensionless ratios, the limits to Eqs. 12.2a are

$$x = \pm 1,$$

$$y = \pm 1, \qquad\qquad (b)$$

and $\qquad\qquad x - y = \pm 1.$

Accordingly, for biaxial stress the yield line is a hexagon as shown in Fig. 12.2; this is the intersection of the yield surface of Eqs. a and the plane $z = 0$.

For combinations of σ_1 and σ_2 represented by the six corners of the hexagon in Fig. 12.2, the expectations of the theory are borne out with good accuracy in ductile metals. For other combinations of the principal stresses, the theory is conservative, that is, it gives values on the safe side. For example, in pure shear, where $\tau_{\max} = |\sigma_1| = |\sigma_2|$, the theory predicts that yield will begin when $\tau_{\max} = \sigma_e/2$, as indicated in Fig. 12.2. The actual experimental value is larger than this, as discussed in the next article.

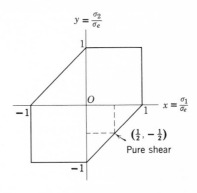

Observe that, in plane stress, the greatest discrepancy between this and the maximum normal-stress theory occurs when $\sigma_1 = -\sigma_2$, or pure shear. With the aid of Figs. 12.1 and 12.2, it is easy to see that the normal-stress theory indicates a strength twice that allowed by the shear-stress theory. It should also be noted, however, that in the first and third quadrants the two figures

FIG. 12.2

are identical. Hence in biaxial stress of the *same* sign, the two theories make the same predictions.

12.4 The Maximum Distortion-Energy Theory. In Article 2.6 we derived the expression for the energy per unit volume stored in a body that obeys Hooke's law when it strains as a result of stress, Eq. 2.9b. Using the principal stresses, we may rewrite that equation in the form

$$\frac{dU}{dV} = \frac{1}{2E} [\sigma_1^2 + \sigma_2^2 + \sigma_3^2 - 2\nu(\sigma_1\sigma_2 + \sigma_2\sigma_3 + \sigma_3\sigma_1)]. \qquad (a)$$

Let us consider this energy of strain to consist of two parts: one part, $(dU/dV)_V$, equals that work expended in changing the volume but not the shape of the unit element; the other, $(dU/dV)_D$, represents the work expended in changing the shape but not the volume of the element. Thus

$$\frac{dU}{dV} = \left(\frac{dU}{dV}\right)_V + \left(\frac{dU}{dV}\right)_D \qquad (b)$$

The distortion-energy theory concerns itself only with the second portion of the total elastic strain energy. It assumes that *yield will commence when the distortion energy in whatever state of stress equals the distortion energy at yielding in uniaxial stress.* To derive the quantitative expression for the yield criterion, we must first evaluate $(dU/dV)_D$.

The change in volume of the original unit element (a unit cube) is

$$e = (1 + \epsilon_1)(1 + \epsilon_2)(1 + \epsilon_3) - 1$$

$$= \epsilon_1 + \epsilon_2 + \epsilon_3, \qquad (c)$$

if the cross products of the strains, which are very small, are ignored. This quantity e is called the *volume strain* or the *dilatation*. By virtue of Hooke's law, this becomes

$$e = \epsilon_1 + \epsilon_2 + \epsilon_3 = \frac{1 - 2\nu}{E}(\sigma_1 + \sigma_2 + \sigma_3). \qquad (d)$$

Since the stress-strain relations are linear we could consider the state of stress to be the result of superposing two states of stress, one corresponding to $(dU/dV)_V$ and the other to $(dU/dV)_D$. Because of isotropy, the principal stresses responsible for the change in volume only must be all equal; let their common magnitude be designated σ_m. Then the principal stresses that account for the distortion of the element are

$$\sigma_1{}' = \sigma_1 - \sigma_m,$$

$$\sigma_2{}' = \sigma_2 - \sigma_m, \qquad (e)$$

and $\qquad\qquad\qquad \sigma_3{}' = \sigma_3 - \sigma_m.$

These are schematically shown in Fig. 12.3. Since the primed stresses do not change the volume of the element, we find by virtue of Eq. d that

$$\sigma_1{}' + \sigma_2{}' + \sigma_3{}' = 0 = \sigma_1 + \sigma_2 + \sigma_3 - 3\sigma_m,$$

whence $\qquad\qquad\qquad \sigma_m = \dfrac{\sigma_1 + \sigma_2 + \sigma_3}{3}, \qquad (f)$

which we see to be the mean or average stress. Substituting this value

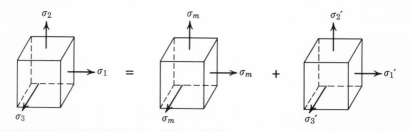

Fig. 12.3

in Eqs. *e*, we find the primed stresses to be

$$\sigma_1' = \frac{2\sigma_1 - \sigma_2 - \sigma_3}{3},$$

$$\sigma_2' = \frac{2\sigma_2 - \sigma_3 - \sigma_1}{3}, \tag{g}$$

and
$$\sigma_3' = \frac{2\sigma_3 - \sigma_1 - \sigma_2}{3}.$$

In advanced work, the tensor whose components are σ_m is called the *isotropic stress tensor*, and that whose components are the primed stresses of Eqs. *g* is called the *deviator stress tensor*.

We can now evaluate the distortion-producing part of the strain energy by substituting in Eq. *a* the primed stresses. After simplification, the result is

$$\left(\frac{dU}{dV}\right)_D = \frac{1 + \nu}{6E}\left[(\sigma_1 - \sigma_2)^2 + (\sigma_2 - \sigma_3)^2 + (\sigma_3 - \sigma_1)^2\right]. \tag{h}$$

It remains now only to find the expression for the distortion energy in uniaxial stress under conditions of yielding. Equation *h* gives this directly when σ_2 and σ_3 are set equal to zero, and σ_e is substituted for σ_1, thus:

$$\left(\frac{dU}{dV}\right)_D = \frac{1 + \nu}{3E}\sigma_e^2. \tag{i}$$

The maximum distortion-energy theory assumes that yielding will start when the quantity given by Eq. *h* just equals that given by Eq. *i*. Performing the indicated operation and simplifying, we derive the criterion for admissible stress values in the statement

$$(\sigma_1 - \sigma_2)^2 + (\sigma_2 - \sigma_3)^2 + (\sigma_3 - \sigma_1)^2 \leqq 2\sigma_e^2. \tag{12.3}$$

Dividing through by σ_e^2 and using the same symbols for the stress ratios as before, we obtain from Eq. 12.3 the limits for admissible stress values in the dimensionless form

$$(x - y)^2 + (y - z)^2 + (z - x)^2 = 2. \tag{j}$$

Thus the yield surface is represented by a right circular cylinder whose axis is the line $x = y = z$ and whose radius is $\sqrt{2/3}$. We observe that

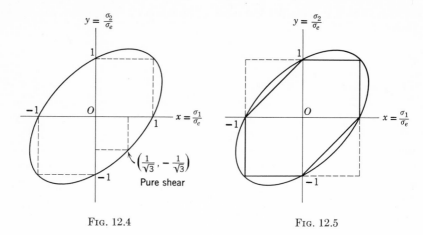

FIG. 12.4   FIG. 12.5

there is no point on this surface for which $x = y = z$; hence this theory predicts that no yielding can take place in either hydrostatic compression or hydrostatic tension.

For plane stress, with $\sigma_3 = 0$, the criterion becomes

$$\sigma_1{}^2 - \sigma_1\sigma_2 + \sigma_2{}^2 \leqq \sigma_e{}^2, \qquad (12.3a)$$

and the corresponding dimensionless form is

$$x^2 - xy + y^2 = 1. \qquad (k)$$

This is the equation of an ellipse whose semimajor axis, of length $\sqrt{2}$, is in the direction $x = y$, and whose semiminor axis is of length $\sqrt{2/3}$, which is the radius of the cylinder of Eq. j. This yield line for biaxial stress is represented in Fig. 12.4; it is the intersection of the yield surface of Eq. j and the plane $z = 0$. It is evident from this figure that, for plane stress, the distortion-energy theory will tolerate without threat of yielding a major principal stress which is *greater* than the uniaxial yield strength of the material, provided there is an accompanying nonzero intermediate principal stress of the *same* sign.

Of all the strength theories, this one based on the distortion energy appears to be the most accurate for predicting yield in ductile metals. For example, the yield stress in pure shear (plane stress) has been shown experimentally to be about $0.56\sigma_e$.* The theory predicts a value of

* A. Nadai, *Plasticity*, p. 68, McGraw-Hill Book Company, New York, 1931, and *Theory of Flow and Fracture of Solids*, pp. 210 and 250, McGraw-Hill Book Company, New York, 1950.

$0.577\sigma_e$, which is obtained from Eq. 12.3a when σ_1 is set equal to $-\sigma_2$, thus:

$$\sigma_1 = -\sigma_2 = \tau_{max} = \frac{\sigma_e}{\sqrt{3}} = 0.577\sigma_e.$$

This is indicated in Fig. 12.4.

Figure 12.5 shows the yield limits for the three theories in plane stress. Observe that the hexagon encloses the smallest common area; this signifies that the maximum shear-stress theory is the most conservative of the three. Although the distortion-energy theory gives the most accurate predictions of yielding in ductile metals, as an over-all theory, and especially for design purposes, the shear-stress theory finds wider application.* This is due to (1) the safer values that it gives and (2) the easier handling inherent in the linearity of its equations.

12.5 Combined Loading: Uniaxial Stress. Load-resisting members may not always be subject only to the simple modes of loading described in the first several chapters. For example, a beam may have superposed on its bending loads axial tension or compression forces; a rotating shaft transmitting power in torsion may at the same time be subjected to bending. In such cases, we assume that the principle of superposition applies, and we obtain the state of stress at some key point by combining the individual states, each due to an elementary mode of loading.

The simplest case of combined loading involves pure bending superposed on simple tension or compression. It is the simplest situation because either mode of loading produces uniaxial stress only and the two axes coincide; hence here superposition is merely algebraic addition of individual stress components. We discussed this briefly in Chapter 9 by way of introducing column action; we consider it here with a different emphasis.

Figure 12.6a represents a tool, such as the common C-clamp used by carpenters, or a fixture, such as the giant presses of heavy industry. At some section such as m-m, the loads induce the combined effects of an axial tension load P and a bending moment $M = Pe$ (see Fig. 12.6b). Unless the quantity e is defined, this would seem to be an indeterminate situation. Based on our knowledge of the elementary cases, however, we note that this need not be so: Inasmuch as the resultant axial load in simple tension must pass through the centroid of the cross-sectional area, in order that the stresses due to this load alone may be assumed uni-

---

* See, for instance, J. D. Lubahn and R. P. Felgar, *Plasticity and Creep of Metals*, p. 284, John Wiley and Sons, New York, 1961.

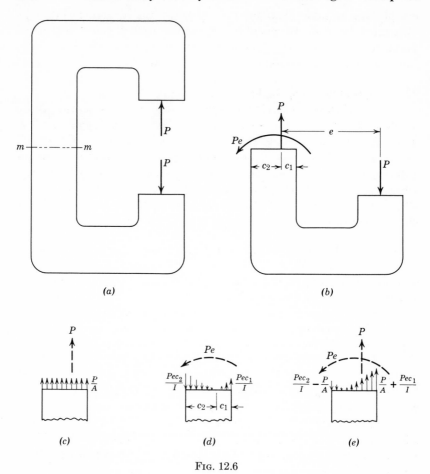

(a)   (b)

(c)   (d)   (e)

FIG. 12.6

formly distributed, the eccentricity e should be measured from the common centroidal line of all sections m-m.

The two stress patterns, a uniformly distributed one of intensity P/A (sketch c), and a uniformly varying one that gives rise to $M = Pe$ as a resultant (sketch d), are superposed to produce the equivalent stress pattern in sketch e. It should be clear that the individual effects are cumulative for points in the cross section nearest to the loads P, whereas for points furthest from P the effects tend to neutralize each other. If the tensile strength of the material is as large as, or smaller than, its compressive strength, and if the two values of c are equal, then it is proper to use the tensile stress at points on the inside face as a basis for establishing an upper limit for P. Otherwise the section should be investigated for compression also. Assuming that P must not induce permanent set, no matter how localized, we state the criterion for the limiting value in the equation

$$\frac{P_{\max}}{A} + \frac{M_{\max}c_1}{I_z} = \frac{P_{\max}}{A} + \frac{(P_{\max}e)c_1}{I_z} = \sigma_e, \qquad (a)$$

where σ_e is the proportional-limit stress in simple tension.

It is instructive to depict graphically the "interaction" between the axial load and the bending load. Let that part of the total stress corresponding to P only be denoted by σ_a, and the stress corresponding to M alone by σ_b. Then the criterion for allowable stress values, of which Eq. a is an upper limit, can be stated thus:

$$\sigma_a + \sigma_b \leqq \sigma_e. \qquad (b)$$

Dividing through by σ_e, and using the symbols x and y for the dimensionless stress ratios, we obtain

$$x + y \leqq 1. \qquad (c)$$

Figure 12.7 shows the graph of Eq. c. We call Eq. c an *interaction* equation, and Fig. 12.7 an *interaction curve*, for the end of elastic action in tension combined with bending. This curve is not to be confused with the yield or failure line discussed in previous articles.

In this particular example, where all dimensions are fixed and the only variable is the load P, the loading is proportional, that is, both the axial load P and the bending moment Pe vary linearly with P and main-

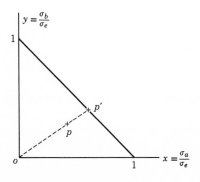

Fig. 12.7

tain the same ratio to each other. Therefore all stress ratios x and y correspond to points lying on a straight line through the origin, such as op' in Fig. 12.7. Then for any P less than the maximum, the distance pp' gives the margin of safety for proportional loading.

Illustrative Example 1. The frame of an industrial punch press, whose profile is represented by Fig. 12.8a, is made of cast iron for which the allowable stresses are 4000 psi in tension and 13,000 psi in compression. If the design had been based on the use of m-m as the controlling section, determine the margin of safety when $P = 4000$ lb.

SOLUTION. The cross section at m-m is shown in Fig. 12.8b; its area is 24 in.^{2} Measured from the inside face, the centroidal distance is $c_1 = [(12)1 + (12)5]/24 = 3$ in. Therefore the eccentricity is $e = 17 + 3 =$

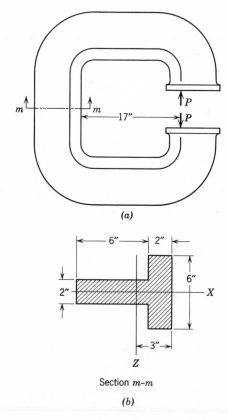

(a)

Section m-m

(b)

FIG. 12.8

20 in. The second-moment of area relative to the centroidal axis Z may now be found, thus:

$$I_z = \frac{6(12)^3}{12} + 12(2)^2 + \frac{2(6)^3}{12} + 12(2)^2 = 136 \text{ in.}^4$$

Then the two stress components are

$$\sigma_a = \frac{P}{A} = \frac{P}{24}$$

and

$$\sigma_b = \frac{Mc_1}{I_z} = \frac{20P(3)}{136}$$

or

$$\sigma_b = \frac{Mc_2}{I_z} = -\frac{20P(5)}{136}.$$

Superposing stress components, we find for the inside face

$$\sigma_i = \frac{P}{24} + \frac{60P}{136} = \frac{197P}{408},$$

and for the outside face

$$\sigma_o = \frac{P}{24} - \frac{100P}{136} = -\frac{283P}{408}.$$

Comparing the relative magnitudes of these two values with the relative magnitudes of the allowable stresses, we conclude that the maximum allowable P should be based on the tensile stress. Accordingly, the controlling equation becomes

$$\frac{197P}{408} = 4000,$$

whence $P_{max} = 8280$ lb.

Finally, the margin of safety is found to be

$$\text{M.S.} = \frac{8280}{4000} - 1 = 1.07. \qquad \qquad Ans.$$

We note that, inasmuch as this is uniaxial stress, all three strength theories give the same value for the margin. In fact, it is altogether unnecessary formally to use any of them.

PROBLEMS

12.1. A tension member with a 2 in. by 2 in. square cross section is to have some material removed from it as shown. How deep may the cut be in order that the maximum tensile stress shall not exceed 1000 psi when the load, centrally applied at each end, is 2000 lb? Ignore any bending deformation.

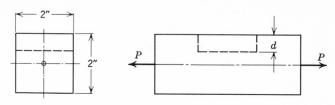

FIG. P12.1

12.2. If F is 6000 lb, how large may P be without the tensile stress in the longitudinal direction exceeding 1500 psi? Ignore deflections due to bending.

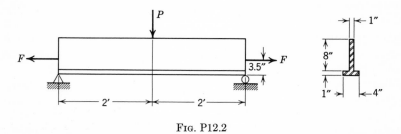

FIG. P12.2

12.3. In Fig. P12.2, if $F = 4P$, how large may P be if the longitudinal tensile stress is not to exceed 1500 psi?

12.4. In the A-frame of Fig. 1.5, design member B, using an allowable tensile stress of 500 psi and assuming a rectangular cross section such that $h = 2b$. Ignore deformation of frame.

12.5. Where must P be applied in order that the longitudinal tensile stress in the rectangular bar will be a maximum? Ignore flexibility of members.

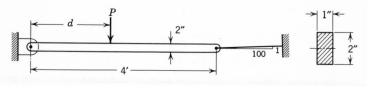

FIG. P12.5

12.6. If the maximum allowable tensile stress in the horizontal member is 11,600 psi and the loads P are each equal to 1000 lb, calculate the margin of safety.

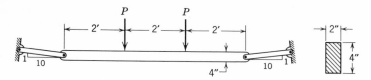

Fig. P12.6

12.6 Combined Loading: Biaxial Stress. When there is biaxiality of stress, one or more of the strength theories must be used to obtain allowable load values or safety margins, or to provide a basis for design. The simplest example of biaxiality among the structural elements we have examined so far is found in the simple shaft. Since the treatment in Chapter 4 made use of allowable shear stress, the maximum shear-stress theory as a basis of strength was implied there. If on the twisting moment is superposed either an axial load, commonly called *thrust*, or a bending moment, or both, then any allowable load components, potential load margins, or necessary dimensions will depend on the particular strength theory employed.

For simple load combinations, the "critical" section to be investigated should obviously be where the maximum twisting moment *and* the maximum bending moment or axial force are transmitted; when this is not obvious, a few likely sections must be looked into. In the process the twisting-moment, bending-moment, and axial-force diagrams will be found helpful. Whenever there is doubt about the criticality of suspected sections, these diagrams should always be sketched alongside the free bodies.

Let σ_x denote the maximum fiber stress due to either bending or thrust or a combination of the two, and let τ_{xy} be the maximum shear stress due to twist at the same section; these are the stress components at points on the periphery of the shaft that are farthest from the neutral axis for pure bending. Whichever sign σ_x has, the resulting principal stresses will always have opposite signs; this can be visualized in Mohr's circle always straddling the τ axis. Equation 10.28 gives the principal stresses, σ_1 and σ_2, thus:

$$\left.\begin{array}{r}\sigma_1\\[1.2em]\sigma_2\end{array}\right\} = \frac{\sigma_x}{2} \pm \sqrt{(\sigma_x/2)^2 + \tau_{xy}{}^2}. \qquad (a)$$

Substituting these values of σ_1 and σ_2 in the criterion for yielding by the maximum shear-stress theory, namely, $\sigma_1 - \sigma_2 = \sigma_e$, we obtain, after simplification,

$$\sigma_x{}^2 + 4\tau_{xy}{}^2 = \sigma_e{}^2. \tag{b}$$

In dimensionless form, the interaction equation becomes

$$x^2 + \frac{y^2}{(\frac{1}{2})^2} = 1, \tag{c}$$

where $x = \sigma_x/\sigma_e$ and $y = \tau_{xy}/\sigma_e$. Figure 12.9 shows the interaction curve "a" which is the graph of Eq. c in the first quadrant. The entire curve is an ellipse with semiaxes of lengths 1 and $\frac{1}{2}$.

Using instead the criterion for yielding by the maximum distortion-energy theory, namely, $\sigma_1{}^2 - \sigma_1\sigma_2 + \sigma_2{}^2 = \sigma_e{}^2$, we obtain

$$\sigma_x{}^2 + 3\tau_{xy}{}^2 = \sigma_e{}^2, \tag{d}$$

which in dimensionless form is

$$x^2 + \frac{y^2}{(1/\sqrt{3})^2} = 1. \tag{e}$$

The interaction curve for the start of yielding by this theory is also an ellipse; its semiaxes have lengths 1 and $1/\sqrt{3}$. The curve marked "b" in Fig. 12.9 is the plot in the first quadrant.

Illustrative Example 2. A solid circular shaft is to transmit a twisting moment of 20,000 in.-lb while resisting a maximum bending moment of 15,000 in.-lb. Using a material with a tensile yield strength of 60,000

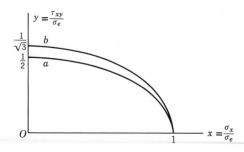

FIG. 12.9

psi, calculate the necessary shaft diameter based (1) on the maximum shear-stress theory, and then (2) on the maximum distortion-energy theory. Apply a safety factor of 3.

SOLUTION. The stress components are

$$\sigma_x = \frac{Mc}{I} = \frac{32M}{\pi d^3} = \frac{32(15,000)}{\pi d^3} \ ; \qquad \sigma_y = 0;$$

$$\tau_{xy} = \frac{Tc}{I_p} = \frac{16T}{\pi d^3} = \frac{16(20,000)}{\pi d^3}.$$

In lieu of σ_e, we will use a working stress of $60,000/3 = 20,000$ psi.

(1) By the maximum shear-stress theory, we find from Eq. b,

$$\left[\frac{32(15,000)}{\pi d^3}\right]^2 + 4\left[\frac{16(20,000)}{\pi d^3}\right]^2 = (20,000)^2,$$

that

$$d^3 = \frac{40}{\pi} = 12.74.$$

This gives

$$d = 2.34 \text{ in.} \qquad\qquad\qquad\qquad Ans.$$

(2) By the maximum distortion-energy theory, we obtain from Eq. d,

$$\left[\frac{32(15,000)}{\pi d^3}\right]^2 + 3\left[\frac{16(20,000)}{\pi d^3}\right]^2 = (20,000)^2,$$

whence

$$d^3 = \frac{8\sqrt{21}}{\pi} = 11.68,$$

and

$$d = 2.27 \text{ in.} \qquad\qquad\qquad\qquad Ans.$$

We note that the preceding results are consistent with the observation that the maximum shear-stress theory is more conservative.

PROBLEMS

12.7. The pulley of negligibly small weight drives a shaft to whose free end it is keyed as shown. At full load, the belt tensions are 150 lb and 50 lb. What should be the shaft diameter if the material has a tensile yield strength of 40,000 psi and a safety factor of 4 is used? Base the design first on (*a*) the maximum shear-stress theory, and then on (*b*) the maximum distortion-energy theory.

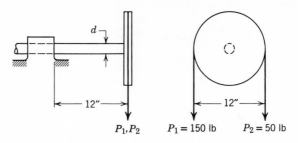

P_1, P_2 $P_1 = 150$ lb $P_2 = 50$ lb

FIG. P12.7

12.8. In the preceding problem, assume the shaft diameter is 1.5 in. For the same torque transmitted, what maximum values may the belt tensions have? Use the same material property and safety factor as above and solve on basis of the maximum shear-stress theory.

12.9. The bent is a 2-in. diameter rod of steel for which the yield strength in simple tension is 36,000 psi. How large must the forces P be in order that the middle 2-ft portion will start to yield

(*a*) according to the maximum shear-stress theory?

(*b*) according to the maximum distortion-energy theory?

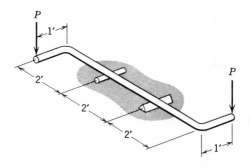

FIG. P12.9

12.10. An equivalent working strength in simple tension of 20,000 psi is to be used in the design of this post. Calculate the minimum wall thickness at the base, where the outside diameter of the hollow tube is 8 in., using

(*a*) the maximum shear-stress theory;

(*b*) the maximum distortion-energy theory.

(*Hint:* Combine vectorially the bending moments about the Y and Z axes at the base.)

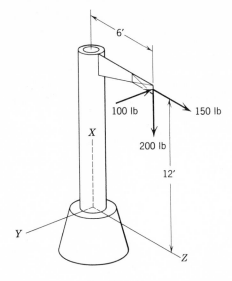

FIG. P12.10

12.11. This wide-flange beam weighs 31 lb per foot. Calculate the maximum allowable load P based on a working tensile stress of 18,000 psi, using first (a) the maximum shear-stress theory and then (b) the maximum distortion-energy theory. (*Hint:* Check the states of stress at points 1 and 2, assuming the shear stresses τ_{xy} and τ_{xz} are as given on Figs. 6.7 and 6.8.)

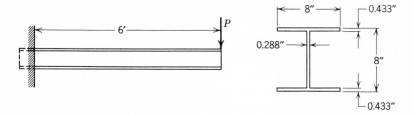

FIG. P12.11

12.12. If the above beam were rectangular in cross section, say 3 in. by 6 in., would there be any difference in the values of P by the two theories? Explain.

12.7 Thin-Walled Pressure Vessels. Pressure vessels are an important class of stressed bodies that are more or less complete structures in themselves. Although it is not typical of any of the simple structural elements we have discussed, the pressure vessel in its entirety may act

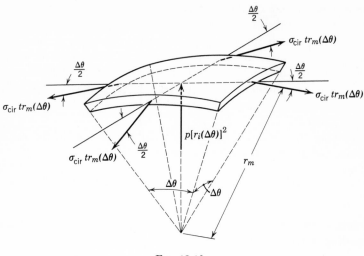

FIG. 12.10

as a tension or compression member, as a torsion member, or sometimes even as a beam. On the other hand, a pressure vessel is at times considered to consist of a series of longitudinal strips acting in unison as beams on an elastic foundation.*

For the storage of industrial gases under moderate pressure, the thin-walled vessel usually has the form of a surface of revolution. In this article we will treat only the two most common forms, the sphere and the cylinder.

Owing to the characteristic nature of fluids at rest, the forces exerted by a confined fluid on the surface of a container are everywhere normal to that surface. If the container walls are curved and very thin, the tensile stresses induced in them by the fluid pressure may be assumed uniform in magnitude across the wall thickness. Essentially, the resultant tensile forces per unit length along the periphery are considered to act tangentially to the median surface. Such stresses are called *membrane stresses*.

Let us consider first the spherical vessel. Imagine a small square element cut out of the pressure vessel's "skin" by two pairs of diametral planes, the two planes of each pair forming a small central angle $\Delta\theta$ (Fig. 12.10). The curved inner surface on which the pressure p acts projects onto the tangent plane as a small square of area $r_i(\Delta\theta)[r_i(\Delta\theta)]$,

---

* For instance, see M. Hetenyi, *Beams on Elastic Foundation*, pp. 30–32, The University of Michigan Press, Ann Arbor, 1946.

where r_i is the inner radius. The resultant pressure force on this differential area is therefore $p[r_i(\Delta\theta)]^2$; it is in the radial direction. The edge of the element lying in each diametral plane has an area $tr_m(\Delta\theta)$, where $t = r_0 - r_i$ is the thickness and $r_m = (r_i + r_0)/2$ is the mean radius. Owing to symmetry, for each edge of the small element the resultant of the circumferential stresses is $\sigma_{\mathrm{cir}}tr_m(\Delta\theta)$, inclined an angle $\Delta\theta/2$ away from the tangent plane. These five resultants are displayed in Fig. 12.10.

Applying the condition of translational equilibrium in the radial direction, and ignoring body forces, we write

$$\Sigma F_{\mathrm{rad}} = 0 = p[r_i(\Delta\theta)]^2 - 4\sigma_{\mathrm{cir}}tr_m(\Delta\theta) \sin\frac{\Delta\theta}{2}. \qquad (a)$$

Passing to the limit, where $\sin(d\theta/2)$ becomes $d\theta/2$, we obtain from the preceding, after dividing through by $d\theta^2$, the result

$$\sigma_{\mathrm{cir}} = \frac{pr_i^{\,2}}{2tr_m} \cong \frac{pr_i}{2t}, \qquad (12.4)$$

since r_i differs but slightly from r_m for small values of t.

The condition of symmetry makes it impossible for any diametral plane to transmit shear stresses. Therefore, except for the comparatively small compressive stress at the inner surface, equal to the fluid pressure itself, each point in the vessel wall is essentially in a state of biaxial tensile stress, the two principal stresses being of the same magnitude: $\sigma_1 = \sigma_2 = pr_i/2t$, and $\sigma_3 \cong 0$. As shown in Chapter 10, the maximum shear stress in such a case is $\tau_{\max} = \sigma_1/2 = pr_i/4t$; it occurs on planes inclined 45 degrees to both the radial and tangential directions.

In the cylindrical pressure vessel, the situation is somewhat different. Although, because of symmetry, all radial (longitudinal) and transverse planes are free of shear stress, distinction must now be made between the circumferential and the longitudinal stresses in the vessel wall. Figure 12.11a shows an edge view of a small element cut out of the vessel wall by two radial planes inclined an angle $\Delta\theta$ to each other and by two transverse planes a distance ΔL apart. This element projects onto the tangent plane as a rectangle of area $r_i(\Delta\theta)\Delta L$; hence the resultant pressure force on its inner surface is $pr_i(\Delta\theta)\Delta L$. The resultant tangential tension force on each of the two longitudinal edges of the element, due to the circumferential stress, is $\sigma_{\mathrm{cir}}t(\Delta L)$. These three resultants are represented in Fig. 12.11a. The two resultant tension forces in the longitudinal direction, due to σ_{long} on each transverse face,

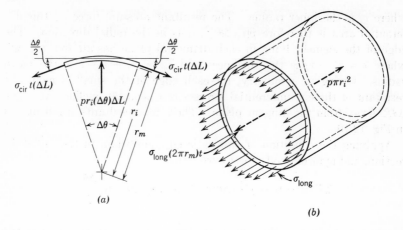

Fig. 12.11

are self-balancing and are not shown in the sketch. As before, translational equilibrium in the radial direction leads to

$$\Sigma F_{\rm rad} = 0 = pr_i(\Delta\theta)\Delta L - 2\sigma_{\rm cir}t(\Delta L)\sin\frac{\Delta\theta}{2},\qquad (b)$$

from which $\qquad\qquad \sigma_{\rm cir} = \dfrac{pr_i}{t}.\qquad\qquad\qquad (12.5)$

To evaluate the longitudinal stresses, we need to consider another free body. One is shown in Fig. 12.11b, which stands for part of the cylinder isolated by a transverse cutting plane. The resultant of the pressure forces in the longitudinal direction is $p\pi r_i{}^2$, where $\pi r_i{}^2$ is the area either of the closed end, if that is flat, or of its projection on a transverse plane, if it is curved. The resultant of the tensile forces due to the longitudinal stress is $\sigma_{\rm long}(2\pi r_m t)$, where $2\pi r_m t$ is approximately the area of the thin ring exposed by the sectioning transverse plane. The radial pressure forces are self-balancing and are not shown in the sketch. Summing forces in the longitudinal direction, thus:

$$\Sigma F_{\rm long} = 0 = p\pi r_i{}^2 - \sigma_{\rm long}2\pi r_m t,\qquad (c)$$

we obtain $\qquad\qquad \sigma_{\rm long} = \dfrac{pr_i{}^2}{2tr_m} \cong \dfrac{pr_i}{2t}.\qquad\qquad (12.6)$

From the preceding two equations we note that the circumferential or hoop stress in thin-walled cylindrical pressure vessels is twice the longitudinal stress. Points in the vessel wall are essentially in a state of biaxial tension, the two principal stresses being unequal in magnitude: $\sigma_1 = pr_i/t$, $\sigma_2 = pr_i/2t$, and $\sigma_3 = 0$. Therefore the maximum shear stresses are of magnitude $\tau_{\max} = \sigma_1/2 = pr_i/2t$, and they occur on planes inclined 45 deg to both the radial and tangential directions but parallel to the longitudinal axis of the cylinder.

Comparison of Eqs. 12.4 and 12.5 reveals that, for the same radius and wall thickness and the same allowable stress in the material, the spherical vessel can withstand twice as much pressure as the cylindrical one.* Were it not for the higher cost of fabrication, the spherical vessel is therefore to be preferred for storage purposes.

Nevertheless, the cylindrical vessel lends itself better to the experimental investigation of the strength theories. By superposing on the system of stresses induced by fluid pressure another system due to an axial tension load, or due to an eccentrically applied transverse load which will produce the combined effects of torsion and bending, or due to combinations of such loads, the resourceful experimenter can vary the ratios of the principal stresses.

Illustrative Example 3. A cylindrical pressure vessel, having an internal diameter of 40 in. and a wall thickness of $\frac{1}{2}$ in., is subjected to an internal pressure of 150 psi. What maximum external twisting moment may be superposed on the pressure load without having the state of the stress in the vessel wall away from the ends considered unsafe? The tensile yield strength of the material is 60,000 psi, and a safety factor of 4 is to be used. Base the solution on the maximum shear-stress theory.

SOLUTION. The membrane stresses are

$$\sigma_x = \sigma_{\text{long}} = \frac{pr_i}{2t} = \frac{150(20)}{2(0.5)} = 3000 \text{ psi};$$

$$\sigma_y = \sigma_{\text{cir}} = \frac{pr_i}{t} = 6000 \text{ psi}.$$

Since the ratio of the wall thickness to the radius is very small, the shear stresses due to the twisting moment may be considered uniform

---

* The cylindrical pressure vessel suffers from a still more serious disadvantage, particularly if the ends are flat. The so-called discontinuity stresses at the junction of cylindrical shell and flat plate, owing to the unequal free deformation of the two, can be several times larger than the simple membrane stresses. Rounding the ends, especially using hemispherical heads, minimizes this condition. See, for instance, J. P. Den Hartog, *Advanced Strength of Materials*, pp. 166–169, McGraw-Hill Book Company, New York, 1952.

in magnitude across the wall; accordingly, the approximate formula, Eq. 4.18, $\tau = T/2At$, may be used to calculate this value. For this we need the area enclosed by the median line: $A = \pi(20 + 0.25)^2 = 1288$ in.^{2} Substituting this in the approximate formula, we find

$$\tau_{xy} = \frac{T}{2At} = \frac{T}{2(1288)(0.5)} = \frac{T}{1288} \text{ psi.}$$

(This value differs from the correct maximum and minimum by only slightly over 1%.)

Since τ_{xy} is as yet undetermined, the principal stresses σ_1 and σ_2 may or may not have the same sign. The correct value of τ_{xy} is that which will be consistent with the relative signs of σ_1 and σ_2. Now, the allowable maximum principal stress in simple tension is $60,000/4 = 15,000$ psi; therefore the upper limit for τ_{max} by the shear-stress theory is $15,000/2 = 7500$ psi. Considering that the mean stress, $\sigma_{mean} = (\sigma_x + \sigma_y)/2 = (3000 + 6000)/2 = 4500$ psi, which locates the center of Mohr's circle, is smaller than the largest $\tau_{max} = 7500$ psi, which gives the radius, we conclude that the circle will necessarily straddle the τ axis, and therefore σ_1 and σ_2 will have opposite signs. Accordingly, the circle shown

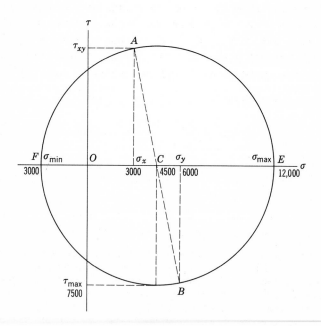

Fig. 12.12

in Fig. 12.12 is the correct one. The value of τ_{xy} is now found from the figure as one arm of the right triangle, whose hypotenuse is the value of the allowable τ_{max}, thus:

$$\tau_{xy} = \sqrt{(7500)^2 - (1500)^2} = 7350 \text{ psi.}$$

Finally, we find the allowable twisting moment T to be

$$T = 1288(7350) = 9.47 \times 10^6 \text{ in.-lb.} \qquad Ans.$$

PROBLEMS

12.13. A spherical pressure vessel with a 12-ft inside diameter is to store gas under 500 psi pressure. If a working tensile stress of 10,000 psi is specified, how thin may the wall be, biaxial stress being assumed? Note that all three theories lead to the same result.

12.14. If the triaxiality in the state of stress at the inner surface is taken into account in the preceding problem, how thin may the wall of the pressure vessel be (a) by the maximum shear-stress theory? (b) By the maximum distortion-energy theory?

12.15. The pressure vessel of Prob. 12.13 is modified into a cylinder with hemispherical ends. For the same conditions, how thin may the cylinder wall be (a) by the maximum shear-stress theory? (b) By the maximum distortion-energy theory? Assume biaxiality of stress.

12.16. Do Prob. 12.15, taking into account the triaxiality in the state of stress at the inner cylindrical surface.

12.17. If $\sigma_1 = 10,000$ psi, $\sigma_2 = 5000$ psi, and $\sigma_3 = -5000$ psi, what percentage of the total strain energy per unit volume is distortive? Assume $\nu = 0.3$.

12.18. In uniaxial tension, what fraction of the total does the distortion energy per unit volume constitute? Use $\nu = 0.3$.

12.19. Derive an expression for the distortion energy per unit volume for plane stress in terms of σ_x, σ_y, and τ_{xy}.

12.20. In pure shear, plane stress, what percentage of the total is the distortion energy per unit volume? (*Note:* Distortion energy is sometimes called shear energy. Does this make sense?)

12.21. A long cylindrical tube with closed ends, with a 10-in. inside diameter and a 0.10-in. wall, is pressurized to 200 psi. How much axial tension may be superimposed if the tensile yield strength of the material is 36,000 psi? Use a safety factor of 4 and analyze first (a) on basis of the maximum shear-stress theory and then (b) on basis of the maximum distortion-energy theory.

12.22. Instead of the tension load, how much torque may be applied on the preceding pressurized tube?

12.23. The steel vessel, whose wall thickness is 0.2 in., is subjected simultaneously to an internal pressure of 500 psi and the eccentric transverse load of 20,000 lb. Calculate the principal stresses at points A and B on the periphery adjacent to the wall support. Assuming proportional loading, calculate how much additional internal pressure and how much additional transverse load would initiate yielding, according to the maximum shear-stress theory. The yield strength of the material in simple tension is 40,000 psi. (*Note:* It is assumed that the cylinder wall will not buckle locally.)

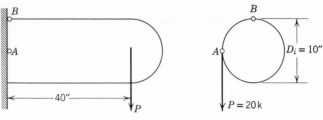

FIG. P12.23

12.24. If two linear strain gages were attached to the surface of a thin-walled pressurized cylinder, away from the ends, one in the axial the other in the circumferential direction, would they register strain readings in the ratio of 1 to 2? Explain.

12.25. Derive an expression for the elastic change in the diameter of a thin-walled sphere due to internal pressure.

13

ENERGY CONCEPTS

13.1 Energy Stored in a Strained Member. As a body deforms on account of impressed forces, it stores energy of strain; this is completely recoverable as useful work so long as the proportional limit is not overstepped anywhere in the body. The total energy obviously equals the sum of the energies stored in all the body's constituent particles. In Chapter 2 we developed an expression (Eq. 2.9) for the energy stored per unit volume of material; this can be stated in terms of the stresses multiplied by their corresponding strains, or as a homogeneous quadratic function of either the stresses only or the strains only. Assuming the stresses are known everywhere in the body, it is clear that we can obtain the total energy stored by performing the above-mentioned summation to be extended throughout the entire volume of the body. Since, as mentioned in Chapter 2, complete solutions to the stress problem exist for but relatively few geometries and loading conditions, we shall develop here explicit forms representing this summation only for the elementary structural elements when subjected to the modes of loading that we have discussed.

For a member in simple tension or compression, all the stress components are zero except σ_x, the X axis being assumed in the direction of the member's longitudinal axis. Therefore Eq. 2.9 becomes (see Eq. 3.2, p. 44)

$$\frac{dU}{dV} = \frac{\sigma_x^2}{2E} = \frac{F^2}{2EA^2}, \tag{a}$$

where F is the local axial force being transmitted. An element of volume that is convenient to handle in dealing with slender members is $dV = A \, dx$, the volume of a thin transverse slice. Substituting this in Eq. a, solving for dU, and integrating, we obtain

$$U = \int_0^L \frac{F^2}{2EA} \, dx. \qquad (13.1)$$

The proper expression for F as a function of x should, of course, be substituted before the integral can be evaluated.

In round solid shafts transmitting torsional moments, the only nonzero stress components are τ_{xy} and τ_{xz}, which, as shown in Chapter 4, combine to give a τ that varies linearly with the distance ρ from the geometric or neutral axis of the member. Then Eq. 2.9 reduces to (see Eq. g, p. 80)

$$\frac{dU}{dV} = \frac{\tau^2}{2G} = \frac{T^2 \rho^2}{2GI_p{}^2}, \qquad (b)$$

where T is the local torque being transmitted. Substituting for dV the equivalent $(dx)\int_A dA$, which is the volume of a thin slice of shaft, and solving for dU, we get

$$dU = \frac{T^2 \, dx}{2GI_p{}^2} \int_A \rho^2 \, dA = \frac{T^2}{2GI_p} \, dx. \qquad (c)$$

Note that ρ has to go inside the integral sign because it is the only variable in the region of integration. From Eq. c we obtain the total energy

$$U = \int_0^L \frac{T^2}{2GI_p} \, dx. \qquad (13.2)$$

In a beam whose transverse sections transmit bending moments as well as shear forces, the two nonzero stress components are σ_x and τ_{xy}.[*] In this case Eq. 2.9 becomes (see Eq. 6.2, p. 146 and Eq. 6.5, p. 155)

$$\frac{dU}{dV} = \frac{\sigma_x{}^2}{2E} + \frac{\tau_{xy}{}^2}{2G} = \frac{M^2 y^2}{2EI^2} + \frac{V^2 Q^2}{2GI^2 t^2}. \qquad (d)$$

---

[*] This is approximately true in the general case. For unusual cross sections, like W̄ and I structural shapes, the component τ_{xz} may be quite appreciable. (See Article 6.5.)

Again, substituting $(dx) \displaystyle\int_A dA$ for dV and solving for dU, we get

$$dU = \frac{M^2\, dx}{2EI^2} \int_A y^2\, dA + \frac{V^2\, dx}{2GI^2} \int_A \left(\frac{Q}{t}\right)^2 dA$$

$$= \frac{M^2}{2EI}\, dx + \frac{V^2\, dx}{2GI^2} \int_A \left(\frac{Q}{t}\right)^2 dA. \qquad (e)$$

Hence $\qquad U = \displaystyle\int_0^L \frac{M^2}{2EI}\, dx + \int_0^L \frac{V^2}{2GI^2} \int_A \left(\frac{Q}{t}\right)^2 dA\, dx. \qquad (13.3)$

If the beam is subject to pure bending only, or if its span-to-depth ratio is of the order of 15 or more, the last term in Eq. 13.3, representing the energy due to shear, may be ignored; then the expression for U simplifies to

$$U = \int_0^L \frac{M^2}{2EI}\, dx. \qquad (13.4)$$

When the loading is a combination of tension or compression, torsion, and bending, the energy stored in a member is obtained as the sum of these magnitudes. This is valid because energy is a scalar quantity that obeys the rules of ordinary addition.

Illustrative Example 1. The right-angle bent ABC of Fig. 13.1, a uniform rod of diameter d and length $3L$, is held in a horizontal plane by a built-in support in the vertical wall at C. It bears a single concentrated vertical load P at the free end A. Ignoring the rod's weight as well as the effects of direct shear, derive the expression for the total energy stored, assuming that the load P is gradually applied.

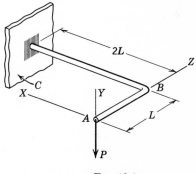

SOLUTION. For the portion AB, the major energy-producing action is bending, whereas for the part BC it is a combination of torsion and bending. Setting up a right-handed

FIG. 13.1

coordinate system with origin at A as shown in the sketch, we define the bending and twisting moments by the following expressions:

From A to B, $M_x = +Pz$, $0 < z < L$,
From B to C, $M_z = -Px$, $0 < x < 2L$,
From B to C, $M_x = T = PL$, $0 < x < 2L$.

Then, by Eqs. 13.2 and 13.4, we have

$$U = \int_0^L \frac{(+Pz)^2}{2EI_x}\, dx + \int_0^{2L} \frac{(-Px)^2}{2EI_z}\, dz + \int_0^{2L} \frac{(PL)^2}{2GI_p}\, dx.$$

Setting $I_x = I_z = \pi d^4/64$ and $I_p = \pi d^4/32$, performing the indicated operations, and simplifying, we obtain

$$U = \frac{32P^2 L^3}{3\pi E d^4}\left(9 + \frac{3E}{G}\right). \qquad Ans.$$

PROBLEMS

13.1. Considering only the energy due to torsion as given by Eq. 13.2, derive an approximate expression for the strain energy stored in a helical spring, of mean coil diameter $D = 2R$, wire diameter d, and shear elasticity modulus G, due to a gradually applied compressive load P. Assume that the coils, numbering N, will not touch at maximum compression.

13.2. Considering only the energy due to bending as given by Eq. 13.4, derive an approximate expression for the strain energy stored in a simply supported uniform beam, of span L, rectangular cross section with depth h and width b, and elasticity modulus E, due to a gradually applied uniformly distributed load of intensity p over the entire span.

13.3. Considering only the energy due to bending, derive an approximate expression for the strain energy stored in a uniformly stressed (variable strength) cantilever beam of rectangular cross section, of uniform depth h, maximum width b, length L, and elasticity modulus E, due to a gradually applied transverse load P at its free end.

13.4. Considering only the energy due to bending, derive an approximate expression for the strain energy stored in a slightly buckled hinged-end Euler column, of initial length l, maximum transverse deflection δ, minimum second-moment of cross-sectional area I, and elasticity modulus E, due to a steady central compressive load P, it being assumed that P remains at the critical Euler value and that the buckled form of the column is sinusoidal.

13.2 Reciprocity of Static Deflections. In the preceding article we expressed the energy stored in a strained body in terms of the *internal* forces and moments being transmitted across the various sections of the body. It is, of course, just as valid to express this energy as the work performed by the *external* forces and moments that constitute the loads on the body: energy conservation is implied in the assumption of elasticity. This alternative way of stating the energy leads to significant relationships which in turn furnish us with powerful tools of analysis.

To provide a physical picture of what is involved, let us consider an elastic body resting on unyielding supports. Imagine two external loads P_1 and P_2 applied gradually on the body at points 1 and 2 (Fig. 13.2) in such a manner that they start acting at the same instant and attain their full magnitudes simultaneously. Assuming that the material itself as well as the body obey Hooke's law, we find the work done by the P's to be

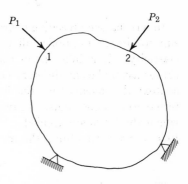

FIG. 13.2

$$U = \frac{P_1\delta_1}{2} + \frac{P_2\delta_2}{2}, \qquad (a)$$

where δ_1 is the deflection of point 1 in the direction of P_1, and δ_2 that of point 2 in the direction of P_2. Note that these are not necessarily the total displacements from the unstrained state; they could be only components of these displacements. In the language of mechanics, we call these the *work-absorbing components* of the total deflections. The deflection δ_1 is due to both P_1 and P_2; similarly, δ_2 is due to both P_1 and P_2. The assumption of Hooke's law allows us to express these deflections as follows:

$$\delta_1 = \alpha_{11}P_1 + \alpha_{12}P_2$$

and $$\delta_2 = \alpha_{21}P_1 + \alpha_{22}P_2. \qquad (b)$$

The α's are called *deflection influence coefficients;* that is, α_{11} reflects the influence of P_1 on the deflection at point 1 in the P_1 direction, and α_{12} that of P_2 on the deflection of point 1 in the P_1 direction, and so on.

Suppose, instead of the two P's coming on simultaneously, P_1 is applied first, followed by P_2 *after* P_1 has attained full magnitude. Then the work done will be

$$U = \frac{P_1(\alpha_{11}P_1)}{2} + \frac{P_2(\alpha_{22}P_2)}{2} + P_1(\alpha_{12}P_2), \qquad (c)$$

where the factor $1/2$ is not needed in the last term because P_1 is fully acting while its point of application is being displaced by P_2. Now let us reverse the order, applying P_2 first, followed by P_1 after P_2 has attained full value. This time we obtain for the work expended,

$$U = \frac{P_2(\alpha_{22}P_2)}{2} + \frac{P_1(\alpha_{11}P_1)}{2} + P_2(\alpha_{21}P_1). \qquad (d)$$

In writing the preceding expressions, we have assumed the principle of superposition; its applicability is guaranteed by the property of linear elasticity. It is inherent in this principle that the order in which the causes act makes no difference on the final over-all effect; in the present context this means that the final energy stored, which equals the external work done, must always be the same regardless of the order in which the loads are applied. Hence, equating the expressions given by Eqs. c and d, we obtain the result

$$\alpha_{12} = \alpha_{21}. \qquad (e)$$

The general proposition is proved as follows. Let the P's stand for *generalized forces* (that is, forces as well as moments), which may include the support reactions; and let the δ's denote the *corresponding generalized displacements* (that is, linear as well as angular shifts). Without loss of generality we will assume that there are n discrete P's, one at each of n distinct sites (continuously distributed forces may always be replaced by an equivalent system of differential resultants). Then, in the format of Eqs. b, we write the generalized deflection at site i as

$$\delta_i = \alpha_{i1}P_1 + \alpha_{i2}P_2 + \cdots + \alpha_{in}P_n$$

$$= \sum_{j=1}^{n} \alpha_{ij}P_j. \qquad (f)$$

Assuming that the P's are applied gradually and simultaneously, we can express the work they perform as follows:

$$U = \frac{P_1\delta_1}{2} + \frac{P_2\delta_2}{2} + \cdots + \frac{P_n\delta_n}{2}$$

$$= \frac{1}{2}\sum_{i=1}^{n} P_i\delta_i = \frac{1}{2}\sum_{i=1}^{n}\sum_{j=1}^{n} \alpha_{ij}P_iP_j, \qquad (13.5)$$

where we have used Eq. f.

It is evident that U is a homogeneous quadratic function of the P's. Now, according to Euler's theorem on homogeneous functions,[*]

$$\sum_{k=1}^{n} P_k \frac{\partial U}{\partial P_k} = 2U. \tag{g}$$

Differentiating U in Eq. 13.5 with respect to P_k, we observe that only two single summations enter into the process: one is the sum of products containing $P_k P_j$, that is, when P_i becomes P_k, and the other is the sum containing $P_i P_k$, that is, when P_j becomes P_k; hence,

$$\frac{\partial U}{\partial P_k} = \frac{1}{2} \sum_{j=1}^{n} \alpha_{kj} P_j + \frac{1}{2} \sum_{i=1}^{n} \alpha_{ik} P_i$$

$$= \frac{1}{2} \sum_{j=1}^{n} \alpha_{kj} P_j + \frac{1}{2} \sum_{j=1}^{n} \alpha_{jk} P_j, \tag{h}$$

since the "dummy" indices indicating the ranges of summation may be changed without altering the meaning of the symbols. Multiplying both sides of Eq. h by P_k and summing, as required by the left-hand side of Eq. g, we obtain

$$\sum_{k=1}^{n} P_k \frac{\partial U}{\partial P_k} = \sum_{k=1}^{n} P_k \left(\frac{1}{2} \sum_{j=1}^{n} \alpha_{kj} P_j + \frac{1}{2} \sum_{j=1}^{n} \alpha_{jk} P_j \right). \tag{i}$$

Since in all the preceding summations the subscripts take on all the values in the same finite range, the outside summation symbol may be placed within each of the inside summation symbols. Therefore

$$\sum_{k=1}^{n} P_k \frac{\partial U}{\partial P_k} = \frac{1}{2} \sum_{j=1}^{n} \sum_{k=1}^{n} \alpha_{kj} P_k P_j + \frac{1}{2} \sum_{j=1}^{n} \sum_{k=1}^{n} \alpha_{jk} P_k P_j. \tag{j}$$

Then, setting the right-hand side of Eq. j equal to $2U$ (see Eq. g), and replacing the dummy subscript k by i, we obtain, by virtue of Eq. 13.5

$$\frac{1}{2} \sum_{i=1}^{n} \sum_{j=1}^{n} \alpha_{ij} P_i P_j + \frac{1}{2} \sum_{i=1}^{n} \sum_{j=1}^{n} \alpha_{ji} P_i P_j = \sum_{i=1}^{n} \sum_{j=1}^{n} \alpha_{ij} P_i P_j. \tag{k}$$

Collecting terms, we get

$$\frac{1}{2} \sum_{i=1}^{n} \sum_{j=1}^{n} \alpha_{ji} P_i P_j = \frac{1}{2} \sum_{i=1}^{n} \sum_{j=1}^{n} \alpha_{ij} P_i P_j, \tag{l}$$

from which it follows that

$$\alpha_{ij} = \alpha_{ji}, \tag{13.6}$$

which was to be proved.

Equation 13.6, of which Eq. *e* is a special case, is a symbolic statement of the reciprocity of static deflections.* The relationship may be loosely expressed in words as follows: *The generalized deflection at point i caused by a generalized force at point j is numerically equal to the generalized deflection at point j caused by a like generalized force at point i.* It is understood that the generalized deflections are in the directions of the generalized forces; this is explicit in the definition of the influence coefficient, which may be given in the equivalent statement: α_{ij} is equal numerically to the deflection at site *i* in a certain specified direction due to a unit load at site *j* in another specified direction, all other loads (but not reactions) being assumed zero.

13.3 Castigliano's Theorem.   Using the results of Eq. 13.6 in Eq. *h* of the preceding article, and making the proper changes in the dummy subscripts, we find

$$\frac{\partial U}{\partial P_i} = \sum_{j=1}^{n} \alpha_{ij} P_j. \qquad (a)$$

Comparison of this with Eq. *f* reveals the right-hand sides to be identical. Therefore there follows the significant relation

$$\frac{\partial U}{\partial P_i} = \delta_i. \qquad (13.7)$$

Equation 13.7 embodies a famous theorem. Formally this is Part II of *Castigliano's theorem*, Part I being

$$\frac{\partial U}{\partial \delta_i} = P_i.\dagger \qquad (b)$$

Starting out with the expressions of the *P*'s as linear functions of the *δ*'s, analogous to Eq. *f* of the preceding article, one can derive Part I of the theorem in much the same way as the foregoing. In the remaining discussion we shall be concerned largely with Part II, Eq. 13.7.

Castigliano's theorem may be stated in words as follows: *The deflection at any point in a loaded body that obeys Hooke's law, in the direction of a force acting there, is given by the first derivative of the total strain energy*

---

* The reciprocity theorem for static deflections is attributed to J. C. Maxwell, who discovered the relationship for two forces, and to E. Betti, who proved it for the general case. Lord Rayleigh extended the principle to dynamical situations. See S. Timoshenko, *History of Strength of Materials*, pp. 207, and 320–321, McGraw-Hill Book Company, New York, 1953.

† See E. S. Andrews, *Elastic Stresses in Structures*, pp. 15–16, Scott, Greenwood and Son, London, 1919. This is a translation of A. Castigliano's *Théorie de l'Équilibre des Systèmes Élastiques et ses Applications*, Turin, 1879.

stored in the body relative to that force. We remark that this theorem should have been anticipated in view of Eqs. 2.10a and b, p. 32, to which the preceding relations are strictly analogous.

Elegant as the mathematical derivation is, it leaves something to be desired. Therefore, although we will not derive the statement anew from a different viewpoint, we should at least mention the salient point in Castigliano's original derivation, partly as a courtesy to him but more importantly because an understanding of the physical situation is essential to a proper interpretation of the sign of the deflection. This is the following.

If the force P_i is given a small increment dP_i *in the sense of* P_i, then the change in the stored energy U will be $dU = \delta_i dP_i$ (this principal part will differ from the total increment by the amount $\alpha_{ii}(dP_i)^2/2$, an infinitesimal of second order), from which Eq. 13.7 follows. Observe that if δ_i agrees in sense with dP_i, dU will be positive. But dP_i has the same sense as P_i. Hence we have the following rule for interpreting the sign of δ_i: *If δ_i as given by Eq. 13.7 comes out positive, it is in the sense of Pi.*

PROBLEM

13.5. Derive Part I of Castigliano's theorem, Eq. b. (*Hint:* First express the P's as linear functions of the δ's, using *force influence coefficients,* β_{ij}.)

13.4 Deflections by Energy Methods. If a structural member, or an entire structure for that matter, has only one external load on it, the deflection at the site and in the direction of the load may be obtained very simply by equating the work done by the lone load to the stored energy in terms of the internal forces induced by the load. For instance, in Example 1, p. 378, equating the work done by P to the stored energy, thus:

$$\frac{P\delta}{2} = \frac{32P^2L^3}{3\pi Ed^4}\left(9 + \frac{3E}{G}\right),$$

we obtain $$\delta = \frac{64PL^3}{3\pi Ed^4}\left(9 + \frac{3E}{G}\right).$$

Note that the same result follows by application of Castigliano's theorem: $\delta = \partial U/\partial P$. (Also see Article 4.8.)

When several loads act on a member or structure and the deflection at some one point is sought, Castigliano's theorem is invaluable. If at the point in question there is, among the given loads, actually a force in the direction the deflection is desired, the total energy may be differentiated directly relative to this force. If, however, there is no force at the point of interest, then a force is applied there in the desired direction, the expression for the total energy is formulated and then differentiated relative to this force, and finally the fictitious (also called auxiliary) force is set equal to zero.

For structures made up of slender members, whose individual energy-storage capabilities are given by Eqs. 13.1 to 13.4, the following symbolic statement will be found useful:

$$\frac{\partial U}{\partial P} = \frac{\partial}{\partial P}\left(\sum \int_0^L \frac{F^2}{2EA}\,dx + \sum \int_0^L \frac{T^2}{2GI_p}\,dx + \sum \int_0^L \frac{M^2}{2EI}\,dx\right)$$

$$= \sum \int_0^L \frac{F(\partial F/\partial P)}{EA}\,dx + \sum \int_0^L \frac{T(\partial T/\partial P)}{GI_p}\,dx$$

$$+ \sum \int_0^L \frac{M(\partial M/\partial P)}{EI}\,dx, \tag{13.8}$$

where there are as many terms inside each summation sign as there are discrete members to which the integrals are applicable. The preceding is predicated on the validity of differentiation under the integral sign. Each integrand (before differentiation) is a continuous function of P and, between singularities, the first derivative of each internal force (or moment) with respect to P is also continuous. Therefore, except at the sites of the singularities themselves, we may say that the integral of the differentiated integrand is the same as the derivative of the integral.* The observant reader will no doubt anticipate that, in order to handle the singularities that are surely bound to arise, we shall bring in the singularity functions of Chapter 5. This will be illustrated in the following example.

Some writers like to attach the following interpretation to the derivatives inside the integral signs. Consider $\partial M/\partial P$, for example; this is the rate of change of the bending moment M with respect to P. If P were replaced by a unit load, then, so long as superposition is applicable, the derivative becomes numerically equal to the bending moment that would be caused by the unit load acting alone, the member being assumed supported in the same manner as under the actual loads. For this reason, there is the so-called *unit-load method* for determining deflections, in connection with which the last integral, say, in Eq. 13.8 is written in the form $\int \frac{Mm}{EI}\,dx$, m standing for the bending moment due to the unit

---

* See F. S. Woods, *Advanced Calculus*, pp. 141–142, Ginn and Company, Boston, 1934.

load. Analogous expressions may be used in lieu of the other integrals. Since this manner of writing the integrals entails no change in the fundamental concept which is at the core of Castigliano's theorem, and, furthermore, since there is really no great gain to speak of (indeed, if one were so careless as to retain m in units of force times length, he could be in for some confusion because a dimensional check would then show the integral to give force times length rather than length as it should) in adopting this "manicuring" viewpoint, we shall stay with the basic form of Eq. 13.8. Of course, nothing prevents us from considering the symbol m (in units of length) as representing $\partial M/\partial P$; it certainly is simpler to write.

Illustrative Example 2. By the energy method, derive the equation of the elastic curve for a simply supported uniform beam bearing a uniformly distributed load throughout its span.

SOLUTION.   Figure 13.3a shows the beam as a free body, together with the bending-moment diagram. Let M_1 denote the bending moment due to the actual load, that is,

$$M_1 = \frac{pLx}{2} - \frac{px^2}{2}.$$

On the beam, free of any load but supported as in the original, let P act by itself at a distance x_1 from the left end (Fig. 13.3b). The bending moment due to P then will be

$$M_2 = \frac{P(L - x_1)x}{L} - P\{x - x_1\}^1.$$

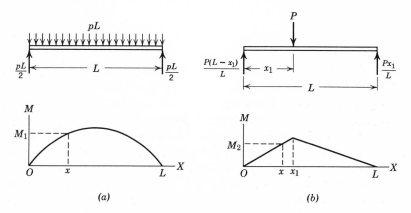

(a)   (b)

Fig. 13.3

If the two loads were now combined, the bending moment would be, by virtue of superposition,

$$M = M_1 + M_2.$$

Now, $$m = \frac{\partial M}{\partial P} = \frac{\partial M_2}{\partial P} = \left(\frac{L - x_1}{L}\right) x - \{x - x_1\}^1,$$

since M_1 does not contain P. Furthermore, since in the actual beam there is no load P, before evaluating the integral we should set the fictitious P equal to zero in the expression for M; this leaves M_1. Hence by Eq. 13.8 we obtain

$$\delta = \left(\frac{\partial U}{\partial P}\right)_{P=0} = \int_0^L \frac{Mm}{EI}\, dx$$

$$= \frac{1}{EI} \int_0^L \left(\frac{pLx}{2} - \frac{px^2}{2}\right)\left[\left(\frac{L - x_1}{L}\right) x - \{x - x_1\}^1\right] dx$$

$$= \frac{1}{EI}\left[\int_0^{x_1} \left(\frac{pLx}{2} - \frac{px^2}{2}\right)\left(\frac{L - x_1}{L}\right) x\, dx \right.$$

$$\left. + \int_{x_1}^L \left(\frac{pLx}{2} - \frac{px^2}{2}\right)\frac{x_1}{L}(L - x)\, dx\right]$$

$$= \frac{p}{24EI}(x^4 - 2Lx^3 + L^3 x),$$

from which the subscript has been dropped, having served its purpose of distinguishing x_1 from the variable of integration. Reference to Fig. 13.3 makes it clear that δ is downward in the sense of P. Therefore, relative to a right-handed x-y system, the equation of the elastic curve is

$$y = -\frac{p}{24EI}(x^4 - 2Lx^3 + L^3 x). \qquad\qquad Ans.$$

It would be instructive for the student to check this result by the double-integration method.

Outside of dispensing with the explicit evaluation of the integration constants, the energy method offers no particular advantage over the repeated-integration technique when it comes to deriving the equations of elastic curves of originally straight members. Even this saving becomes questionable in the face of longer computation (the student should fill in the algebra missing from the last example) brought about by the singularity of the fictitious or auxiliary force. Nevertheless, if the deflection is sought at a specified (nongeneric) site, Castigliano's theorem does achieve what is often claimed to be the principal advantage of such techniques as the area-moment and conjugate-beam methods: it gives the deflection directly without "bothering" with the integration constants. In such situations, all three methods share the common characteristic of lending themselves better to semigraphical computation. It is in handling nonstraight slender members subjected to combined loading, however, that we can truly appreciate the niceties of Castigliano's theorem and realize its power.

Illustrative Example 3. A uniform slender rod, of specific weight γ and cross-sectional area A, is bent in the form of a quadrant of a circle whose mean radius is R. It is built into a vertical wall at one end and supported there so that its plane is horizontal. Determine the vertical deflection of its free end due to the weight of the rod. Assume that the formulas for bending and torsion developed for straight members are applicable, and ignore the effects of direct shear.

SOLUTION. There being no force at the free end with respect to which the energy may be differentiated, we apply an auxiliary force P there, as shown in Figs. 13.4a and b. We will determine the bending and twisting moments produced by P first; this will make the derivation of the moments due to the earth pull on the rod easier to understand.

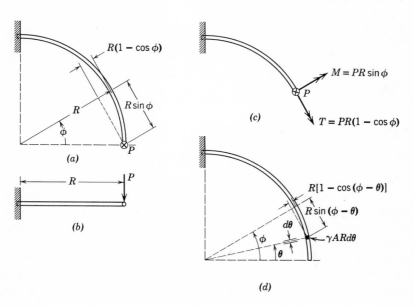

Fig. 13.4

At any transverse section of the rod defined by the angle ϕ from the free end, the force P exerts the following moments: through the lever arm of length $R \sin \phi$ (see sketch a), the bending moment $M = PR \sin \phi$; through the lever arm of length $R(1 - \cos \phi)$, the twisting moment $T = PR(1 - \cos \phi)$. These are shown in sketch c, where for completeness the force P is also indicated. Note that the force system shown in sketch c is statically equivalent to the original P of sketch a and may be considered derived from it by a shift of P to a parallel position at the interior transverse section of the rod. We can now establish the rates of change of the moments relative to P, thus:

$$m = \frac{\partial M}{\partial P} = R \sin \phi$$

and
$$t = \frac{\partial T}{\partial P} = R(1 - \cos \phi).$$

Figure 13.4d defines the location of the differential resultant earth pull, $(\gamma AR)d\theta$, with respect to the generic section. This differential force produces the following moments at that section: through a lever arm of length $R \sin (\phi - \theta)$, the differential bending moment $dM = \gamma AR^2 \sin (\phi - \theta)d\theta$; through a lever arm of length $R[1 - \cos (\phi - \theta)]$, the differential twisting moment $dT = \gamma AR^2[1 - \cos (\phi - \theta)]$. The aggregate of all such differential moments, from $\theta = 0$ to $\theta = \phi$, constitute the generic moments. Performing the summations, we obtain

$$M = \int_0^{\phi} \gamma AR^2 \sin (\phi - \theta) \, d\theta$$

$$= \gamma AR^2(1 - \cos \phi),$$

and
$$T = \int_0^{\phi} \gamma AR^2[1 - \cos (\phi - \theta)] \, d\theta$$

$$= \gamma AR^2(\phi - \sin \phi).$$

We may now evaluate the deflection at the free end, as follows:

$$\delta = \left(\frac{\partial U}{\partial P}\right)_{P=0} = \int_0^{\pi/2} \frac{Mm}{EI} R \, d\phi + \int_0^{\pi/2} \frac{Tt}{GI_p} R \, d\phi$$

$$= \int_0^{\pi/2} \frac{\gamma AR^4(1 - \cos \phi) \sin \phi}{EI} \, d\phi$$

$$+ \int_0^{\pi/2} \frac{\gamma AR^4(\phi - \sin \phi)(1 - \cos \phi)}{GI_p} \, d\phi$$

$$= \frac{\gamma A R^4}{EI} \left[-\cos \phi - \frac{1}{2} \sin^2 \phi \right]_0^{\pi/2}$$

$$+ \frac{\gamma A R^4}{GI_p} \left[\frac{\phi^2}{2} - \phi \sin \phi + \frac{\sin^2 \phi}{2} \right]_0^{\pi/2},$$

from which we obtain, after using $I_p = 2I$ (for a circular cross section) and simplifying,

$$\delta = \frac{\gamma A R^4}{8EI} \left[4 + \frac{E}{2G} (\pi^2 - 4\pi + 4) \right]. \qquad Ans.$$

It is evident that this is a downward deflection in the sense of the auxiliary P.

PROBLEMS

13.6. Show that, by applying Castigliano's theorem on Eq. 13.1, one can derive Eq. 3.3.

13.7. By equating the external work done to the torsional strain energy stored, solve for the deflection of a helical spring and hence check Eq. 4.17. See Prob. 13.1.

13.8. Do the above by differentiating the expression for the strain energy as derived in Prob. 13.1 with respect to P.

13.9. The small ring is held in place by two identical wires symmetrically anchored as shown. Each wire is of length L, cross-sectional area A, and has an elasticity modulus E. Using energy concepts, derive an expression for the deflection of the ring due to a gradually applied load P. (*Hint:* Assume the deflection to be so small that the initial position of the system remains substantially unchanged.)

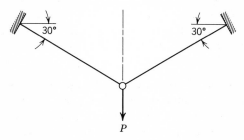

FIG. P13.9

13.10. In the truss of Fig. 3.8, assume all bars to have the same elasticity modulus E, all tension bars to have the same cross-sectional area A_t, and all compression bars to have the same cross-sectional area A_c. Assuming all compression members to remain straight, calculate the deflection of joint E due to the 12,000-lb load there. (*Suggestion:* A tabular arrangement of the computation will be convenient and helpful.)

13.11. Using Castigliano's theorem, find the deflection at the free end of a uniform cantilever beam due to a transverse load P there.

13.12. Using Castigliano's theorem, find the deflection at midspan of a uniformly loaded simply supported beam.

13.13. In Fig. 13.1 of Example 1, imagine the load P rotated clockwise until it is parallel to BC and is directed toward the wall. Again ignoring the earth pull on the rod and considering bending energy only, calculate the total deflection of the end A.

13.14. A uniform slender rod of diameter d is bent into the form of a semicircle with a mean radius R. One end A is hinged to an immovable support and the other end C rests on rollers. A small force P along AC is gradually applied. Derive approximate expressions for the deflections at C and B.

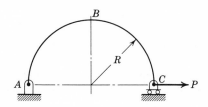

FIG. P13.14

13.15. In Fig. P13.14, imagine the roller support at C removed and the end A completely fixed (built in). Find the deflection of the end C where the load is applied.

13.16. For the rod of Example 3, Fig. 13.4, determine the deflection of the free end due to a vertical load P there as shown in sketch b.

13.17. Derive Eq. b of Article 9.5, p. 273, expressing the relationship between the longitudinal and transverse deflections of a slightly buckled column with hinged ends. (*Hint:* Assume that the compression load P remains at the Euler value as the column bends into a full arch of a sine wave. Consider energy due to bending action only.) See Prob. 13.4.

13.5   Application to Redundantly Supported Systems. When a loaded body is redundantly supported in such a manner that, at the site of the extra supports, the deflections in the directions of the reactions there are zero or negligibly small, application of Castigliano's theorem yields a set of equations of the form

$$\frac{\partial U}{\partial R_i} = 0, \qquad i = 1, 2, 3, \cdots, n, \qquad (a)$$

where n is the degree of redundancy. These n equations, together with the necessary conditions of equilibrium, will then constitute a sufficient set for a complete determination of the reactions. In the opening para-

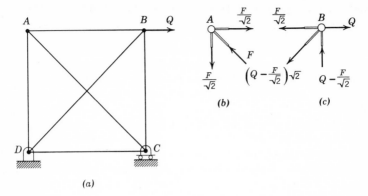

(a)

Fig. 13.5

graphs of Chapter 8, we pointed out that the n unknowns (representing n redundant, hence, dispensable reaction components) may be looked upon as independent variables in terms of which the remaining unknowns (corresponding to the determinate system) may then be expressed. Therefore, the equations that arise out of Castigliano's theorem will contain the first derivatives of the stored energy relative to the independent variables. Now, the condition that these derivatives be zero is precisely the criterion for a stationary U. Since it is intuitively evident from physical considerations that a stationary U must correspond to a minimum rather than a maximum, Castigliano's theorem points to the following *incidental* conclusion: *The redundant reaction components (in a system with perfect initial fit) must have such magnitudes as will make the stored energy a minimum.* It is for this reason that this application to redundantly supported systems is sometimes called the *Theorem of Least Work.* Castigliano himself called it so and designated it his third theorem, or Part III of the basic proposition.*

Observe that Eqs. *a* are analogous to the set of equations that describe the boundary conditions in the repeated-integration method of handling statically indeterminate beams. The energy method is, of course, applicable to much more than beams. This brings up the question of how to proceed when "internal" rather than "external" redundants are involved. For instance, the two-dimensional truss in Fig. 13.5a, although externally determinate, is internally indeterminate: it has one redundant member, say, AC. If we designate the unknown axial force in AC as F, then by Castigliano we must have $\partial U/\partial F = 0$. But what, we might ask, does this signify? To visualize the zero deflection

* Andrews, *op. cit.* on p. 382.

implied, let us imagine member AC cut by a transverse plane; then, as the load Q deforms the structure, the exposed faces of AC where it was cut will not displace relative to each other. Hence it is correct to say that the deflection at the site of F must be zero and, furthermore, that F must have such a value as to make the energy stored by the truss a minimum.

The internal forces P_i can always be expressed in terms of F and the given load, since, as already mentioned, F may be considered an independent variable. Reference to Figs. 13.5b and c will help make this clear. Analysis of joint A (sketch b) shows that, if F is assumed known, the remaining force system is completely solvable; similarly, at joint B (sketch c), with the force in member AB taken as $F/\sqrt{2}$ (or any other value), the remaining unknown forces become determinate. Therefore the derivatives $\partial P_i/\partial F$ can be established, and the one equation, independent of equilibrium, which completes the set of relations that will suffice for a full solution is

$$\frac{\partial U}{\partial F} = 0 = \sum \frac{P_i(\partial P_i/\partial F)L_i{}^*}{A_iE_i}. \qquad (b)$$

The extension to several internal redundants is obvious. Considering the redundant unknowns as the independent variables, one determines the values of the remaining forces in terms of these redundants and any loads on the structure; then, applying Castigliano's theorem, he obtains as many relations like Eq. b as there are redundants. These, combined with the equilibrium equations, will then permit a complete solution for the unknowns. Once again, the incidental conclusion is that the values of the redundants must be such as to make the stored energy a minimum.

One final question remains to be settled. Suppose the deflection is desired at a site where there is no force; in applying the fictitious or auxiliary force, would we be faced with the necessity of first evaluating the auxiliary force distribution in the indeterminate system before we can apply Castigliano's theorem? Does this mean that we would have to solve *two* indeterminate systems (the actual and then the auxiliary) before we can evaluate the desired deflection? The answer is to be found in the expressions typified by Eqs. a and b. The differential relations, of the form $\partial U/\partial F = 0$, may also be interpreted to mean that U does not change as the F's are varied; this relationship is independent of the values of the F's, including zero. Therefore it would simplify matters greatly if, in applying the auxiliary force, we removed all redundants (this is equivalent to setting the forces due to them equal to zero).

---

* It is assumed that compression members will not buckle.

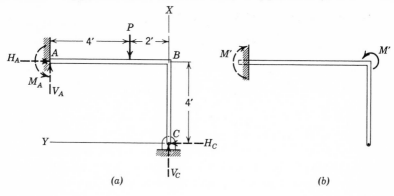

FIG. 13.6

Then, the system corresponding to the fictitious force becomes determinate and therefore easily solvable.   This is shown in the following.

Illustrative Example 4.   The two-dimensional bent in Fig. 13.6a is built into the wall at A and supported on a smooth hinge at C. It bears the single concentrated load P and behaves in such a manner that the bend at B remains a right angle. Taking into account only the bending energy and ignoring the weight, determine (1) all components of the reactive system and (2) the rotation of the corner B as P is gradually applied. Assume EI is constant throughout the member.

SOLUTION.   The reaction components are indicated by dashed lines in sketch a. Observe that the force system is indeterminate to the second degree (there are five unknowns and only three equilibrium equations). Inspection of the figure shows that H_C and V_C may be considered the two redundants: obviously, the built-in support at A would be fully adequate to maintain equilibrium and stability. Let us therefore consider H_C and V_C the independent variables. Setting up a coordinate system with origin at C as indicated in Fig. 13.6a, we write out the bending moments as follows:

From C to B, $M_z = H_C x$, $0 < x < 4$.
From B to A, $M_z = 4H_C - V_C y + P\{y - 2\}^1$, $0 < y < 6$.

Then, $\dfrac{\partial M}{\partial H_C} = x$, $0 < x < 4$,

                 $= 4$, $0 < y < 6$,

and $\dfrac{\partial M}{\partial V_C} = -y$, $0 < y < 6$.

Applying Castigliano's theorem, we have

$$\frac{\partial U}{\partial H_C} = 0 = \int_0^4 \frac{H_C x(x)}{EI}\,dx$$

$$+ \int_0^6 \frac{(4H_C - V_C y + P\{y - 2\}^1)(4)}{EI}\,dy$$

$$= \frac{1}{EI}\left[H_C \left(\frac{x^3}{3}\right)\Big|_0^4 + 16H_C y - 4V_C \left(\frac{y^2}{2}\right)\Big|_0^6 \right.$$

$$\left. + 4P\,\frac{(y - 2)^2}{2}\Big|_2^6 \right],$$

from which, after simplification, we get

$$0 = 44H_C - 27V_C + 12P. \tag{1}$$

Also,

$$\frac{\partial U}{\partial V_C} = 0 = \int_0^6 \frac{(4H_C - V_C y + P\{y - 2\}^1)(-y)}{EI}\,dy$$

$$= \frac{1}{EI}\left[-4H_C \left(\frac{y^2}{2}\right) + V_C \left(\frac{y^3}{3}\right)\Big|_0^6 - P\left(\frac{y^3}{3} - y^2\right)\Big|_2^6 \right],$$

whence

$$0 = -27H_C + 27V_C - 14P. \tag{2}$$

Solving Eqs. 1 and 2 simultaneously, we obtain

$$H_C = \tfrac{2}{17}P = 0.1176P \qquad \text{and} \qquad V_C = \tfrac{292}{459}P = 0.636P. \qquad Ans.$$

Three equilibrium equations will then give

$$H_A = 0.1176P, \qquad V_A = 0.364P, \qquad \text{and} \qquad M_A = 0.654P. \qquad Ans.$$

The senses of all five components are as shown in Fig. 13.6a.

To find the rotational deflection of the corner B, we apply an auxiliary moment M' at B, on the nonredundantly supported bent, as shown in Fig. 13.6b. Then

$$M_z = 0, \qquad \text{hence} \qquad \frac{\partial M}{\partial M'} = 0, \qquad 0 < x < 4,$$

and $M_z = -M'$,   hence $\dfrac{\partial M}{\partial M'} = -1,\qquad 0 < y < 6.$

By Castigliano, we have

$$\left(\frac{\partial U}{\partial M'}\right)_{M'=0} = \theta_B = \int_0^6 \frac{(4H_C - V_C y + P\{y - 2\}^1)(-1)}{EI}\,dy$$

$$= \frac{1}{EI}\left[-4H_C y + V_C \left(\frac{y^2}{2}\right)\Big|_0^6 - P\,\frac{(y - 2)^2}{2}\Big|_2^6 \right].$$

Substituting the values of H_C and V_C previously found, we finally obtain

$$\theta_B = 0.626 \frac{P}{EI}, \quad \text{counterclockwise.} \qquad Ans.$$

PROBLEMS

13.18. In Fig. 8.2a, using energy methods, (a) solve for the reactions on the re-strained bar, and (b) determine the longitudinal deflection at $x = a$, due to the axial load P. Compare the results with those in Example 1 of Chapter 8.

13.19. In Fig. 8.3a, using energy methods, (a) solve for the reactions on the re-strained torsion member, and (b) determine the twist deflection at $x = a$, due to the torsion load T_0. Compare the results with those in Example 2 of Chapter 8.

13.20. The small ring is supported by three wires in the same vertical plane, all having the same cross-sectional area A and the same elasticity modulus E. Assuming there is perfect initial fit, which is to say that no wire is initially slack while the others are taut, determine (a) the tension in each wire and (b) the deflection of the small ring, due to the vertical load P.

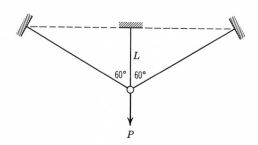

Fig. P13.20

13.21. The truss of Fig. 13.5 is in the shape of a square with edge of length L. Each member in compression has a cross-sectional area $2A$, and each member in tension has a cross-sectional area A. All members are of the same material. Assuming the compression members will remain straight even though unstable, calculate (a) the force in each member and (b) the deflection of joint B, due to the gradually applied load Q there.

13.22. In Fig. 8.4a, using energy methods and ignoring the energy due to direct shear, (a) solve for the reactions on the restrained beam, and (b) determine the transverse deflection at $x = 0.579L$, due to the uniformly distributed load. Compare the results with those in Example 3 of Chapter 8.

13.23. In the bent of Example 4, Fig. 13.6a, calculate the vertical deflection at the site where P is applied. Consider energy due to bending only.

13.24. In Fig. 13.6a, replace the hinge support at C by a roller support, thus reducing the degree of constraint redundancy of the bent by one.   Solve for the reaction components.   Consider energy due to bending only.

13.25. In Fig. 13.6a, replace the hinge support at C by a built-in support, thus increasing the degree of constraint redundancy by one.   Solve for the reaction components.   Consider energy due to bending only.

13.26. A slender rod of uniform diameter d is bent into a semicircular ring of mean radius R; its ends are then secured to smooth hinges without prestrain.   A symmetrically placed vertical load P is gradually applied.   Determine (a) the reaction components and (b) the deflection at the site of P.

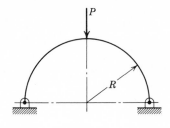

Fig. P13.26

13.27. Do the preceding problem with both ends of the ring built in rather than hinged.

13.28. A uniform slender rod of diameter d is bent into a circular ring of mean radius R.   The ring is loaded by collinear forces P at the ends of a mean diameter. Determine (a) the bending moment at A, (b) the bending moment at B, (c) the increase in the mean diameter parallel to P, and (d) the decrease in the mean diameter perpendicular to P.   Ignore the energy due to direct shear.

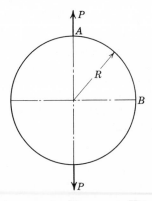

Fig. P13.28

CHAPTER

14

THE ROLE OF DUCTILITY
IN STATIC LOADING

14.1 Introduction. Ductility is that material property which enables a loaded body to withstand extensive deformation without fracture under high levels of stress. It is related to malleability, which is extreme deformability under low levels of stress. These two properties are usually associated only with metals. No completely satisfactory simple measure exists for this important property of ductility. The two most commonly employed indices are the percentage elongation and the percentage reduction in cross-sectional area of a simple tension piece. Sometimes the cold bend is used to indicate the degree of ductility.

Materials are described qualitatively as ranging from the very ductile to the extremely brittle. Of the structurally important metals, pure iron represents the extreme in ductility (gold is the most malleable), whereas magnesium is one of the most brittle. Alloying decreases the ductility of iron and increases that of magnesium, although the disparity between the extremes is still enormous.

On par with strength, ductility occupies the most important position in the list of properties that endow metals with truly remarkable structural usefulness. It is noteworthy that, until comparatively recently, little more than lip service had been paid ductility in strength considerations. Ignored in strength theory, it has nevertheless played in practice the all-important role of providing the saving grace for omissions and uncertainties. In this chapter we will do quite a bit more than merely pay it lip service; we will take it into account—albeit in an elementary but nonetheless meaningful and useful fashion—and incorporate it in the theory.

The basic role of ductility in static loading is that *it makes possible a readjustment in the stress distribution whereby a closer approximation to the ideal of full material utilization can develop.* Although it is only in the tension member of uniform cross section where this ideal can be achieved, in other structural elements where it is theoretically unattainable it still represents a useful upper limit on which can be based a more realistic measure of usable strength.

14.2 Tension and Compression. For quantitative analysis, it is convenient to describe ductility in terms of the stress-strain diagram. Practically all the structurally significant alloys obey Hooke's law, with but minor deviations within the elastic limit. In this region, therefore, the diagram is correctly represented by a straight line whose slope gives the elasticity modulus. Beyond the proportional limit, in the region of imperfect elasticity, the form of the diagram for slowly applied tension or compression depends on the particular alloy. For example, the stress-strain curve for very ductile mild steel displays a "knee" almost immediately after the proportional limit—a yield *point* in a sense—followed by a flat part parallel to the strain axis and extending to a total strain of 2000 to 3000 percent of the proportional-limit strain. In this region the material "flows," or, more properly, it *strain hardens* at a *zero* rate. With the accumulation of permanent strain, the steel then begins to strain harden at a positive rate and deforms up to as much as 30,000 percent of the proportional-limit strain. A tension specimen would then be very near fracture; a compression one would keep on strain hardening, its transverse dimensions increasing all the while. What happens far beyond the flat part of the stress-strain curve is important to the metallurgist; it does not particularly concern us.

The less ductile alloys exhibit no yield points and no such marked flatness in their stress-strain diagrams beyond the proportional limit, but rather display continuously varying rates of strain hardening. In such materials, there is generally more disparity in this region between the tension and compression curves, when plotted on the same axes, than in mild steel. Thus, for the region beyond the proportional limit, it is not easy to represent the stress-strain curve by simple functions, and idealizations become necessary.

For mild steel this idealization is represented by a straight-line segment starting at the proportonial limit and running parallel to the strain

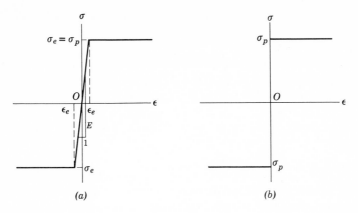

FIG. 14.1

axis, as shown in Fig. 14.1a. The stress-strain diagram in tension then consists of two straight lines and is a plot of the equation

$$\sigma = E\epsilon - E\{\epsilon - \epsilon_e\}, \tag{14.1}$$

where ϵ_e is the proportional-limit strain, and the braced term is to be ignored when negative. The compression part of the diagram is assumed symmetrical to the tension part relative to the origin. Figure 14.1a and Eq. 14.1 characterize a *perfectly elastic-plastic material*. If the total deformations involved are so large that elastic components become negligible, then a further simplification may be made as shown in Fig. 14.1b; the corresponding equation is

$$\sigma = \sigma_p, \tag{a}$$

where σ_p denotes the "plastic" stress, equal in magnitude to σ_e. Figure 14.1b and Eq. a characterize a *perfectly plastic material*. Note that the strain ϵ is indeterminate, as it also is in Eq. 14.1 for all ϵ larger than ϵ_e.

For less ductile materials, any comparably simple idealization necessarily entails a rougher approximation. One such diagram is shown in Fig. 14.2a, for which the equation is

$$\sigma = E_1\epsilon - (E_1 - E_2)\{\epsilon - \epsilon_e\}, \tag{14.2}$$

where E_1 is the initial modulus and E_2 is the final modulus or the constant rate of strain hardening. Observe that, when E_2 is zero, Eq. 14.2 reduces to Eq. 14.1. As previously, if elastic deformations are a negligible part of over-all deformations, a further simplification may be made such that (Fig. 14.2b)

$$\sigma = \sigma_p + E_2\epsilon, \tag{b}$$

where σ_p signifies the *onset* of flow.   Such materials are said to possess *limiting rates of strain hardening*.

Of the two approximations, the first one, which assumes a zero rate of strain hardening, leads to simpler results; furthermore, measures of *limit strength* based on it are more definitive.   Throughout the rest of the chapter, except the article on columns, we shall assume material ductility as depicted in either Fig. 14.1a or 14.1b.   Although this appears rather restrictive since it applies strictly only to mild steel, the resulting theory is still of significance if only (1) because mild steel continues to be of major structural importance and (2) because limit strengths so derived represent lower bounds for values that are actually realizable in materials exhibiting strain hardening.

In a nonredundantly supported simple tension member of uniform cross section subjected to end forces only, the *limit strength*, corresponding to over-all yielding of the material, is

$$P_L = \sigma_p A. \tag{14.3}$$

Since σ_e and σ_p are assumed equal, this is no different from the elastic strength; likewise, the beginning of excessive deformation coincides with the proportional limit if the load is the independent variable.   Hence, for such a member, there is no difference between the value of usable strength obtained by applying the safety factor on the stress and that obtained by applying the same factor on the load.

When axial forces act not only at the ends but also at sections in between, P_L is the strength of the worst loaded section.   The analysis is as explained in Example 2 of Chapter 3.

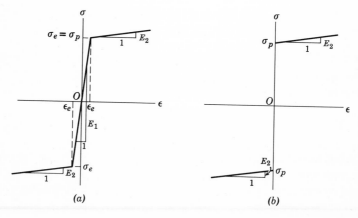

(a)   (b)

Fig. 14.2

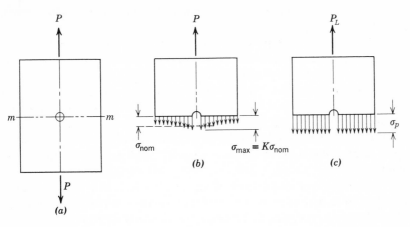

$$F_{IG}.\ 14.3$$

If the member is of nonuniform cross section, the area A to use in Eq. 14.3 is that of the weakest section. For instance, in a tension bar with a hole (Fig. 14.3a), the area that controls is that at m-m; that is,

$$P_L = \sigma_p A_{m\text{-}m}. \qquad (c)$$

Within the proportional limit, the stresses across section m-m are not uniformly distributed; the maximum, which occurs at the edge of the hole, has the magnitude

$$\sigma_{\max} = K\sigma_{\text{nom}}, \qquad (d)$$

where σ_{nom} is the *nominal* stress $P/A_{m\text{-}m}$ and $K > 1$ is a *stress-concentration factor* (Fig. 14.3b). A hole is an example of a *stress raiser*. Mathematical theory of elasticity shows that K depends on the geometry of the piece, and for this particular stress raiser the limiting magnitude of K is 3.* If P is to be governed by σ_e such that there will be no permanent set at all, no matter how localized, then the maximum value P_e will depend not only on σ_e and $A_{m\text{-}m}$ but also on K, thus:

$$P_e = \frac{\sigma_e A_{m\text{-}m}}{K}. \qquad (e)$$

As P is increased beyond this value, the material will yield, the region of plastic flow spreading outward from the edge of the hole until the immediate vicinity of m-m is fully plastic and the stress distribution equal-

* C. T. Wang, *Applied Elasticity*, pp. 58–61, McGraw-Hill Book Company, New York, 1953.

ized, Fig. 14.3c. When this stage is reached, P attains its limiting value as given by Eq. c.

It should be clear from Eqs. c and e that applying a safety factor on P_L leads to a different working P from that derived by applying the factor on σ_e. For static loading, and *if* the stress raiser is not so severe as to prevent full plastic flow from developing in its vicinity, P_L gives a more realistic measure of strength than does P_e because it is based on full utilization of the material in the weakest section. Moreover, *over-all* deformation corresponding to P_L is of the same order of magnitude as that corresponding to P_e since the plastic flow is confined to narrow limits.

How severe a stress concentration can be and still allow material ductility to come into play beyond the proportional limit necessarily depends on this very ductility. Hence, until a precise measure is devised for this property, the *full* influence of stress raisers must remain describable partly in qualitative terms. Throughout the rest of our discussion, no stress raisers of any appreciable severity will be assumed present.

The major implication of ductility to structural strength can best be understood in relation to redundantly supported members. To illustrate this, let us return to Example 1 of Chapter 8.

Illustrative Example 1. The redundantly supported uniform bar in Fig. 14.4a is of an elastic-plastic material. Under the axial loading shown, investigate the performance of the bar beyond the proportional limit.

ANALYSIS. When $b > a$, the stresses within the proportional limit are

$$\sigma_a = \frac{Pb}{AL} \quad \text{and} \quad \sigma_b = \frac{Pa}{AL}, \qquad (f)$$

and the maximum deflection is

$$\delta_{\max} = \frac{Pab}{AEL} = \frac{\sigma_a a}{E} = \frac{\sigma_b b}{E}. \qquad (g)$$

Based on the proportional-limit stress, the maximum load that the bar may carry is found from the first of Eqs. f to be

$$P_e = \frac{\sigma_e AL}{b}, \qquad (h)$$

and the corresponding maximum deflection, from Eq. g, is

$$\delta_e = \frac{P_e ab}{AEL} = \frac{\sigma_e a}{E}. \qquad (i)$$

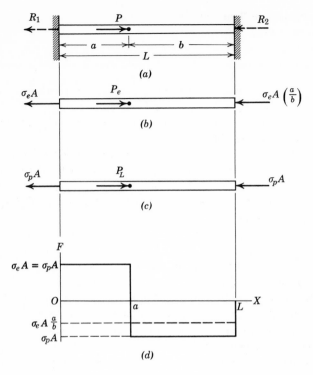

Fig. 14.4

With this load on the bar, the portion of length a is on the verge of yielding (in tension); the portion of length b, however, is stressed (in compression) only to the level

$$\sigma_b = \frac{P_e a}{AL} = \frac{\sigma_e a}{b},\tag{j}$$

which is below the proportional limit, and therefore remains perfectly elastic. Consequently, there is no tendency for uncontrolled over-all deformation of the bar.

As P is increased beyond P_e, the portion a goes plastic, thereby losing its ability to control the deformation, although it maintains constant resistance to the load. Meanwhile, the portion b continues to increase its resistance and hence maintains control on the deformation. Since this part of the bar still obeys Hooke's law, over-all deformation remains of the order of δ_e. The limit of P is reached when the increasing stress in b attains the value σ_e. Then (Fig. 14.4c),

$$P_L = 2\sigma_e A = 2\sigma_p A,\tag{k}$$

and the maximum deflection becomes

$$\delta_L = \frac{\sigma_e b}{E}. \qquad (l)$$

Under this load, the entire bar goes plastic, the portion a yielding in tension and the portion b beginning to do so in compression; this marks the start of uncontrolled deformation or collapse. The axial-force diagram is shown in Fig. 14.4d.

The relationship between P and the maximum deflection is displayed in Fig. 14.5. The first stage, OC, is that of elastic deformation, the second, CD, that of controlled plastic deformation, and the third, beyond D, that of uncontrolled plastic deformation. For practical purposes, the third stage is considered synonymous with collapse.

Comparison of Eqs. h and k reveals that so long as b exceeds a (hence exceeds $L/2$), P_L is always larger than P_e; the two become equal only for $a = b = L/2$. It follows therefore that the working value of P obtained by applying the safety factor on P_L is larger than that derived when the factor is applied on σ_e, except when $a = b$. Since P_L is based on full material utilization at a maximum number of transverse sections, it represents a more realistic measure of the bar's load-carrying capacity than does P_e, and hence is the more logical basis for a working P.

Let us see what happens when a redundantly supported member on the verge of collapse due to limit loading is relieved of this load. To explain this we will make use of the fact that metallic bodies obey

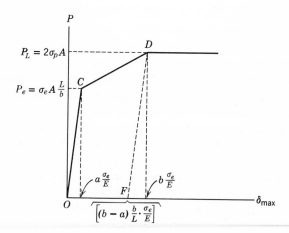

FIG. 14.5

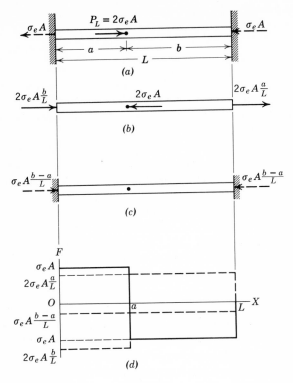

$$P_L = 2\sigma_e A$$

$\sigma_e A$ $\sigma_e A$

a b

L

(a)

$2\sigma_e A \frac{b}{L}$ $2\sigma_e A$ $2\sigma_e A \frac{a}{L}$

(b)

$\sigma_e A \frac{b-a}{L}$ $\sigma_e A \frac{b-a}{L}$

(c)

F

$\sigma_e A$
$2\sigma_e A \frac{a}{L}$

O a L X

$\sigma_e A \frac{b-a}{L}$

$\sigma_e A$

$2\sigma_e A \frac{b}{L}$ (d)

FIG. 14.6

Hooke's law during unloading.* Relief of load is accomplished by super-posing a load equal and opposite to the original. Figure 14.6a represents the redundantly supported bar on the verge of collapse. The load $P_L = 2\sigma_e A$ and the wall reactions are each of magnitude $\sigma_e A$; the deflection at the site of the load is $\delta_L = \sigma_e b/E$. Imagine now a similar bar (Fig. 14.6b), carrying a load of magnitude $2\sigma_e A$ but of a sense opposite to P_L in Fig. 14.6a, and behaving according to Hooke's law. From the results of Example 1, Chapter 8, we know that the reactions of this second bar are $R_1 = Pb/L = 2\sigma_e A(b/L)$ and $R_2 = Pa/L = 2\sigma_e A(a/L)$, and that the maximum deflection is $\delta_{\max} = Pab/AEL = 2\sigma_e ab/EL$; these quantities are all oppositely directed to those in Fig. 14.6a. Super-position of the two systems results in Fig. 14.6c, showing the still sup-ported unloaded bar. The residual reactions are obtained as the algebraic sums of the two sets of reactions, thus:

* See footnote on page 51.

$$2\sigma_e A \left(\frac{b}{L}\right) - \sigma_e A = \sigma_e A \left(\frac{b-a}{L}\right)$$

and
$$\sigma_e A - 2\sigma_e A \left(\frac{a}{L}\right) = \sigma_e A \left(\frac{b-a}{L}\right).$$

Figure 14.6d depicts this superposition. These residual reactions are compressive, implying that there are residual compressive stresses in the bar, of intensity $\sigma_e(b-a)/L$, and consequently that the bar would elongate an amount $\sigma_e(b-a)/E$ if the wall supports were removed. Similarly, the permanent set of the unloaded built-in bar, at the site of the original load, is found by adding the two deflections, as follows:

$$\delta_{\text{set}} = \frac{\sigma_e b}{E} - \frac{2\sigma_e ab}{EL} = \frac{\sigma_e b}{E}\left(\frac{b-a}{L}\right).$$

Note that this quantity may be obtained directly from the load-deformation diagram by drawing the inclined line DF parallel to the part OC of the loading curve and evaluating the intercept on the δ axis, as indicated in Fig. 14.5.

The final significant remark is that if the bar of Fig. 14.6c were now reloaded in the same sense as the original load, it would behave according to the line FD in Fig. 14.5 and no additional permanent deformation would develop for all P up to just a shade less than P_L. In other words, the redundantly supported bar would, during reloading, obey Hooke's law, *displaying a higher elastic strength than originally*, even though the material itself had the same proportional limit. It must be clearly understood that this behavior of utmost practical significance is made possible *only* by the material property of ductility. We will take this up repeatedly in the following articles.

PROBLEMS

14.1. This uniform bar of cross-sectional area A is of a mild steel whose yield strength in uniaxial stress is σ_p. (a) What will be the value of each P that will induce uncontrolled deformation? (b) What will be the residual reactions when the system is unloaded from near collapse, perfect initial fit being assumed?

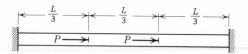

Fig. P14.1

14.2. In the bar of Prob. 14.1, reverse one of the P's and then solve.

14.3. In the bar of Prob. 14.1, change the left-hand load to $2P$ and then solve.

14.3 Torsion. Because of the difference in their stress distribution patterns, a torsion member is necessarily less efficient than a tension member in regard to material utiliza-
tion. In Chapter 4 it was shown that the utilization factor for a round solid shaft is only $\frac{1}{2}$ and that, although this can be increased by hollowing out the shaft, the ideal value of unity can never be attained. Further improvement can be accomplished only through yielding in plastic flow.

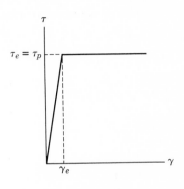

FIG. 14.7

The following applies only to shafts of uniform circular cross section. We make the same assumptions as those in Article 4.3, but now amend the second one to include perfect plasticity beyond the proportional limit. Let Fig. 14.7 represent the stress-strain diagram in shear.

A solid shaft cross section can transmit a maximum elastic twisting moment of

$$T_e = \frac{\tau_e I_p}{r} = \frac{\pi r^3 \tau_e}{2}, \qquad (a)$$

which corresponds to an angle of twist per unit length of

$$\frac{\phi_e}{l} = \frac{T_e}{GI_p} = \frac{\tau_e}{Gr}. \qquad (b)$$

Figure 14.8a shows the stress distribution produced by T_e. As T increases, the outermost material yields and the plastic flow spreads inward so that, at any instant during this stage of contained plastic deformation, there is left an elastic core of radius r_e (Fig. 14.8b). Effectively the shaft then is two shafts in one: an outer plastic shell of thickness $r - r_e$, in a state of uniform and constant shear stress $\tau_e = \tau_p$ incapable of controlling the angle of twist; and an inner core of radius r_e which behaves according to Hooke's law and therefore still controls the angular deflection. The contributions to the total T are

$$\int \rho \tau \, dA = \tau_e \int_0^{2\pi} \int_{r_e}^{r} \rho^2 \, d\rho \, d\theta = \frac{2\pi \tau_e}{3}(r^3 - r_e^3) \qquad (c)$$

from the plastic shell, and

$$\frac{\tau_e(I_p)_e}{r_e} = \frac{\pi r_e^3 \tau_e}{2} \tag{d}$$

from the elastic core. Therefore, corresponding to any degree of yielding, the twisting-moment capacity is

$$T = \frac{2\pi\tau_e}{3}(r^3 - r_e^3) + \frac{\pi r_e^3 \tau_e}{2}$$

$$= \frac{\pi\tau_e}{6}(4r^3 - r_e^3). \tag{e}$$

The unit angle of twist, dependent only on the elastic core, is

$$\frac{\phi}{l} = \frac{\tau_e}{Gr_e} = \frac{6T}{\pi Gr_e(4r^3 - r_e^3)}. \tag{f}$$

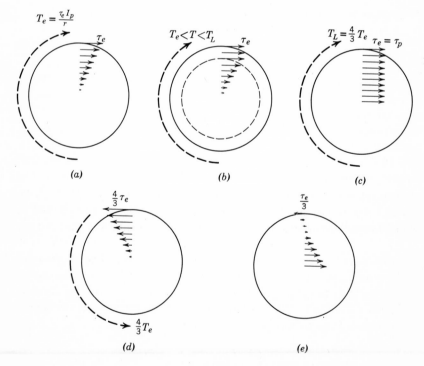

Fig. 14.8

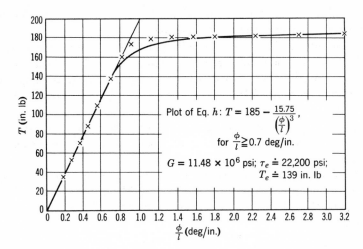

Plot of Eq. h: $T = 185 - \dfrac{15.75}{\left(\frac{\phi}{l}\right)^3}$,

for $\dfrac{\phi}{l} \geq 0.7$ deg/in.

$G = 11.48 \times 10^6$ psi; $\tau_e \doteq 22{,}200$ psi;
$T_e \doteq 139$ in. lb

$\frac{\phi}{l}$ (deg/in.)

F\textsc{ig}. 14.9　　Results of the torsion test of a $\frac{5}{16}$-in. commercial hot-rolled mild steel rod.

We note from Eqs. e and f that, whereas T has the limit

$$T_L = \frac{2\pi r^3 \tau_e}{3} = \frac{4}{3} T_e, \tag{14.4}$$

as r_e approaches zero, the unit angle of twist goes to infinity. Theoretically, the fully plastic twisting moment T_L cannot, of course, be realized since the elastic core can never disappear altogether in view of the assumption that diameters remain straight. Practically, however, because of strain hardening in the material, the limit strength defined by Eq. 14.4 is attainable within finite limits of the angle of twist per unit length. Figure 14.9 displays experimental evidence to this effect. The crosses represent laboratory values from the torsion test of a $\frac{5}{16}$-in. round hot-rolled steel rod.* The full line is a plot of Eqs. g and h, derived as follows. Equation g is from Chapter 4 (Eq. 4.6):

$$T = \frac{I_p G \phi}{l} = \frac{\pi r^2 G}{2}\left(\frac{\phi}{l}\right), \qquad \frac{\phi}{l} \leq \frac{\tau_e}{Gr}. \tag{g}$$

Solved for T in terms of ϕ/l, Eqs. e and f give

$$T = \frac{\pi \tau_e}{6}\left[4r^3 - \frac{\tau_e{}^3}{G^3(\phi/l)^3}\right], \qquad \frac{\phi}{l} \geq \frac{\tau_e}{Gr}. \tag{h}$$

* Typical test data of a laboratory class in strength of materials, Union College, Schenectady, New York, 1961.

The modulus G and the proportional-limit stress τ_e were calculated from the straight-line part of the test record.

Unloading the shaft from the fully plastic state leaves the system of residual stresses shown in Fig. 14.8e. This is derived on the assumption that the material obeys Hooke's law during unloading, as suggested in Fig. 14.8d. Superposition of Fig. 14.8d on Fig. 14.8c results in Fig. 14.8e. Subsequent reloading will produce no additional plastic deformation provided the load is in the same sense as, and does not exceed, the previous maximum. The shaft would behave as if it were made of a stronger material than originally.

For a hollow shaft, the unit angle of twist has a finite limit and therefore T_L is theoretically attainable. If r_o is the outside radius and r_i the inside one, then the equations corresponding to Eqs. e and f for the solid member are

$$T = \frac{\pi \tau_e}{6}\left(4r_0{}^3 - r_e{}^3 - 3\frac{r_i{}^4}{r_e}\right) \qquad (i)$$

and

$$\frac{\phi}{l} = \frac{6T}{\pi G r_e(4r_0{}^3 - r_e{}^3 - 3r_i{}^4/r_e)}. \qquad (j)$$

These give the limit values

$$T_L = \frac{2}{3}\pi\tau_e(r_0{}^3 - r_i{}^3) = \frac{4}{3}T_e\left[\frac{1 - (r_i/r_o)^3}{1 - (r_i/r_o)^4}\right], \qquad (14.4a)$$

and

$$\frac{\phi_L}{l} = \frac{\tau_e}{G r_i} = \frac{3T_L}{2\pi G r_i(r_o{}^3 - r_i{}^3)}. \qquad (k)$$

As mentioned in the preceding article, ductility shows up to best advantage in redundantly supported members. To illustrate this in torsion, let us return to Example 2 of Chapter 8.

Illustrative Example 2. The solid shaft of Fig. 14.10a is built into unyielding walls at both ends. Analyze the member for the limit twisting load $(T_0)_L$, and calculate the residual reactions that will remain after unloading from $(T_0)_L$, based on the assumption of an elastic-plastic material.

ANALYSIS. The maximum elastic twisting load is that which will induce τ_e in the worst stressed portion. If $b > a$, then, by Example 2 of Chapter 8, the external load $(T_0)_e$ will be

$$(T_0)_e = \frac{\pi r^3 L \tau_e}{2b}, \qquad (l)$$

and the wall reactions will be

$$(T_0)_e \left(\frac{b}{L}\right) = \frac{\pi r^3 \tau_e}{2} \quad \text{and} \quad (T_0)_e \left(\frac{a}{L}\right) = \frac{\pi r^3 \tau_e}{2} \left(\frac{a}{b}\right). \qquad (m)$$

As T_0 is increased, the shaft will become plastic, first in the region a and finally in the region b, until uncontrolled deformation begins. This will take place when both portions of the member are contributing simultaneously their full limit strengths as given by Eq. 14.4. Hence the limit twisting load will be

$$(T_0)_L = 2 \left(\frac{2}{3} \pi r^3 \tau_e\right) = \frac{4}{3} \pi r^3 \tau_e. \qquad Ans. \quad (n)$$

The twisting-moment diagram under these conditions is shown in Fig. 14.10d.

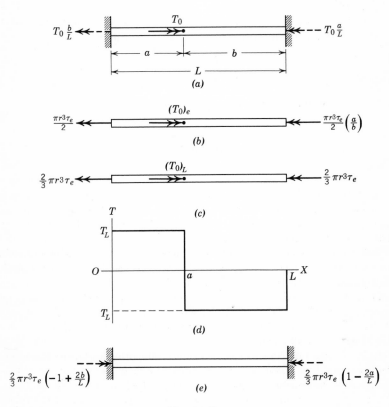

Fig. 14.10

Unloading the member is like superposing on $(T_0)_L$ an equal but opposite load; this superposed load will then be reacted elastically by the wall twisting moments, $(T_0)_L(b/L)$ and $(T_0)_L(a/L)$, in virtue of Eqs. m. Hence relieving the member of the collapse load will leave the residual reactions:

$$(T_0)_L \left(\frac{b}{L}\right) - \frac{(T_0)_L}{2} = \frac{2\pi r^3 \tau_e}{3} \left(\frac{2b - L}{L}\right)$$

and $$\frac{(T_0)_L}{2} - (T_0)_L \left(\frac{a}{L}\right) = \frac{2\pi r^3 \tau_e}{3} \left(\frac{L - 2a}{L}\right),$$ *Ans.*

which must, of course, be equal in magnitude and are therefore in balance. The free-body diagram of the unloaded but still supported shaft is shown in Fig. 14.10e. These locked-in reactions insure the subsequent elastic functioning of the member when reloaded in the original sense; it would then behave as if it were made of a stronger material than originally.

Special attention is called to the reserve in the load-carrying capacity of the redundantly supported shaft, implied in the ratio

$$\frac{(T_0)_L}{(T_0)_e} = \frac{8b}{3L},$$ (o)

which is between $\frac{4}{3}$ and $\frac{8}{3}$, since $L/2 < b < L$.

PROBLEMS

14.4. A solid round shaft 3 in. in diameter is of a mild steel for which $\tau_e = \tau_p = 20{,}000$ psi. What twisting moment can the shaft transmit corresponding to an elastic core $\frac{1}{2}$ in. in diameter? What percentage of the elastic-limit torque is this? Of the limit torque? If $G = 12 \times 10^6$ psi, what is the corresponding angle of twist per unit length in the shaft?

14.5. A solid round shaft of mild steel for which $\tau_e = \tau_p = 20{,}000$ psi transmits a twisting moment of 100,000 in.-lb. What is the diameter of the shaft if the remaining elastic core has a diameter half as large?

14.6. A hollow shaft of mild steel for which $\tau_e = \tau_p = 20{,}000$ psi has an outside diameter of 3 in. and an inside diameter of 1 in. Calculate the limit twisting strength. If $G = 12 \times 10^6$ psi, what is the angle of twist per unit length at the beginning of over-all yielding?

14.7. The shaft of Prob. 14.6 is redundantly supported as shown in the sketch. Perfect initial fit is assumed. (a) What torque load T_0 will initiate collapse? (b) What is the corresponding angle of twist deflection at the site of T_0? (c) What will be the residual wall twisting moments upon removal of the collapse load?

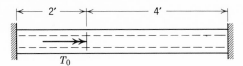

FIG. P14.7

14.4 Bending. In Chapter 6 we learned the reason for structural shapes such as the **I**- and **WF**-sections—to increase the efficiency of material utilization. Just as in the torsion member, so too in a beam the utilization factor can never be unity and, for any given cross section, further improvement can come about only through plastic action.

To explain beam action beyond the proportional limit, we make use of the same assumptions cited in Chapter 6; in addition we extend assumption 4 to include perfect plasticity beyond Hooke's law. The following need to be emphasized: (1) that the beam cross section is symmetrical about an axis that lies in the plane of loading, and (2) that the material has a stress-strain curve in tension and compression which is symmetrical with respect to the origin, which means that the modulus of elasticity and the elastic-limit stress in tension are equal to those in compression. (See Fig. 14.1).

The maximum elastic bending moment that a beam section can transmit is

$$M_e = \frac{\sigma_e I}{c}, \qquad (a)$$

where the dimension c is the larger of the two values c_1 and c_2 in sections with only one axis of symmetry. If c_1 is the larger c, then the maximum stress of opposite sign will be $\sigma_e c_2/c_1$. (See Fig. 14.11a.) As M is increased beyond M_e, the furthest material from the centroidal axis will yield, throwing the burden of increasing resistance on the material nearer this axis. This will proceed until the material at the c_2 edge reaches the proportional limit; then the stress pattern will be as shown in Fig. 14.11b. Note that there will be a shift e_1 in the position of the neutral axis. Of the total depth h, the still elastic portion will be h_e and the plastic part h_p. With continued increase in M, further yielding will shrink the elastic portion, which now separates the two plastic regions, and there will be further shifting of the neutral axis. While this is happening, the plastic parts of the cross section maintain their resistance to the bending moment but are incapable of controlling the rotation of the section; on the other hand, the elastic core, because it still obeys Hooke's law, continues to offer increasing resistance and

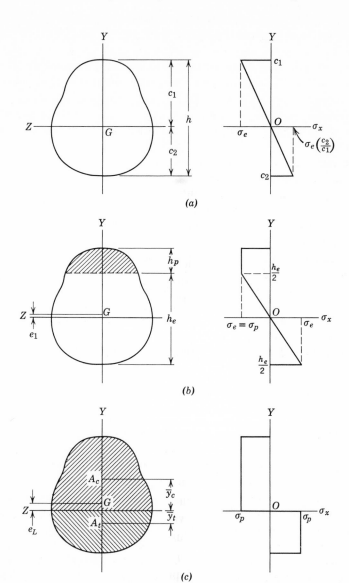

Fig. 14.11

hence to exert control over the angular rotation. Before long, however, because the lever arms of the elastic forces remain small and continually decrease, the contribution to the total resisting moment of the still elastic core will become relatively insignificant. Thus, although theoretically the elastic core can never disappear (because of the assumption that transverse planes remain plane), the limit resisting moment M_L, corresponding to the stress pattern of Fig. 14.11c, and the limiting shift e_L of the neutral axis from the centroidal axis, may be assumed practically attainable. With this moment being transmitted, the entire cross section goes plastic and the internal resistance to deformation becomes nil. The beam section is then aptly described as a *yield hinge*, because it will act as a hinge with a constant frictional resisting moment. The expression for M_L is derived as follows.

Let A_c stand for the area in compression and A_t for that in tension. Then, for pure bending, the system of forces normal to the transverse section must reduce to a moment; or that $\Sigma F = 0$ and $\Sigma M = M_L$. From the first equilibrium equation,

$$\Sigma F = 0 = -\sigma_p A_c + \sigma_p A_t, \tag{b}$$

we find that

$$A_c = A_t = \frac{A}{2}. \tag{14.5}$$

This significant result means the following: For elastic-plastic materials with "symmetrical" properties, *the neutral axis in a fully plastic beam section subject to bending only is that line perpendicular to the plane of loading which divides the cross-sectional area into two halves.* In cross sections having two axes of symmetry, the neutral axis stays put at the original centroidal position and no shift takes place.

Taking moments about the neutral axis just located, we have

$$\Sigma M = M_L = \int_A \sigma_p y \, dA = \sigma_y \int_{A_c} y_c \, dA + \sigma_p \int_{A_t} y_t \, dA, \tag{c}$$

whence

$$M_L = \sigma_p(\bar{y}_c A_c + \bar{y}_t A_t) = \sigma_p \left[\frac{A}{2} (\bar{y}_c + \bar{y}_t) \right], \tag{14.6}$$

in which the combined first-moment of the two halves of the cross-sectional area with respect to the neutral axis constitutes the *plastic section modulus*. Dividing M_L by M_e and using $\sigma_p = \sigma_e$, we obtain

$$\frac{M_L}{M_e} = \frac{\bar{y}_c A_c + \bar{y}_t A_t}{I/c} = F_p, \tag{14.7}$$

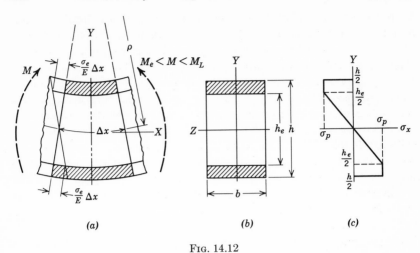

(a)   (b)   (c)

FIG. 14.12

where F_p, the ratio of the plastic section modulus to the elastic section modulus, is called the *plastic form factor*. It can be shown without difficulty that F_p is $\frac{3}{2}$ for a rectangle and $\frac{16}{3\pi}$ for a circle. For standard **W**- and **I**-sections, F_p is of the order of 1.1 to 1.2. (See the Appendix Tables I and II.)

Corresponding to any instant during the stage of contained plastic deformation, the depth of the elastic core, the shift of the neutral axis, the radius of curvature of the elastic curve, and the elasto-plastic moment being transmitted can all be evaluated. Except for the simplest of cross sections, however, the algebra becomes quite involved and the resulting expressions unwieldy; * we will therefore discuss only the rectangular section.

Sketch a of Fig. 14.12 shows a small length of beam in the vicinity of the section in question, in which the shaded areas represent the yielded regions. Sketch b shows the transverse section and sketch c the stress distribution. The assumption that transverse planes remain plane allows us to write (see sketch a)

$$\frac{\sigma_e(dx)/E}{h_e/2} = \frac{dx}{\rho},$$

from which $$\frac{1}{\rho} = \frac{2\sigma_e}{Eh_e}. \qquad (d)$$

---

* For instance, see A. Phillips, *Introduction to Plasticity*, pp. 55–63, The Ronald Press Company, New York, 1956.

For uniaxially symmetrical sections, Eq. d gives the curvature at the level of the *neutral* axis rather than the centroidal axis. Since, however, the shift of the neutral axis is but a small quantity, even for such sections the preceding may still be considered the curvature at the level of the *centroidal* axis.

The resisting moment contributed by the elastic core is

$$M_1 = \frac{\sigma_e b h_e^2}{6}, \tag{e}$$

and that contributed by the plastic regions is (sketches b and c, Fig. 14.12)

$$M_2 = \sigma_e b \left(\frac{h - h_e}{2}\right)\left(\frac{h + h_e}{2}\right) = \frac{\sigma_e b(h^2 - h_e^2)}{4}. \tag{f}$$

Therefore, the total elasto-plastic moment is

$$M = M_1 + M_2 = \frac{\sigma_e b}{12}(3h^2 - h_e^2). \tag{g}$$

Solved for h_e, Eq. g gives

$$h_e = 3h^2 - \frac{12M}{\sigma_e b}. \tag{h}$$

Substituting this in Eq. d, we obtain

$$\frac{1}{\rho} = \frac{2\sigma_e}{E\sqrt{3h^2 - 12M/\sigma_e b}}, \tag{i}$$

where $\sigma_e b h^2/6 \leqq M < \sigma_e b h^2/4$. When $M = \sigma_e b h^2/6 = M_e$, Eq. i reduces to $1/\rho = M_e/EI$, as it should; on the other hand, when $M \doteq \sigma_e b h^2/4 = M_L$, $1/\rho$ becomes infinite, which means that at the yield hinge a kink develops—precisely what a hinge implies.

A beam section unloaded from beyond the proportional limit will have stored in it residual stresses of such distribution that repeated reloading and unloading will produce no additional plastic deformation, provided the subsequent loads neither reverse nor exceed the original maximum. The pattern of these residual stresses may be established with the aid of the assumption that, during unloading, a beam section obeys Hooke's law. Let us demonstrate this for a rectangular section unloaded from the fully plastic condition.

In Fig. 14.13a are shown the stress distribution pattern (right sketch) and the stress resultants (left sketch) for a rectangular section of width b and depth h, when acting as a yield hinge. Figure 14.13b shows the

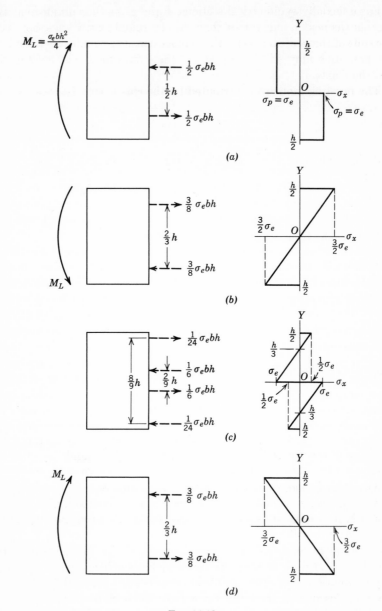

$$M_L = \frac{\sigma_e bh^2}{4}$$

$\frac{1}{2}\sigma_e bh$

$\frac{1}{2}h$

$\frac{1}{2}\sigma_e bh$

$\sigma_p = \sigma_e$

$\sigma_p = \sigma_e$

$\frac{h}{2}$

$\frac{h}{2}$

(a)

$\frac{3}{8}\sigma_e bh$

$\frac{2}{3}h$

$\frac{3}{8}\sigma_e bh$

M_L

$\frac{3}{2}\sigma_e$

$\frac{3}{2}\sigma_e$

$\frac{h}{2}$

$\frac{h}{2}$

(b)

$\frac{1}{24}\sigma_e bh$

$\frac{1}{6}\sigma_e bh$

$\frac{1}{6}\sigma_e bh$

$\frac{1}{24}\sigma_e bh$

$\frac{8}{9}h$

$\frac{2}{9}h$

$\frac{h}{3}$

σ_e

$\frac{1}{2}\sigma_e$

$\frac{1}{2}\sigma_e$

σ_e

$\frac{h}{3}$

$\frac{h}{2}$

$\frac{h}{2}$

(c)

M_L

$\frac{3}{8}\sigma_e bh$

$\frac{2}{3}h$

$\frac{3}{8}\sigma_e bh$

$\frac{3}{2}\sigma_e$

$\frac{3}{2}\sigma_e$

$\frac{h}{2}$

$\frac{h}{2}$

(d)

Fig. 14.13

same section elastically transmitting an opposite but equal moment M_L, and the corresponding stress distribution and stress resultants. The apparent maximum stress is $\frac{3}{2}$ the original σ_e. Superposition of the two systems results in Fig. 14.13c, which shows the residual stress pattern and the residual stress resultants. Note that the internal force system is in equilibrium. Reloading is equivalent to superposing the stress pattern of sketch d on that of sketch c, which results in the pattern of sketch a.

The presence of these residual stresses can be demonstrated by cold bending a bar of steel into a U- or V-shape. If some material from either the convex or the concave side were then removed, the bent bar would open up measurably. Reference to Fig. 14.13c shows that removal of some material from the top or bottom would destroy the equilibrating effect of the exterior couple; the interior couple would then cause the section to rotate, partly relieving the residual stresses.

These residual stresses, made possible by the material's ductility, are put to practical use in mechanical springs. For instance, in the manufacture of leaf springs, one of the last steps is to prestrain the spring in the sense of normal service loading so as to cause permanent deformation. The stored stresses then will confer on the spring additional elastic strength, which effect is equivalent to the material possessing a higher elastic limit than originally (Fig. 14.13d).

So far we have a relatively simple yet entirely reasonable theory valid for beam sections that transmit bending moments only. When we apply these concepts to whole beams which transmit not only bending moments but shear forces as well, we are no longer sure of our ground. In such cases, we must consider any prediction of the theory as a first approximation only.* How good the approximation is we can establish by experiment; this is in keeping with the engineering approach.

Illustrative Example 3. The simply supported beam of an elastic-plastic material is loaded at its third points as indicated in Fig. 14.14a. An analysis is desired as a basis for predicting the load that will cause collapse.

ANALYSIS. Since the beam is nonredundantly supported, the bending moments everywhere bear constant relationships to P; therefore the relative form of the bending-moment diagram (Fig. 14.14b) remains unaltered. It is clear that the middle third of the beam is subject to bending moment unaccompanied by shear force; hence the results de-

---

* For a mathematically rigorous treatment, see P. G. Hodge, Jr., *Plastic Analysis of Structures*, pp. 206–213, McGraw-Hill Book Company, New York, 1959.

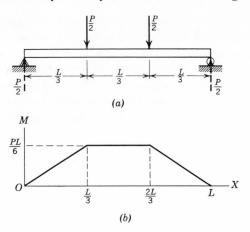

Fig. 14.14

rived from the elementary theory in the foregoing apply strictly to this middle portion, except those sections immediately next to the point loads $P/2$.

The maximum elastic load P_e is found by equating the maximum bending moment to the elastic bending strength of the beam section, thus:

$$\frac{P_e L}{6} = M_e,$$

from which

$$P_e = \frac{6M_e}{L}. \tag{j}$$

As the load is increased beyond this value, yielding will take place simultaneously throughout the middle third of the beam, starting at the outermost material where the elastic stresses are highest and gradually spreading inward toward the neutral surface. The maximum bending moment will remain $PL/6$. Assuming that it is possible for all the beam sections in this middle third to become fully plastic, we find the limit load P_L simply by equating the maximum bending moment to the plastic bending strength. Doing this, we get

$$\frac{P_L L}{6} = M_L = F_p M_e.$$

This gives

$$P_L = \frac{6M_L}{L} = \frac{6F_p M_e}{L} = F_p P_e. \tag{k}$$

Thus the ratio of P_L to P_e is nothing more than the plastic form factor F_p. This is true of any statically determinate prismatic beam, provided the loading is proportional.

Let us now look at some experimental results. A bar of hot-rolled mild steel, of $\frac{5}{8}$ in. by $\frac{5}{8}$ in. square cross section, was tested as a simple beam on a 12.5-in. span. The beam was loaded at its third points as in the preceding example. In separate tests on specimens prepared from the same bar stock, the tension and compression yield strengths had been found to be both 33,300 psi. Assuming that this is the same as the elastic-limit stress, we find the elastic strength of the beam section to be

$$M_e = \frac{\sigma_e b h^2}{6} = \frac{33,300(0.625)^3}{6}$$

$$= 1355 \text{ in.-lb.}$$

Therefore, by Eq. j,

$$P_e = \frac{6M_e}{L} = \frac{6(1355)}{12.5} = 650 \text{ lb.}$$

Since the plastic form factor for a square cross section is 1.5, limit theory predicts that the plastic bending strength is

$$M_L = 1.5(1355) = 2033 \text{ in.-lb,}$$

and, by Eq. k, that $\quad P_L = 1.5(650) = 975 \text{ lb.}$

Figure 14.15 shows a plot of the test results,[*] the load P against the midspan deflection δ. Note that the value $P = 650$ lb lies well within the straight-line part of the fitted curve, in fact, below the 780 lb estimated to be the end of the linear relationship.[†] The remarkable evidence here is that at $P = 975$ lb, which the theory predicts to be the limit load, the curve displays a markedly flat and almost horizontal part.

Illustrative Example 4. We now extend the concepts of limit analysis to redundantly supported beams and thereby bring out again the deeper significance of material ductility. Figure 14.16a shows a beam similar to that in Fig. 14.14a, except that there is an extra restraining moment

[*] From F. Panlilio, "The Theory of Limit Design Applied to Magnesium Alloy and Aluminum Alloy Structures," *J. Roy. Aero. Soc.*, Vol. 51, No. 438 (June, 1947).

[†] This fact, although interesting in itself, is of little import here. It is explained in part by the well-known property of an "upper" yield point as distinct from a "lower" yield point observed in mild steel (the 33,300 psi marked the lower point), and in part by the fact that, in beams, the proportional limit is even more difficult to pinpoint than in simple tension or compression pieces.

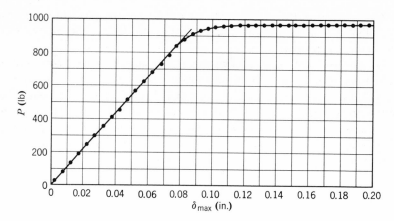

Fig. 14.15. Results of the bend test of a $\frac{5}{8}$-in. by $\frac{5}{8}$-in. hot-rolled mild steel beam on a 12.5-in. span. (By permission of The Royal Aeronautical Society.)

at one end. Analyze the beam's post-elastic performance, assuming that the yield hinge concept applies even in the presence of shear force.

ANALYSIS. For a beam with perfect initial fit, the bending-moment diagram up to the proportional limit is as shown in Fig. 14.16b. There are two sections of greatest bending moment, one at the wall and one at the section of the further load. From $P_e L/6 = M_e$, we find

$$P_e = \frac{6M_e}{L}. \qquad (l)$$

As P is increased beyond this value, the section at the wall becomes elasto-plastic and will begin to taper off its ability to increase resistance to bending; in other words, the bending moment at the wall will cease to be proportional to the rotation of that section and hence also to P. Meanwhile, all other sections continue to increase their resisting moments, linearly with their respective rotations but no longer linearly with P. This will proceed until the section at the outer load reaches the elastic limit and its resisting moment becomes M_e. Figure 14.16c shows a possible bending-moment diagram. The actual instantaneous value of M_A can be determined only by bringing in elasto-plastic deflections,* which we will not take up in this introductory treatment. Any further increase in P will make section C elasto-plastic. Section A becoming fully plastic means the formation of a yield hinge at the wall;

* Phillips, *op. cit.* on p. 416, Chapter 5.

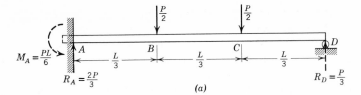

$M_A = \dfrac{PL}{6}$ $R_A = \dfrac{2P}{3}$ $R_D = \dfrac{P}{3}$

(a)

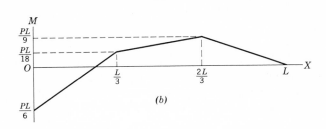

(b)

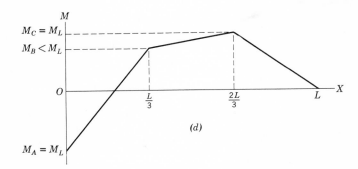

(c)

$M_C = M_e$

M_B

$M_L \geqq M_A > M_e$

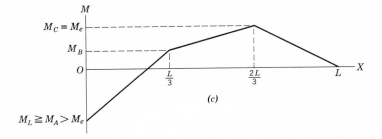

(d)

$M_C = M_L$

$M_B < M_L$

$M_A = M_L$

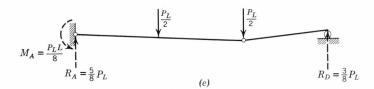

$M_A = \dfrac{P_L L}{8}$ $R_A = \dfrac{5}{8} P_L$ $R_D = \dfrac{3}{8} P_L$

(e)

Fig. 14.16

hence this section completely loses its ability to restrain rotation, but maintains its resisting moment. So long as no other section has become a yield hinge, the deflections of the beam, which is now statically determinate, will remain of the order of elastic deformations. In the limit, a yield hinge will form at section C also. The limit bending-moment diagram is shown in Fig. 14.16d. Provided with the two hinges at A and at C, the beam then becomes a *mechanism* (Fig. 14.16e) and collapse threatens.

The collapse load P_L is calculated from statics alone. This is accomplished either with the aid of free-body diagrams or by directly applying the defining equation for the bending moment at any section. Using the latter method, we write the bending moment at C in terms of forces to the right, thus:

$$M_C = \frac{R_D L}{3} = M_L.$$

This gives the limit value of the reaction at D,

$$R_D = \frac{3M_L}{L}.$$

Again, writing the bending moment at the wall in terms of forces to the right, we have

$$M_A = R_D L - \frac{P_L L}{2} = -M_L,$$

from which, after substituting the value of R_D just found, we get the limit load

$$P_L = \frac{8M_L}{L}. \qquad (m)$$

The final bending moment at B is found to be $2M_L/3$, which is well within the capacity of the beam section to develop; hence no hinge will form at B. Nevertheless, permanent set may occur at this section if the plastic form factor F_p is less than $\frac{3}{2}$.

It is interesting to note how much potential strength a beam really has when redundantly supported. Dividing P_L from Eq. m by P_e from Eq. l, we obtain

$$\frac{P_L}{P_e} = \frac{8M_L}{6M_e} = \frac{4}{3} F_p. \qquad (n)$$

For a beam of rectangular cross section, this ratio is 2. We can appreciate how this considerable margin of strength beyond maximum elastic conditions comes about by remembering that the limit load corresponds to full material utilization at the largest possible number of transverse sections. Once again, it is appropriate to remark that it is more reasonable to apply the safety factor on P_L in Eq. m than on σ_e in Eq. l to obtain a working value for P, when the goal of the design is to achieve a margin of safety against collapse under static load.

The residual reactions which remain after the beam is relieved of its collapse load can be evaluated in the usual manner by the technique of superposition. Figure 14.17a presents the free-body diagram of the beam under limit conditions; Fig. 14.17b shows that of a beam elastically carrying equal but opposite loads. Superposing the two gives Fig. 14.17c, showing the residual reactions. From this last sketch we note that, if the right support were removed, that end would deflect downward; or if the restraining moment were relieved, the beam would arch upward.

Let us turn once again to the results of experiment. In Fig. 14.18 is shown schematically how the simple beam of Fig. 14.14a can be provided with the redundant restraining moment of Fig. 14.16a. This is achieved with a beam that is twice as long, supported symmetrically at the ends and at the middle, and loaded symmetrically on the two spans. Symmetry assures a horizontal tangent at the middle support; hence one-

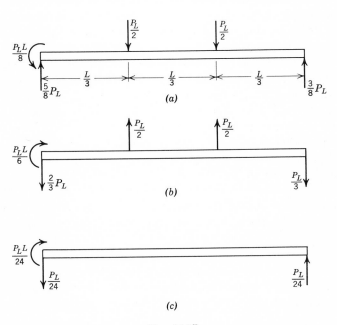

Fig. 14.17

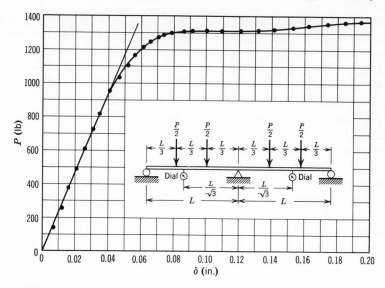

FIG. 14.18   Results of the bend test of a $\frac{5}{8}$-in. by $\frac{5}{8}$-in. hot-rolled mild steel beam redundantly supported on a 12.5-in. span.   (By permission of The Royal Aeronautical Society.)

half of this long beam is equivalent to the beam of Fig. 14.16a.   Analysis shows that the maximum elastic deflection occurs at a distance of $L/\sqrt{3}$ from the middle support.

The beam tested was of the same size and from the same stock as the simple beam cited earlier.   Plotted in Fig. 14.18 are the test results,* total load P on one span versus the deflection at $L/\sqrt{3}$.   For this beam section, $M_e = 1355$ in.-lb and $M_L = 2033$ in.-lb, as computed earlier. Equation l predicts P_e to be no larger than 650 lb; the load-deflection curve shows that the apparent proportional-limit load was in the neighborhood of 880 lb.   Noteworthy is the agreement between the predicted and the practical limit load: by Eq. m we should expect a leveling off at $P_L = 1300$ lb; note that the curve exhibits a plateau at $P = 1309$ lb. In this connection, we observe that under $P = 1300$ lb the deflection was only about twice the proportional-limit deformation and does not in any sense suggest runaway conditions.

Thus, our rather crude assumption, that the relations derived expressly for pure bending only may be applied to bending when accompanied by shear force, leads to very respectable approximations indeed, at least in mild steel.

* Panlilio, op. cit. on p. 421.

PROBLEMS

14.8. Evaluate the plastic form factor of a solid circular beam section in pure bending, assuming the material to be elastic-plastic.

14.9. Evaluate the plastic form factor of a hollow circular beam section in pure bending, if the outside diameter is twice the inside diameter.

14.10. Evaluate the plastic form factor of a solid beam section in pure bending whose form is that of an isoceles triangle with the neutral axis coinciding with the axis of symmetry.

14.11. Evaluate the plastic form factor of the wide-flange beam section shown in Fig. 6.4.

14.12. Evaluate the plastic form factor of the T-shaped beam section shown in Fig. 6.10b.

14.13. Evaluate the plastic form factor of the T-shaped beam section shown in Fig. 6.11b.

14.14. A beam of mild steel for which $\sigma_e = \sigma_p = 36{,}000$ psi has a rectangular section, 3 in. deep by 2 in. wide. It transmits a pure moment in a plane parallel to the 3-in. dimension such that the elastic core remaining is 1 in. deep. (*a*) Calculate this moment. (*b*) Calculate the radius of curvature at the level of the centroid, using $E = 30 \times 10^6$ psi. (*c*) What percentage of the limit bending strength is this moment?

14.15. Calculate the collapse load P_L for this uniform beam in terms of the limit bending strength M_L of the beam section. Assuming perfect initial fit, calculate the residual reactions when the beam is unloaded from near collapse.

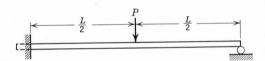

Fɪɢ. P14.15

14.16. Replace the roller support of the beam in Fig. P14.15 by a wall like that at the other end, thus increasing the degree of constraint redundancy by one. Calculate the collapse load P_L in terms of the limit moment M_L.

14.17. Assume both ends of the beam in Fig. 14.16a to be built in. Calculate the collapse load P_L in terms of M_L. When unloaded from near collapse, what will be the residual reactions on the beam?

14.18. Determine the limit load intensity p_L that will initiate excessive deformation in the beam of Fig. 8.4a. The limit bending strength of the section is M_L. (*Hint:* The algebraic maximum bending moment is still where the shear changes sign; this relation from statics remains valid.)

14.19. Assume both ends of the beam of Prob. 14.18 to be fixed and then solve.

14.20. If in the beam of Fig. 8.4a the uniformly distributed load is only over the left half of the span, what is the limit p_L? (See hint in Prob. 14.18.)

14.21. In the beam of Fig. 8.4a assume the uniformly distributed load is only over the right half of the span. Calculate p_L.

14.22. Determine the limit load intensity p_L for this beam in terms of the limit bending moment M_L. (See hint in Prob. 14.18. Solve the cubic by trial.)

FIG. P14.22

14.23. Determine the limit load intensity p_L for this beam in terms of M_L.

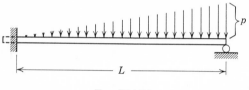

FIG. P14.23

14.5   Column Action.   Inelastic column action will be discussed from two viewpoints: (1) when the material is perfectly plastic beyond the proportional limit, and (2) when the material is capable of strain hardening at a continuously varying rate. We have not considered the other structural elements from the second viewpoint because for such materials the definition of limit strength is uncertain, hence, arbitrary; this aspect is taken up in the more advanced treatises on plasticity. On the other hand, the limit strength of a column remains sharply defined regardless of the degree of ductility possessed by its material.

Let us assume for convenience that the column cross section is rectangular and that its material has a stress-strain curve as shown in Fig. 14.1. The column is also assumed to have hinged ends and a slenderness larger than critical. Imagine now that the column bears the critical load $P_{cr} = \pi^2 EI/l^2$; it is then in a state of *elastic instability*. Sketch a of Fig. 14.19 represents the stress distribution, in which $\sigma = P_{cr}/A$ is less than σ_e. Immediately after buckling, the stress pattern is something like that in sketch b, where the maximum stress is still less than σ_e. With continuing deformation of the column, before long the compression stress in the concave side reaches the proportional limit (sketch c) and

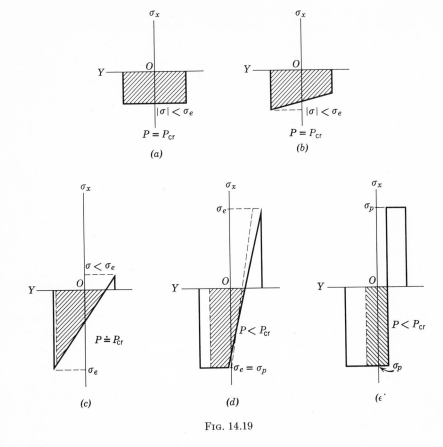

FIG. 14.19

yielding begins. Up to this point, the load-carrying capacity of the column remains approximately constant at the level P_{cr}; hence during this stage the column is in a state of *neutral elastic equilibrium*. The interval between states a and c (Fig. 14.19), as well as whether or not the stress in the convex side reverses, depends on the slenderness: the nearer this is to critical, the shorter the interval and the sooner do the stresses reverse. After further straining, the column becomes elasto-plastic and concomitantly its strength begins to taper off. Sketch d shows the stress distribution when the convex side reaches the proportion limit (in tension). Any further straining will make the convex side yield, as suggested by the dotted line in sketch d. As in the beam, assuming that the fully plastic condition can develop, we represent the stress distribution by the two rectangles in sketch e, where the shaded area stands for the remanent load-carrying capacity of the column, now considerably less than P_{cr}.

The difference between a fully plastic column and a fully plastic beam is that, in the former, continuing deformation brings on decreasing strength (the shaded area in sketch e shrinks, although it cannot disappear altogether), whereas in the latter the strength of the yield hinge remains constant or even tends to increase. Unlike a beam, a column after buckling can no longer control its deflection. Summing up, we observe that a long column made of an elastic-plastic material will approach the fully plastic state *gradually*, the more slender the column the more gradual this approach.

Let us now turn to the short column. Under a load $P_e = \sigma_c A$, the stress distribution is as in sketch a of Fig. 14.19, where the upper limit for σ is used. The material then begins to yield. Although there is theoretically no reason why the column should not remain straight while yielding, it nevertheless will buckle because plastic flow across the transverse section cannot possibly remain absolutely uniform for any length of time. Thus, under the load P_e, the short column is said to be in a state of *plastic instability*. Immediately after buckling, the stress distribution goes over into the pattern of sketch d or even sketch e, with an accompanying *sudden* decrease in the load-carrying capacity. In brief, then, a short column of an elastic-plastic material undergoes in buckling a violent transition from plastic instability to the fully plastic condition of combined bending and thrust, with consequent rapidly decreasing strength, there being *no* stage of neutral equilibrium in transition.

When the material has a stress-strain characteristic like that depicted in Fig. 14.20, inelastic column action presents some differences from that just discussed, relatively minor in the long column but quite significant in the short column range. The behavior of a long column and its stress patterns up until σ_e is first reached are similar to those of any other long column. Figure 14.21a shows the stress distribution after buckling when σ_e is first reached in the concave side. Sketch b shows a later pattern after permanent deformation has set in. Owing to the character of the stress-strain curve, the compressive stresses in the concave side build up with deformation, making it possible for the load-carrying capacity to remain at the previous level or, at least, to decrease from this level more slowly than would be the case were the column of an elastic-plastic material. Sketch c is for the stage when the stress in the convex side reaches the proportional limit in tension, and sketch d represents any later instant. Thus the main difference in the behavior of long columns made of these two kinds of material lies in the rate at which the column loses its strength after buckling: the nonzero strain-hardening

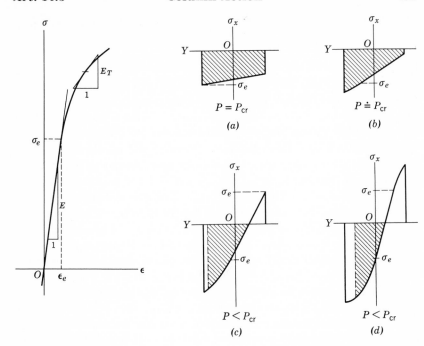

rate of the less ductile material confers on the column a greater tenacity, so to speak. For emphasis, we repeat that the *limit* strength of a long column depends only on the elasticity modulus, all other things being equal, and that ductility of material has nothing to do with this strength.

We come now to the most interesting case of the short column made of a material with a continuously varying rate of strain hardening. The column delivers its elastic strength P_e when the stresses across a transverse section are uniformly distributed at the intensity σ_e. Since the material has no yield point as such, there is no tendency for "runaway" plastic deformation; hence (1) it is less likely for the column to buckle because of nonuniform yielding, and (2) it is possible for the load on it to increase while the column remains straight. Let it be so assumed. The question then is: What load will bring the column to the critical condition of instability?

The Euler formula, $P_{cr} = \pi^2 EI/l^2$, is derived from the solution $y = \delta \sin \pi x/l$ of the differential equation $d^2y/dx^2 = M/EI$, an approximate form of the basic relation $1/\rho = M/EI$. With the discussion in Article 9.4, p. 269, as background, we can say without doing violence to the truth that, when $\delta = 0$, the expression $y = \delta \sin \pi x/l$ is a solution of the exact differential equation

$$\frac{d^2y/dx^2}{[1 + (dy/dx)^2]^{3/2}} = \frac{M}{EI}.$$

Now, the elasticity modulus E may be interpreted as a measure of the material's stiffness, that is, of the amount by which the stress needs to be changed to effect a unit change in the strain. Within the proportional limit, this rate (of change of stress relative to strain) is constant and independent of the stress level. Beyond the proportional limit, however, this rate depends on the stress level. We touched on this briefly in Chapter 3. The rate is called the *tangent modulus* E_T at a specified stress level. Note that this is merely another designation of the local rate of strain hardening.

Considering all this, especially that the column is assumed to remain straight ($\delta = 0$) up to the critical state, so that P_{cr}/A is truly the stress at every point in the transverse section of the member, we find the idea not only attractive but eminently reasonable of substituting for E in Euler's formula the tangent modulus E_T, thus:

$$P_{cr} = \frac{\pi^2 E_T I}{l^2}, \tag{14.8}$$

where E_T and $P_{cr}/A = \sigma$ are to be paired off according to the compression stress-strain curve of the material.

The above formula was suggested in 1889 by F. Engesser. For many years after, this starkly simple and uncomplicated relation was held suspect and preference leaned toward a similar equation in which the E term purported to take into account not only the geometry of the cross section but also the two moduli ascribed to the column: one for the concave side, which is the tangent modulus, and another for the convex side, which is assumed to unload and finally go over into tension during buckling. This *double modulus column formula* (based on the work of A. Considère, of Engesser himself, and later of T. von Karman, and still later of R. V. Southwell, independently) was generally accepted as correct until 1947. That year F. Shanley showed that there was some inconsistency in the double modulus theory and that the true critical load of a short column, although somewhat higher, is substantially as given by the original Engesser equation. The definition of the critical load contained in Eq. 14.8 is now accepted as representing the limit strength of a short column.*

---

* For an interesting account, see F. Bleich, *Buckling Strength of Metal Structures*, pp. 8–21, McGraw-Hill Book Company, New York, 1952.

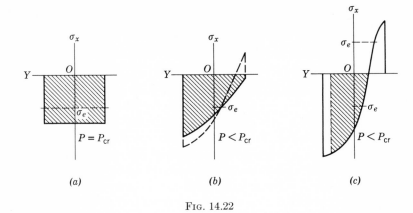

Fɪɢ. 14.22

The stress distribution patterns are shown in Fig. 14.22. Sketch *a* represents the instant when the column is in a state of *inelastic instability*. Sketch *b* shows two possible patterns soon after buckling, and sketch *c* depicts any later state.

We have now come full circle. Since E is also E_T within the proportional limit, Eq. 14.8 defines the strength of a column for all slenderness values. It should thus be properly called the *Euler-Engesser formula*. Interestingly enough, this equation does not apply to short columns made of elastic-plastic materials, inasmuch as, when $E_T = 0$, it requires that the column has zero strength, which we know is not so. Evidently this conclusion is in order: The Euler-Van den Broek equation (see Eq. 9.6) gives the *limit* strength of all columns made of elastic-plastic materials or the *elastic* strength of all columns made of any other material with a proportional limit; the Euler-Engesser equation gives the *limit* strength of all columns made of materials whose tangent modulus remains positive.

The last discussion will illustrate how the Euler-Engesser column curve is obtained from the stress-strain diagram of a given material. In Fig. 14.23*a* is shown the compression stress-strain curve of a typical grade of cold-rolled steel and, derived from it, a curve showing the variation of E_T with stress level. Rewriting Eq. 14.8 in the form

$$\frac{P_{\text{cr}}}{A} = \frac{\pi^2 E_T}{(l/k)^2},$$ (14.8a)

and substituting for P_{cr}/A and E_T the coordinates of points on the $\sigma\text{-}E_T$ curve, we calculate the values of the slenderness l/k that satisfy

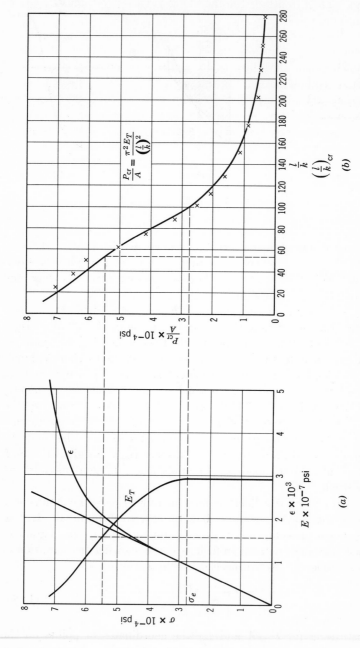

FIG. 14.23 Showing the Euler-Engesser column curve. Crosses represent test results on $\frac{5}{16}$-in. commercial cold-rolled steel columns.

Eq. 14.8a. Then, plotting the matching values of l/k and P_{cr}/A, we obtain the curve in Fig. 14.23b.

Many researchers have long since verified the buckling strength of a short column to be virtually that predicted by Eq. 14.8. Even in a modestly equipped laboratory, it is a simple matter to demonstrate the basic facts of column action. In Fig. 14.23b the crosses shown are plots of data from actual hinged-end column tests.[*] The specimens were $\frac{5}{16}$-in. commercial cold-rolled steel rods provided with semispherical ends bearing on flat carboloy blocks.

PROBLEM

14.24. Run through the calculation for the slenderness value of a column with hinged ends that will match a plastic buckling load per unit area P_{cr}/A of 60,000 psi according to the Euler-Engesser equation. The material properties are as shown in Fig. 14.23a.

14.6 Limit Design.[†] This is a method of design whereby the specified or assumed working loads are multiplied by an overload factor and the member or structure then designed so that, when subjected to this maximum loading, it is at or comes close to the state of collapse. The method presupposes not only material ductility but member ductility as well.

In actual use, the method bypasses altogether the stages of elastic and contained plastic deformation and instead considers limit conditions immediately. In the light of earlier discussion in this chapter, we anticipate that limit design promises to be of advantage primarily where redundancy of constraint is involved; then the justification for considering limit conditions directly is found in the sure knowledge that up to collapse through a mechanism the deformations involved will remain within the order of maximum *elastic* deformations. This concept was expressed by Van den Broek as follows:

When in a well designed, and especially a properly detailed, n-fold redundant structure n redundant members are stressed to their elastic limit or up to their critical buckling load, the deformations involved are of the order of elastic deformations until an $(n + 1)th$ *member has reached its elastic limit, or its critical buckling capacity.*[‡]

[*] Typical test data of a laboratory class in strength of materials, Union College, Schenectady, New York, 1961.

[†] The terminology is due to J. A. Van den Broek. See his *Theory of Limit Design*, John Wiley and Sons, New York, 1948.

[‡] Van den Broek, *op. cit.*, p. 32.

This spells out the principal feature of limit design, that the static strength of a structural member or of an entire structure should be based not on the proportional-limit stress being attained at some one site but rather on the load-carrying capacity that obtains at or near collapse.

Although Van den Broek's principle remains valid, in the form as originally stated it can be applied strictly only to relatively simple structures. Since his time the concept has been refined, expanded, and amplified so as to include such items as local as distinguished from over-all collapse, upper and lower bounds of the collapse load, shakedown, etc.; now limit design is considered but a special aspect of the more general theory of plastic structural analysis.* In this introductory treatment, the preceding statement will serve adequately to give us an idea of the underlying philosophy of limit design.

In bypassing the intermediate stages of structural behavior, one would probably wonder whether a knowledge of the elastic performance is necessary to a successful application of limit design: specifically, is it not important to know which $n + 1$ elements should be considered? There is no question but that a full knowledge of the elastic behavior of a structure would indicate which elements will control the strength, namely the $n + 1$ most highly stressed elements; hence such knowledge would be a distinct asset. Nevertheless, the answer to the preceding question is that it is not necessary at all to know about the elastic performance of the structure for one successfully to apply limit design. In order to appreciate this, let us consider what is actually involved in an elastic analysis.

In the analysis that necessarily precedes design, the tried and true engineering approach has been to assume sizes and forms (sometimes also the material to employ) for the elements of the structure being designed. The hypothetical structure is then analyzed for internal stresses, and their maximum (so-called critical) values compared with specifica-tions. Changes are then made as indicated by the comparison: those elements that are overstressed are strengthened, whereas the under-stressed ones are weakened. The process is repeated until a reasonably efficient utilization of the materials is achieved. Thus, even for only moderately complex structures, what might be considered a full know-ledge of the structure's elastic behavior could be obtained only after a long and tedious process which, in essence, is a cut-and-try affair. This is no longer a drawback in itself in view of the fact that electronic computers can take the drudgery out of such work. Notwithstanding this,

---

* For instance, see Hodge, *op. cit.* on p. 419.

the fundamental objection remains that elastic behavior has never furnished a realistic *basis* for strength determination in static loading. Moreover, although it is easy enough in the analysis to assume perfect structural fit, it is next to impossible to insure the same in the actual construction; a slight error or misfit could render meaningless the results of much elaborate calculation. Inevitably one is forced to the realization that elastic design with ductile materials is actually a game of make believe and, with tongue in cheek, one then submits that any numbers obtained in an elastic analysis are merely "thinking numbers."

This is not to dismiss as unimportant the techniques and theory of elastic analysis which, after all, are a main concern of this book. Nonetheless, as a basis for structural design, elastic performance need not be held sacrosanct since in practice it is hardly ever completely preserved.

To repeat, it is not necessary to have prior knowledge of elastic performance in applying limit design. We quote here the earliest articulation of this concept. In 1917, speaking of steel construction, N. C. Kist propounded:

> *"In the design of a redundant structure, it is not necessary to use the equations of elasticity to determine the redundants; it is only necessary to assume values for them, any assumptions at all but preferably the most advantageous ones, provided such assumptions are compatible with the conditions of equilibrium."* *

Obviously, the most advantageous value to assume for a redundant is its limit strength or value.

In a nutshell then, combining the Van den Broek and Kist principles, all we need to do in limit design is (1) *assume limit values for the n redundants and for one additional element or constraint* and then (2) *solve for any remaining unknowns, including the limit or collapse load, by the equations of equilibrium.* Clearly, this simplifies the solutions of problems involving statically indeterminate elements. Furthermore, because material ductility is taken advantage of, the possibility of slight initial misfit in the actual construction is no longer significant: *Ductility endows the structural components with the ability to adjust themselves to and compensate for small constructional errors.*

There remains, however, one fly in the ointment. If several groupings of the redundants are possible, as pointed out in the introduction of Chapter 8, the question arises as to which grouping to work with. The answer is: try all possibilites; *the correct collapse mechanism is that which corresponds to the smallest load.*† We find then that even with limit design

---

* Van den Broek, *op. cit.* on p. 435, p. 39.
† Phillips, *op. cit.* on p. 416, p. 37.

a certain amount of cutting and trying cannot be avoided. Fortunately, for every set of unknowns assumed, the remaining system is statically determinate and its solution presents no difficulties.

To illustrate the foregoing concepts, let us return to the beam of Example 4, Article 14.4. Through our previous discussion of redundancy (Chapter 8), we know that the system is redundant to the first degree; this we have to know. As far as the external force system is concerned, we can decide immediately which of the restraints is redundant: either the moment at the wall or the reaction of the roller support. On the other hand, in the internal force system, if the moment at any transverse section between ends is assumed known, the remaining system also becomes determinate. Hence we can assume the moment at any one of an infinite number of transverse sections, including that at the wall, and then that at any other section in addition ($n = 1$ and $n + 1 = 2$). Does this mean that we are now faced with the prospect of dealing with a double infinity of possible solutions? At this point, we must make use of previous knowledge, gleaned not from elastic analysis but from basic statics. We recall that, when there are concentrated forces among the transverse loads on a beam, the bending moment diagram invariably manifests a local peak at the site of each such force. Taking advantage of this fact, we conclude that only the three sections A, B, and C of the beam need be considered (Fig. 14.16b). Then, grouping these two at a time, we find that it will suffice to investigate only three cases: (1) hinges at A and B, (2) hinges at A and C, and (3) hinges at B and C.

Figure 14.24 shows the three possible mechanisms in which the three sketches correspond, respectively, to these three cases. The relation between P and the limit bending strength M_L of the yield hinge is illustrated for Case 1 as follows. The bending moment at B in terms of forces to the right is

$$R_D \left(\frac{2L}{3}\right) - \frac{P}{2}\left(\frac{L}{3}\right) = M_L.$$

Similarly, the bending moment at A in terms of forces to the right is

$$R_D(L) - \frac{P}{2}\left(\frac{2L}{3}\right) - \frac{P}{2}\left(\frac{L}{3}\right) = -M_L.$$

Solving these two equations for P, we obtain

$$P = \frac{10M_L}{L}. \qquad (a)$$

Repeating this process for the other two cases, each time using only the forces that lie to the *same* side of the sections (always those to the right or always those to the left), we find these two other values of P:

$$P = \frac{8M_L}{L} \tag{b}$$

for Case 2 and
$$P = \frac{18M_L}{L} \tag{c}$$

for Case 3. Of these three values, the smallest one as given by Eq. b is the correct collapse load. This value agrees with that previously obtained, as it should. Note that the earlier value was arrived at as the culmination of inelastic action, with P increasing beyond P_e.

It is not the intent here to suggest that limit design is confined to beams only. In an elementary textbook, however, there is little room for much else. Since the main objective in this treatment is to acquaint the student only with the basic philosophy of limit design as a criterion of usefulness, the beam has been chosen as the most convenient vehicle for illustration because it continues to be the most important one of the structural elements. Furthermore, experimental data in partial confirmation of limit analysis can be obtained from beam tests with little difficulty even in the most modest laboratory. The only other simple vehicle, the riveted joint, which represents the oldest and continuing successful application of limit design, is treated in the next article.

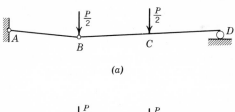

(a)

(b)

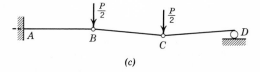

(c)

Fig. 14.24

When other elements such as tension or compression members or both are involved in a structure, let it suffice here to say that the limit strength to use for tension and ordinary compression is simply $\sigma_p A$; for long slender members, the Euler buckling strength should be used. We leave unsettled the question of what should be the assumed limit strength for compression members of intermediate slenderness. The reason for this was brought out in Chapter 9 (see Fig. 9.8): Among columns, only the very slender ones actually behave in a ductile manner, allowing other elements to catch up, so to speak, while they themselves continue to deliver full strength. An intermediate column displays no such unusual behavior, its remanent load-carrying capacity after buckling tapering off more or less rapidly. Notwithstanding this lack of definitiveness, we remark that limit design can still be applied in such cases. Guided by Kist's principle, we may assume, for short or intermediate columns, strengths considerably below their limit capacities.* Ultimately, such procedure must lean heavily on value judgment; this is something that not even the best of engineers can teach, let alone an author through his textbook.

PROBLEMS

14.25. The three wires are to be of the same diameter. Assuming that they all are of an elastic-plastic material, for which $\sigma_e = \sigma_p = 40,000$ psi, select the right size wire that will support a static load of $P = 100,000$ lb (this includes the weight of the rigid bar) with a safety factor of 2. Under the collapse load of 200,000 lb, what approximately will be the deflection of the rigid bar if E is 30×10^6 psi? See opposite page for figure.

14.26. Repeat Prob. 14.25 with the outer wires inclined 15 deg away from the center wire, their lengths remaining the same as before.

14.27. In Fig. P14.15, $L = 10$ ft and $P = 50,000$ lb. Select from Table II of the Appendix a W^F-section that will carry the load with a safety factor of 2, assuming $\sigma_e = \sigma_p = 40,000$ psi. Ignore the effect of the beam's weight on the bending moments.

14.28. Do Prob. 14.27 for a beam built in at both ends.

14.29. In Fig. 14.16a, $L = 18$ ft and $P = 100,000$ lb. Select from Table II of the Appendix a W^F-section that will carry the load with a safety factor of 2, assuming $\sigma_e = \sigma_p = 40,000$ psi. Ignore the effect of the beam's weight on the bending moments.

14.30. Do Prob. 14.29 for a beam built in at both ends.

* The reader interested in the early pros and cons of this philosophy will want to read the prize winning paper, which is a milestone in strength theory and structural design practice: J. A. Van den Broek, "Theory of Limit Design," *Trans. Amer. Soc. Civ. Engrs.*, Vol. 105 (1940), pp. 638–730; this includes discussion by nineteen distinguished structural engineers and engineering educators.

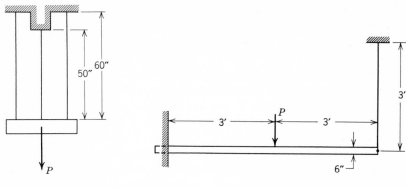

FIG. P14.25   FIG. P14.31

14.31. The mild steel beam has a 6 in. by 4 in. rectangular cross section. The slender rod, hinged to the end of the beam and representing a redundant constraint, is also of mild steel; like the beam it has a $\sigma_e = \sigma_p = 36{,}000$ psi. (a) Assuming that the rod is of a size adequate to permit the beam to become a mechanism at collapse, calculate the collapse load P_L. (b) Assuming that this collapse load P_L acts on the beam, select the optimum cross-sectional area A for the rod. Explain your reasoning.

14.32. In Fig. 13.5a, the truss has the shape of a square with $AB = AD = 6$ ft. All bars are of mild steel, for which $\sigma_e = \sigma_p = 36{,}000$ psi and $E = 30 \times 10^6$ psi, and all have square cross sections. The load Q is 50,000 lb. Using the principles of limit design, select a set of bar sizes that will provide the truss with a load-carrying capacity at a safety factor of 3. Carefully state your assumptions and explain why you select one set rather than another.

14.7   The Riveted Connection. Ever since iron came into use as a construction material, long before the middle of the nineteenth century when first the Bessemer and a little later the Siemens process of steel manufacture began to make this remarkable alloy of iron widely available, the rivet had been a satisfactory fastener. It was, however, with the advent of industrial steel that the riveted connection came of age, so to speak, and it has remained one of the two principal methods of effecting continuity in composite load-bearing structures. This success has been due in the main to the generous supply of ductility possessed by the rivet material. It is therefore not surprising that the attempt to use the light metal alloys of magnesium for rivets in aircraft met with unsatisfactory results, and that the slightly heavier aluminum, practically unalloyed, had to be substituted. The reason: aluminum is a great deal more ductile than the softest magnesium alloy, which is still quite brittle.

Unwittingly, the earliest designers of riveted joints stumbled on limit design when, faced with the utter complexity of the composite structure consisting of multiperforated plates joined together by discrete cylindrical fasteners, they adopted what to them was the sound engineering approach: Assume for the redundant unknowns some force values that are compatible with equilibrium, and then solve the resulting determinate system by basic statics. Observation of this and similar practices in early iron and steel construction must have led Professor Kist to his basic principle.

So widespread and important a structure as the riveted joint was bound sooner or later to receive the attention of many investigators, at first experimental and later analytical also.* The outstanding aspect of a joint's behavior which the early workers seemed to have found disquieting (which we now, with the advantage of hindsight, think rather curious) is contained in the following paraphrase of two writers cited by de Jonge. In 1869, C. Reilly of England, discussing a paper by J. Gaudard of Switzerland, remarked that the ultimate strength did not in the least interest the engineer, who is primarily concerned with the strength at working loads. Writing in 1920, J. Montgomerie of Scotland claimed that, although the knowledge of the ultimate strength of the joint is valuable, the really important question is the behavior of the joint at working stresses. Since then, much has been learned concerning this behavior. Nevertheless, it can be said without distorting the truth that this knowledge has not significantly altered the basic philosophy of rivet-joint design from what it had always been, at least in static applications.

The deep-seated and prevalent distrust of limit design reflected in the preceding comments took a long time to overcome, especially in this country. Almost half a century passed, after the Dutch and other Europeans had been using limit design and had recognized its principles formally in their specifications, before we in the United States finally followed suit. Forming an official part of the American Institute of Steel Construction's Specification for the Design, Fabrication and Erection of Structural Steel for Buildings, adopted December 4, 1958, limit design has finally arrived and now occupies a deserved and honored position in American structural engineering practice.

The two basic types of riveted connection are the *lap joint* and the *butt joint*. In the lap joint (Fig. 14.25a), the two plates are simply overlapped and fastened together, the number of rivet rows being counted in the direction of the load; for example, a triple riveted joint has three rows of rivets. In the butt joint (Fig. 14.25b), the two *main plates* are

* See A. E. R. de Jonge, *Riveted Joints*, A Research Publication of the American Society of Mechanical Engineers, New York, 1945.

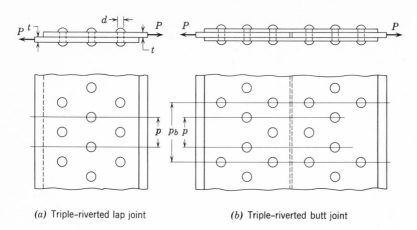

(a) Triple–riveted lap joint   *(b)* Triple–riveted butt joint

Fɪɢ. 14.25

butted or brought together edge to edge and provided with *butt straps* or *cover plates*, which are then fastened to them. For the same number of rows, a butt joint has twice as many rivets as a lap joint, because the rows counted are only those to one side of the butt line.

Since the butt joint is essentially two lap joints combined, there is no tendency in such a setup for the main plates to bend and hence the rivets are in a state of pure shear (approximately). On the other hand, in the lap joint, owing to the slight noncollinearity of the end forces, there is some bending of the plates, as a consequence of which the rivets may be subject to some tension along with the shear.

When joints, such as those in boilers and tanks, contain several columns of rivets clustered in repeating patterns, it is customary to consider in the analysis or design only the least width of joint that includes a complete pattern; for example, a width equal to the *pitch p*, in Fig. 14.25a, or a width equal to the *back pitch* p_b, in Fig. 14.25b.

Out of long experience have empirically evolved certain proportions in the dimensions of riveted joints * which insure that the load-carrying capacity will depend on the stress that develops in one or more of only these three ways: (1) in shear of a rivet, (2) in tension of a plate across the net area at a row of rivet holes, and (3) in compression or bearing between a rivet and a plate. In the analyses to follow, all joints will be assumed so proportioned that only these stresses need be considered. Furthermore, bending and tension of the rivets will be ignored.

---

* For a brief summary of what these proportions are, see R. I. Roark, *Formulas for Stress and Strain*, p. 295, McGraw-Hill Book Company, New York, 1954.

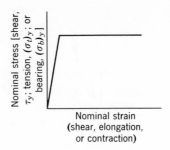

FIG. 14.26

An approximate analysis of load distribution in a riveted joint, based on behavior according to Hooke's law and on the compatibility condition that the differences in the elastic tensile deformations between the overlapping plates (assumed uniform between rivet holes) are accounted for by the cumulative shear deformations of the connecting rivets, shows (1) that the outermost rivets are the most highly stressed and (2) that the farther a rivet is from the edge of the joint the less shear stress it experiences.* Accordingly, if the load-carrying capacity of a riveted joint were based only on elastic action, with no stresses exceeding proportional-limit values, it would be governed exclusively by the elastic shear strength of an outermost rivet, or by the elastic compressive strength of a rivet as it bears on a plate, or by the elastic tensile strength of a plate between holes at the outermost row, whichever of these three leads to the least value. This is the correct and safe practice where nonstatic conditions are involved, as when vibrations are encountered or if a great many cycles of load-unload repetitions and reversals are likely. For ordinary static loading (which could include a *few* load reversals), however, although such an approach would still be valid, it would be unduly tedious and, worse yet, would lead to uneconomical and inefficient material utilization.

The limit analysis or design of riveted connections is predicated on the following two assumptions.

(1) The stress-strain characteristics of rivet and plate materials are as schematically represented in Fig. 14.26. It is *not* to be construed from the sketch that the nominal yield stresses, τ_y in shear, $(\sigma_t)_y$ in tension, and $(\sigma_b)_y$ in bearing, all have equal magnitudes or that they attain these

* This is the conclusion of many investigators as reported by de Jonge, *op. cit.* on p. 442. For a readily available analysis, see F. R. Shanley, *Strength of Materials*, pp. 720–723, McGraw-Hill Book Company, New York, 1957.

values simultaneously. The figure merely suggests that the materials are "equally" ductile in shear, in tension, and in bearing.

(2) The stresses at yield are uniformly distributed across the pertinent areas, which are (a) for shear, the rivet cross-sectional area, $\pi d^2/4$; (b) for tension, the net area of the transverse section of a plate at a row of rivet holes $(p_b - nd)t$, where n is the number of rivets in the row and t is the plate thickness; and (c) for bearing, the projected area of the contact surface between rivet and plate, td. See Figs. 14.27a, b, and c.

Hence the individual sectional strengths are defined as follows:

$$(a) \text{ in shear,} \quad (F_s)_y = \tau_y \left(\frac{\pi d^2}{4}\right),$$

$$(b) \text{ in tension,} \quad (F_t)_y = (\sigma_t)_y (p_b - nd)t,$$

and
$$(c) \text{ in bearing,} \quad (F_b)_y = (\sigma_b)_y (td);$$

which is to say that no one section of an individual element in the connection may transmit, upon yielding, a force larger than the applicable magnitude above.

Between $(F_s)_y$ and $(F_b)_y$ there is an immediate and direct interplay. The ability of a rivet to transmit shear force depends on the ability of the plate it bears against to react with the necessary balancing bearing

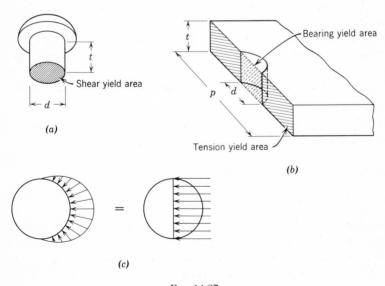

(a)

Shear yield area

(b)

Bearing yield area

Tension yield area

(c)

FIG. 14.27

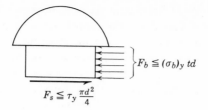

$$F_b \leqq (\sigma_b)_y\, td$$

$$F_s \leqq \tau_y \frac{\pi d^2}{4}$$

Fig. 14.28

force.   In Fig. 14.28, representing *single shear*, the bearing force F_b may not exceed $(F_b)_y = (\sigma_b)_y(td)$, whereas the shear force F_s may not exceed $(F_s)_y = \tau_y(\pi d^2/4)$.   Regardless of their upper limits, however, F_s and F_b must always have equal magnitudes to preserve equilibrium.   Hence the maximum force that can be transmitted at the site of any one rivet, from one plate to the rivet to the other plate, will be the smaller of the two, $(F_b)_y$ and $(F_s)_y$.   Ideally, they should be made equal by proper proportioning of the rivet diameter d to the plate thickness t.

The simplest analysis is that of a lap joint with one column of rivets. An understanding of the limit action in such an elementary connection will make much easier the analysis of more complex arrangements.

Illustrative Example 5.   In the triple riveted lap joint of Fig. 14.29a, the following are given: width of plates, $p = 3$ in.; thickness of each plate, $t = \frac{3}{16}$ in.; diameter of rivet, $d = \frac{1}{2}$ in., assumed the same as the hole diameter; $\tau_y = 44,000$ psi, $(\sigma_t)_y = 55,000$ psi, and $(\sigma_b)_y = 95,000$ psi. (*Note:* in mechanical engineering practice, these stress values for steel rivet and plate materials are often quoted as the *ultimate* rather than the yield.   This does not affect the basic procedure involved.)   Calculate the tension load-carrying capacity of the connection and determine its efficiency.

SOLUTION.   Any one of the three rivets in single shear can transmit, in yield, the smaller of $(F_s)_y$ and $(F_b)_y$, which values

are $(F_s)_y = (44,000)\dfrac{\pi(0.5)^2}{4} = 8640$ lb,

and $(F_b)_y = (95,000)(0.5)(0.1875) = 8900$ lb.

Therefore, at each rivet site, we may count on *not* more than 8640 lb being transmitted from plate to plate.

Figure 14.29b shows the free-body diagram of one plate, together with the three rivets cut at the shear plane.   Observe that the system is redundant to the second degree: two of the rivets (or, equivalently, two of the F's) can certainly be removed with equilibrium still being possible. Invoking Kist's and Van den Broek's principles, we now assume the most favorable values for the $n + 1 = 3$ forces, namely, 8640 lb apiece. This being assumed, we then find P from the equilibrium of the plate in sketch b, thus:

$$\Sigma F = 0 = P - 3(8640),$$

whence
$$P = 25{,}920 \text{ lb.}$$

This would be the correct load-carrying capacity if the net area of the plate cross section at the outermost row (row 1 of the lower plate or row 3 of the upper plate) had the tension capacity; in other words, the free body in sketch c can be in equilibrium, when $F_1 = F_2 = F_3 = 8640$ lb, only if F_t can at least equal their sum of 25,920 lb. Now, the upper limit for F_t is

$$(F_t)_y = 55{,}000(3 - 0.5)(0.1875) = 25{,}800 \text{ lb.}$$

This means that the three rivets, *as a group*, will not be able to deliver full strength. Hence, from the free-body diagram of sketch d, we find the stength of the connection to be

$$P_L = 25{,}800 \text{ lb.} \qquad\qquad Ans.$$

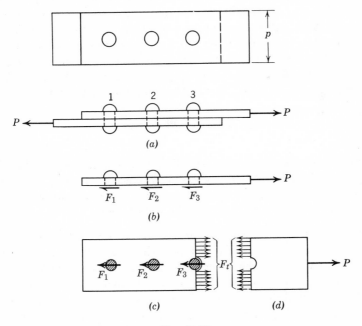

(a)

(b)

(c)   (d)

Fig. 14.29

Amplifying on the preceding results, we say that, under a tension load of 25,800 lb, the plates of the joint will begin to yield at the outermost narrowest cross sections, threatening uncontrolled plastic deformation and collapse. As to what the individual values of F_1, F_2, and F_3 will be is not essential information; suffice it to say that whatever their values, they will be in the realm of possibility because all three can come up to 8640 lb each and therefore their total can more than adequately account for the 25,800 lb. Even so, based on the fact that, during the elastic stage of a well-made joint's performance, the outermost rivets are more highly loaded than the inner ones, we can make a reasonably accurate estimate of the actual load distribution at yield: rivets 1 and 3 each will transmit 8640 lb, whereas rivet 1 will account for the remainder of $25,800 - 2(8640) = 8420$ lb, which is within its capacity. Using these values, we can then establish approximate magnitudes for the net internal tension forces being transmitted by each plate across the two noncritical rows; it should be obvious that both these values will be less than 25,800 lb each.

In the spirit of the philosophy of strength which, we hope, we have succeeded to infuse into the student's consciousness, we now remark that any working load capacity of this connection should be based on the limit value of 25,800 lb. A load of 8600 lb, for example, corresponding to a safety factor of 3, should cause no undue concern for the actual stress distribution throughout the joint. One thing is certain: whatever the actual stresses, they will not be in proportion to the above estimates.

The so-called *efficiency* of the joint is the ratio of its limit strength to the limit strength of the same size unperforated plate. This base figure is $55,000(3)(0.1875) = 30,900$ lb. Therefore the efficiency is

$$\eta = \frac{25,800}{30,900} = 0.835 \text{ or } 83.5\%. \qquad Ans.$$

This has practically the same significance as our factor of utilization. In view of the fact that boring holes in the plate always results in a lessening of the tension-force transmission area, it is obvious that the efficiency of a riveted joint can never be 100 percent.

The analysis of butt joints is similar to the foregoing, one principal difference stemming from the fact that the rivets are in double shear; this obtains whenever the cover plates are of the same length. A joint with cover plates of unequal lengths, which involves a combination of single and double shear action, represents as complicated a situation as we should properly look into. (Increasing the number of rivet rows makes any problem longer, not necessarily more complicated.) Let us then consider for our last example a butt joint with unsymmetrical cover plates.

Illustrative Example 6. Figure 14.30a shows two views of a triple riveted butt joint with one cover plate shorter (narrower) than the other. The main plate thickness is $\frac{1}{2}$ in. and that of each cover plate is

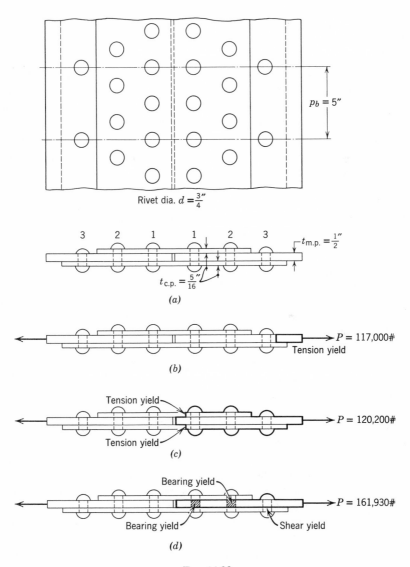

Rivet dia. $d = \frac{3''}{4}$

(a)

(b)

(c)

(d)

Fig. 14.30

$\frac{5}{16}$ in. The rivets are $\frac{3}{4}$ in. in diameter, and the back pitch is 5 in. Assume the same yield (ultimate) stress values as in Example 5. Determine the strength and efficiency of the joint.

SOLUTION. First we calculate the shear and bearing strength of each rivet. A rivet transverse section can transmit a maximum shear force of

$$(F_s)_y = (44,000) \frac{\pi(0.75)^2}{4} = 19,430 \text{ lb.}$$

The cover plate can exert in bearing, on each rivet, a maximum compression force of $95,000(0.75)(0.3125) = 22,300$ lb. Therefore, between cover plate and rivet, there can be transmitted no more than 19,430 lb, as governed by the shear yield stress in the rivet. The main plate, on the other hand, can deliver in bearing, on each rivet, a maximum compression force of only $95,000(0.75)(0.5) = 35,600$ lb, which is less than the double shear strength of one rivet. Hence between main plate and each rivet in double shear no more than 35,600 lb can pass, although between main plate and each rivet in single shear the full 19,430 lb can develop. With this information, we now go about analyzing the joint for failure as follows.

First we introduce the notion of local as opposed to over-all failure or total collapse. Local failure is understood to take place when the least maximum force any row is capable of transmitting from butt straps to main plate is in effect. In butt joints with multiple rows of rivets, only *two* possibilities of over-all failure exist which involve only *one* row apiece: (1) the main plate yielding in tension at the outermost row or (2) the cover plates yielding in tension at the innermost row. Any other possibility of over-all failure must involve a combination of local failures, one for every row, including those at the outermost and innermost rows which do not, of themselves, constitute over-all failure. With the aid of the joint's edge view as shown in Fig. 14.30a, over-all failure can best be visualized as an actual separation. A mode of failure can be represented as an actual cut of the joint in an unbroken jagged line; this line will consist of transverse segments across the plates (to represent tension failure), segments across the rivets (to represent either shear or bearing failure, whichever corresponds to the smaller local force being transmitted), and the common boundaries between plates in various combinations. The rule to remember is: *Draw transverse line segments to represent tension yielding across plates to that side of the rivet row away from the bearing area, outward from a rivet in the main plate and inward from a rivet in a cover plate.* For instance, to depict over-all failure due to the main plate yielding at Row 3, draw a transverse line across the main plate near Row 3 but outward from it, as in Fig. 14.30b. To depict overall failure by tension yielding of the two cover plates, draw transverse lines across the cover plates near Row 1 but inward from it, as shown in Fig. 14.30c. Observe that in both figures, the jagged but unbroken line separates one part of the connection cleanly from the other.

Because there are several possibilities of local failure, which must be combined to produce total collapse, it is best to arrange the computations as follows:

Local Failure	Corresponding Local Force Being Transmitted
Row 1, (1) Two cover plates in tension	$2(0.3125)[5 - 2(0.75)]55,000$ $= 120,200$ lb
(2) Main plate in tension	$0.5[5 - 2(0.75)]55,000 = 96,250$
(3) Main plate bearing on 2 rivets	$2(35,600) = 71,200$
Row 2, (1) Main plate bearing on 2 rivets	$71,200$
Row 3, (1) One rivet in single shear	$19,430$
(2) Main plate in tension	$0.5(5 - 0.75)55,000 = 117,000$

Note that the entry under any inner row need include only the smallest value, whereas that under any extreme row, outermost or innermost, need not include more than two, one being the smallest value among those that do not spell over-all failure.

Then, only three possible modes of total collapse need be evaluated. These are the following (refer to the preceding tabulation):

Combination of Local Failures	Collapse Load
A. Row 3, (2) 117,000	117,000
B. Row 1, (1) 120,200	120,200
C. Row 1, (3) 71,200	
Row 2, (1) 71,200	
Row 3, (1) 19,430	
161,930	161,930

The smallest of the preceding gives the strength of the joint,

$$P_L = 117,000 \text{ lb per 5 in. of repeating width.} \qquad Ans.$$

The unperforated plate can transmit a tension yield force of 55,000(5) (0.5) = 137,500 lb. Hence the efficiency is

$$\eta = \frac{117,000}{137,500} = 0.851 \text{ or } 85.1\%. \qquad Ans.$$

Figures 14.30b, c, and d, respectively, represent the preceding three possibilities of over-all failure. As a test of his understanding, the student should set up for himself the free-body diagrams of the various elements of the joint, singly and in combinations, for each of the failure modes.

PROBLEMS

14.33. In Example 5, Fig. 14.29, keeping the width of the plates fixed at 3 in., how would you improve the efficiency of the joint? Show numerical results.

14.34. In Fig. 14.25a, the plates are each $\frac{1}{2}$ in. thick and the rivet diameter is 1 in. Using the material properties of Example 5, determine (a) the pitch p for optimum conditions and (b) the corresponding joint efficiency.

14.35. In the triple riveted butt joint of Fig. 14.25b, the main plate is $\frac{9}{16}$ in. thick, the butt straps are each $\frac{5}{16}$ in. thick, the rivets are $\frac{3}{4}$ in. in diameter, and the back pitch is 6 in. Assume the same yield stress values as in Example 5. Determine the strength and efficiency of the joint.

APPENDIX TABLES

TABLE I
ROLLED STEEL SHAPES

American Standard I Sections

PROPERTIES FOR DESIGN

Nominal Size	Weight per Foot	Area	Depth	Flange Width	Flange Thickness	Web Thickness	Axis X-X				Axis Y-Y		
							I	$\frac{I}{c}$	F_p	k	I	$\frac{I}{c}$	k
in.	lb	in.²	in.	in.	in.	in.	in.⁴	in.³		in.	in.⁴	in.³	in.
24 × 7⅞	120.0	35.13	24.00	8.048	1.102	0.798	3010.8	250.9	1.188	9.26	84.9	21.1	1.56
	105.9	30.98	24.00	7.875	1.102	.625	2811.5	234.3	1.165	9.53	78.9	20.0	1.60
24 × 7	100.0	29.25	24.00	7.247	0.871	.747	2371.8	197.6	1.208	9.05	48.4	13.4	1.29
	90.0	26.30	24.00	7.124	.871	.624	2230.1	185.8	1.187	9.21	45.5	12.8	1.32
	79.9	23.33	24.00	7.000	.871	.500	2087.2	173.9	1.167	9.46	42.9	12.2	1.36
20 × 7	95.0	27.74	20.00	7.200	.916	.800	1599.7	160.0	1.200	7.59	50.5	14.0	1.35
	85.0	24.80	20.00	7.053	.916	.653	1501.7	150.2	1.180	7.78	47.0	13.3	1.38

Section												
20 × 6¼	75.0	21.90	20.00	6.391	.789	.641	1263.5	126.3	1.200	7.60	30.1	9.4	1.17
	65.4	19.08	20.00	6.250	.789	.500	1169.5	116.9	1.174	7.83	27.9	8.9	1.21
18 × 6	70.0	20.46	18.00	6.251	.691	.711	917.5	101.9	1.215	6.70	24.5	7.8	1.09
	54.7	15.94	18.00	6.000	.691	.460	795.5	88.4	1.171	7.07	21.2	7.1	1.15
15 × 5½	50.0	14.59	15.00	5.640	.622	.550	481.1	64.2	1.191	5.74	16.0	5.7	1.05
	42.9	12.49	15.00	5.500	.622	.410	441.8	58.9	1.165	5.95	14.6	5.3	1.08
12 × 5¼	50.0	14.57	12.00	5.477	.659	.687	301.6	50.3	1.207	4.55	16.0	5.8	1.05
	40.8	11.84	12.00	5.250	.659	.460	268.9	44.8	1.169	4.77	13.8	5.3	1.08
12 × 5	35.0	10.20	12.00	5.078	.544	.428	227.0	37.8	1.175	4.72	10.0	3.9	0.99
	31.8	9.26	12.00	5.000	.544	.350	215.8	36.0	1.156	4.83	9.5	3.8	1.01
10 × 4⅝	35.0	10.22	10.00	4.944	.491	.594	145.8	29.2	1.205	3.78	8.5	3.4	0.91
	25.4	7.38	10.00	4.660	.491	.310	122.1	24.4	1.148	4.07	6.9	3.0	.97
8 × 4	23.0	6.71	8.00	4.171	.425	.441	64.2	16.0	1.200	3.09	4.4	2.1	.81
	18.4	5.34	8.00	4.000	.425	.270	56.9	14.2	1.148	3.26	3.8	1.9	.84
7 × 3⅝	20.0	5.83	7.00	3.860	.392	.450	41.9	12.0	1.200	2.68	3.1	1.6	.74
	15.3	4.43	7.00	3.660	.392	.250	36.2	10.4	1.144	2.86	2.7	1.5	.78
6 × 3⅜	17.25	5.02	6.00	3.565	.359	.465	26.0	8.7	1.207	2.28	2.3	1.3	.68
	12.5	3.61	6.00	3.330	.359	.230	21.8	7.3	1.151	2.46	1.8	1.1	.72
5 × 3	14.75	4.29	5.00	3.284	.326	.494	15.0	6.0	1.234	1.87	1.7	1.0	.63
	10.0	2.87	5.00	3.000	.326	.210	12.1	4.8	1.167	2.05	1.2	0.82	.65
4 × 2⅝	9.5	2.76	4.00	2.796	.293	.326	6.7	3.3	1.212	1.56	0.91	.65	.58
	7.7	2.21	4.00	2.660	.293	.190	6.0	3.0	1.167	1.64	.77	.58	.59
3 × 2⅜	7.5	2.17	3.00	2.509	.260	.349	2.9	1.9	1.210	1.15	.59	.47	.52
	5.7	1.64	3.00	2.330	.260	.170	2.5	1.7	1.118	1.23	.46	.40	.53

By permission of the American Institute of Steel Construction.

TABLE II
ROLLED STEEL SHAPES

Wide-Flange Sections
(Abridged Listing)

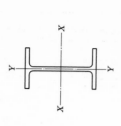

PROPERTIES FOR DESIGN

Nominal Size	Weight per Foot	Area	Depth	Flange Width	Flange Thickness	Web Thickness	Axis X-X				Axis Y-Y		
							I	$\dfrac{I}{c}$	F_p	k	I	$\dfrac{I}{c}$	k
in.	lb	in.²	in.	in.	in.	in.	in.⁴	in.³		in.	in.⁴	in.³	in.
36 × 16½	230	67.73	35.88	16.475	1.260	0.765	14988.4	835.5	1.128	14.88	870.9	105.7	3.59
36 × 12	150	44.16	35.84	11.972	0.940	.625	9012.1	502.9	1.153	14.29	250.4	41.8	2.38
33 × 15¾	200	58.79	33.00	15.750	1.150	.715	11048.2	669.6	1.127	13.71	691.7	87.8	3.43
33 × 11½	130	38.26	33.10	11.510	0.855	.580	6699.0	404.8	1.152	13.23	201.4	35.0	2.29

Section													
30 × 15	172	50.65	29.88	14.985	1.065	.655	7891.5	528.2	1.123	12.48	550.1	73.4	3.30
30 × 10½	108	31.77	29.82	10.484	0.760	.548	4461.0	299.2	1.155	11.85	135.1	25.8	2.06
27 × 14	145	42.68	26.88	13.965	.975	.600	5414.3	402.9	1.122	11.26	406.9	58.3	3.09
27 × 10	94	27.65	26.91	9.990	.747	.490	3266.7	242.8	1.143	10.87	115.1	23.0	2.04
24 × 14	130	38.21	24.25	14.000	.900	.565	4009.5	330.7	1.117	10.24	375.2	53.6	3.13
24 × 12	100	29.43	24.00	12.000	.775	.468	2987.3	248.9	1.118	10.08	203.5	33.9	2.63
24 × 9	76	22.37	23.91	8.985	.682	.440	2096.4	175.4	1.141	9.68	76.5	15.0	1.85
21 × 13	112	32.93	21.00	13.000	.865	.527	2620.6	249.6	1.114	8.92	289.7	44.6	2.96
21 × 9	82	24.10	20.86	8.962	.795	.499	1752.4	168.0	1.141	8.53	89.6	20.0	1.93
21 × 8¼	62	18.23	20.99	8.240	.615	.400	1326.8	126.4	1.140	8.53	53.1	12.9	1.71
18 × 11¾	96	28.22	18.16	11.750	.831	.512	1674.7	184.4	1.117	7.70	206.8	35.2	2.71
18 × 8¾	64	18.80	17.87	8.715	.686	.403	1045.8	117.0	1.126	7.46	70.3	16.1	1.93
18 × 7½	50	14.71	18.00	7.500	.570	.358	800.6	89.0	1.133	7.38	37.2	9.9	1.59
16 × 11½	88	25.87	16.16	11.502	.795	.504	1222.6	151.3	1.117	6.87	185.2	32.2	2.67
16 × 8½	58	17.04	15.86	8.464	.645	.407	746.4	94.1	1.128	6.62	60.5	14.3	1.88
16 × 7	50	14.70	16.25	7.073	.628	.380	655.4	80.7	1.149	6.68	34.8	9.8	1.54
	36	10.59	15.85	6.992	.428	.299	446.3	56.3	1.135	6.49	22.1	6.3	1.45
14 × 16	142	41.85	14.75	15.500	1.063	.680	1672.2	226.7	1.124	6.32	660.1	85.2	3.97
14 × 14½	87	25.56	14.00	14.500	0.688	.420	966.9	138.1	1.095	6.15	349.7	48.2	3.70
14 × 12	84	24.71	14.18	12.023	.778	.451	928.4	130.9	1.110	6.13	225.5	37.5	3.02
	78	22.94	14.06	12.000	.718	.428	851.2	121.1	1.106	6.09	206.9	34.5	3.00
14 × 10	74	21.76	14.19	10.072	.783	.450	796.8	112.3	1.118	6.05	133.5	26.5	2.48
	68	20.00	14.06	10.040	.718	.418	724.1	103.0	1.115	6.02	121.2	24.1	2.46

TABLE II (*Continued*)

Nominal Size	Weight per Foot	Area	Depth	Flange		Web Thickness	Axis X-X				Axis Y-Y		
				Width	Thickness		I	$\frac{I}{c}$	F_p	k	I	$\frac{I}{c}$	k
in.	lb	in.²	in.	in.	in.	in.	in.⁴	in.³		in.	in.⁴	in.³	in.
14 × 10	61	17.94	13.91	10.000	0.643	0.378	641.5	92.2	1.110	5.98	107.3	21.5	2.45
14 × 8	53	15.59	13.94	8.062	.658	.370	542.1	77.8	1.120	5.90	57.5	14.3	1.92
	43	12.65	13.68	8.000	.528	.308	429.0	62.7	1.251	5.82	45.1	11.3	1.89
14 × 6¾	38	11.17	14.12	6.776	.513	.313	385.3	54.6	1.126	5.87	24.6	7.3	1.49
	34	10.00	14.00	6.750	.453	.287	339.2	48.5	1.124	5.83	21.3	6.3	1.46
	30	8.81	13.86	6.733	.383	.270	289.6	41.8	1.127	5.73	17.5	5.2	1.41
12 × 12	85	24.98	12.50	12.105	.796	.495	723.3	115.7	1.116	5.38	235.5	38.9	3.07
	65	19.11	12.12	12.000	.606	.390	533.4	88.0	1.102	5.28	174.6	29.1	3.02
12 × 10	53	15.59	12.06	10.000	.576	.345	426.2	70.7	1.106	5.23	96.1	19.2	2.48
12 × 8	40	11.77	11.94	8.000	.516	.294	310.1	51.9	1.110	5.13	44.1	11.0	1.94
12 × 6½	36	10.59	12.24	6.565	.540	.305	280.8	45.9	1.120	5.15	23.7	7.2	1.50
	31	9.12	12.09	6.525	.465	.265	238.4	39.4	1.117	5.11	19.8	6.1	1.47
	27	7.97	11.95	6.500	.400	.240	204.1	34.1	1.115	5.06	16.6	5.1	1.44

Section													
10 × 10	112	32.92	11.38	10.415	1.248	.755	718.7	126.3	1.168	4.67	235.4	45.2	2.67
	100	29.43	11.12	10.345	1.118	.685	625.0	112.4	1.158	4.61	206.6	39.9	2.65
	89	26.19	10.88	10.275	0.998	.615	542.4	99.7	1.147	4.55	180.6	35.2	2.63
	77	22.67	10.62	10.195	.868	.535	457.2	86.1	1.145	4.49	153.4	30.1	2.60
	49	14.40	10.00	10.000	.558	.340	272.9	54.6	1.105	4.35	93.0	18.6	2.54
10 × 8	45	13.24	10.12	8.022	.618	.350	248.6	49.1	1.120	4.33	53.2	13.3	2.00
	39	11.48	9.94	7.990	.528	.318	209.7	42.2	1.114	4.27	44.9	11.2	1.98
	33	9.71	9.75	7.964	.433	.292	170.9	35.0	1.108	4.20	36.5	9.2	1.94
10 × 5¾	29	8.53	10.22	5.799	.500	.289	157.3	30.8	1.126	4.29	15.2	5.2	1.34
	21	6.19	9.90	5.750	.340	.240	106.3	21.5	1.121	4.14	9.7	3.4	1.25
8 × 8	67	19.70	9.00	8.287	.933	.575	271.8	60.4	1.160	3.71	88.6	21.4	2.12
	58	17.06	8.75	8.222	.808	.510	227.3	52.0	1.152	3.65	74.9	18.2	2.10
	48	14.11	8.50	8.117	.683	.405	183.7	43.2	1.134	3.61	60.9	15.0	2.08
	40	11.76	8.25	8.077	.558	.365	146.3	35.5	1.124	3.53	49.0	12.1	2.04
	35	10.30	8.12	8.027	.493	.315	126.5	31.1	1.116	3.50	42.5	10.6	2.03
	31	9.12	8.00	8.000	.433	.288	109.7	27.4	1.109	3.47	37.0	9.2	2.01
8 × 6½	28	8.23	8.06	6.540	.463	.285	97.8	24.3	1.115	3.45	21.6	6.6	1.62
	24	7.06	7.93	6.500	.398	.245	82.5	20.8	1.110	3.42	18.2	5.6	1.61
8 × 5¼	20	5.88	8.14	5.268	.378	.248	69.2	17.0	1.124	3.43	8.5	3.2	1.20
	17	5.00	8.00	5.250	.308	.230	56.4	14.1	1.120	3.36	6.7	2.6	1.16
6 × 6	20	5.90	6.20	6.018	.367	.258	41.7	13.4	1.119	2.66	13.3	4.4	1.50
	15.5	4.62	6.00	6.000	.269	.240	30.3	10.1	1.119	2.56	9.69	3.2	1.45
5 × 5	16	4.70	5.00	5.000	.360	.240	21.3	8.53	1.125	2.13	7.51	3.00	1.26

By permission of the American Institute of Steel Construction.

TABLE III
ROLLED STEEL SHAPES

Equal-Leg Angles
(Abridged Listing)

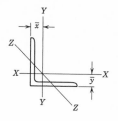

PROPERTIES FOR DESIGN

Size	Thick-ness	Weight per Foot	Area	Axis X-X and Axis Y-Y			Axis Z-Z
				I	k	$\bar{x}$ or $\bar{y}$	k
in.	in.	lb	in.²	in.⁴	in.	in.	in.
8 × 8	$1\frac{1}{8}$	56.9	16.73	98.0	2.42	2.41	1.56
	1	51.0	15.00	89.0	2.44	2.37	1.56
	$\frac{7}{8}$	45.0	13.23	79.6	2.45	2.32	1.57
	$\frac{3}{4}$	38.9	11.44	69.7	2.47	2.28	1.57
	$\frac{5}{8}$	32.7	9.61	59.4	2.49	2.23	1.58
	$\frac{1}{2}$	26.4	7.75	48.6	2.50	2.19	1.59
6 × 6	1	37.4	11.00	35.5	1.80	1.86	1.17
	$\frac{7}{8}$	33.1	9.73	31.9	1.81	1.82	1.17
	$\frac{3}{4}$	28.7	8.44	28.2	1.83	1.78	1.17
	$\frac{9}{16}$	21.9	6.43	22.1	1.85	1.71	1.18
	$\frac{3}{8}$	14.9	4.36	15.4	1.88	1.64	1.19
	$\frac{5}{16}$	12.5	3.66	13.0	1.89	1.61	1.19
5 × 5	$\frac{7}{8}$	27.2	7.98	17.8	1.49	1.57	0.97
	$\frac{5}{8}$	20.0	5.86	13.6	1.52	1.48	.98
	$\frac{7}{16}$	14.3	4.18	10.0	1.55	1.41	.98
	$\frac{5}{16}$	10.3	3.03	7.4	1.57	1.37	.99
4 × 4	$\frac{3}{4}$	18.5	5.44	7.7	1.19	1.27	.78
	$\frac{5}{8}$	15.7	4.61	6.7	1.20	1.23	.78
	$\frac{1}{2}$	12.8	3.75	5.6	1.22	1.18	.78
	$\frac{3}{8}$	9.8	2.86	4.4	1.23	1.14	.79
	$\frac{1}{4}$	6.6	1.94	3.0	1.25	1.09	.80
$3\frac{1}{2} \times 3\frac{1}{2}$	$\frac{1}{2}$	11.1	3.25	3.6	1.06	1.06	.68
	$\frac{7}{16}$	9.8	2.87	3.3	1.07	1.04	.68
	$\frac{3}{8}$	8.5	2.48	2.9	1.07	1.01	.69

TABLE III (*Continued*)

Size	Thick-ness	Weight per Foot	Area	Axis X-X and Axis Y-Y			Axis Z-Z
				I	k	$\bar{x}$ or $\bar{y}$	k
in.	in.	lb	in.^{2}	in.^{4}	in.	in.	in.
$3\frac{1}{2} \times 3\frac{1}{2}$	$\frac{5}{16}$	7.2	2.09	2.5	1.08	0.99	0.69
	$\frac{1}{4}$	5.8	1.69	2.0	1.09	.97	.69
3×3	$\frac{1}{2}$	9.4	2.75	2.2	0.90	.93	.58
	$\frac{7}{16}$	8.3	2.43	2.0	.91	.91	.58
	$\frac{3}{8}$	7.2	2.11	1.8	.91	.89	.58
	$\frac{5}{16}$	6.1	1.78	1.5	.92	.87	.59
	$\frac{1}{4}$	4.9	1.44	1.2	.93	.84	.59
	$\frac{3}{16}$	3.71	1.09	0.96	.94	.82	.59
$2\frac{1}{2} \times 2\frac{1}{2}$	$\frac{1}{2}$	7.7	2.25	1.2	.74	.81	.49
	$\frac{3}{8}$	5.9	1.73	0.98	.75	.76	.49
	$\frac{5}{16}$	5.0	1.47	.85	.76	.74	.49
	$\frac{1}{4}$	4.1	1.19	.70	.77	.72	.49
	$\frac{3}{16}$	3.07	0.90	.55	.78	.69	.49
2×2	$\frac{3}{8}$	4.7	1.36	.48	.59	.64	.39
	$\frac{5}{16}$	3.92	1.15	.42	.60	.61	.39
	$\frac{1}{4}$	3.19	0.94	.35	.61	.59	.39
	$\frac{3}{16}$	2.44	.71	.27	.62	.57	.39
	$\frac{1}{8}$	1.65	.48	.19	.63	.55	.40
$1\frac{3}{4} \times 1\frac{3}{4}$	$\frac{1}{4}$	2.77	.81	.23	.53	.53	.34
	$\frac{3}{16}$	2.12	.62	.18	.54	.51	.34
	$\frac{1}{8}$	1.44	.42	.13	.55	.48	.35
$1\frac{1}{2} \times 1\frac{1}{2}$	$\frac{1}{4}$	2.34	.69	.14	.45	.47	.29
	$\frac{3}{16}$	1.80	.53	.11	.46	.44	.29
$1\frac{1}{4} \times 1\frac{1}{4}$	$\frac{1}{4}$	1.92	.56	.08	.37	.40	.24
	$\frac{1}{8}$	1.01	.30	.04	.38	.36	.25
1×1	$\frac{1}{4}$	1.49	.44	.04	.29	.34	.20
	$\frac{1}{8}$	0.80	.23	.02	.30	.30	.20

By permission of the American Institute of Steel Construction.

ANSWERS TO EVEN-NUMBERED PROBLEMS

Most of the numerical values given were obtained with the aid of a 20-in. slide rule

Chapter 1

1.2 $M_{RL} = 100x$ ft-lb
1.4 $H_{RL} = 147.2$ lb, $V_{RL} = 125$ lb, $M_{RL} = 420$ ft-lb
1.6 $R_{A1} = 1.543P$

Chapter 2

2.12 These are all possible systems of stresses, and, for the boundary conditions they satisfy, they are also all correct.

Chapter 3

3.2 2.0003 in. by 2.5003 in. by 19.9919 in. $\Delta V = -0.0129$ in.^{3}
3.4 $\Delta L = -0.00714$ in.
3.8 $\Delta L = 0.00475$ in.
3.10 $P_{max} = 17,640$ lb. $\delta_{max} = 0.348$ in.
3.12 $P_{max} = 125,000$ lb
3.14 O.D. = 6.87 in.
3.16 $P_{max} = 417$ lb. $x = 2.375$ in.
3 18 $P_{max} = 252$ lb
3.20 $\theta = 2.12$ deg
3 22 $P_{max} = 15,000$ lb
3.24 $V = 10.17$ in.^{3}
3.26 $\theta = 20.4$ deg. $P_{max} = 409$ lb
3.28 $\sigma_{max} = 20,720$ psi; 17,760 psi; and 11,840 psi
3.30 $\delta = 0.0515$ in.
3.32 $\delta_{max} = 0.005$ in.; $\delta_{total} = 0.0015$ in.; $x = 40$ in. and 75 in.

3.34 $\delta = 38.2 \times 10^{-6}$ in.

3.38 $P = 22,000$ lb

3.40 $P = 28,000$ lb acting at 0.9285 in. from left edge on diagonal of symmetry

Chapter 4

4.2 $P = 16,800$ lb; $\tau_{\text{maple}} = 525$ psi; $\tau_{\text{hickory}} = 700$ psi

4.4 $T_{\max} = 625$ in.-lb

4.6 0.59

4.8 $T_{\max} = 67,000$ ft-lb; $\phi = 1.58$ deg

4.10 $L = 87.25$ in.

4.12 $\dfrac{32TL}{3\pi G(D-d)}\left(\dfrac{1}{d^3} - \dfrac{1}{D^3}\right)$; $\phi = 0.001357\ T$ deg

4.14 $\phi = -\dfrac{100x}{GI_p}$; $\phi = -\dfrac{1}{GI_p}[100x - 5(x-2)^2]$;

$\phi = -\dfrac{1}{GI_p}[100x - 5(x-2)^2 + 5(x-7)^2]$

4.16 $T_{\max} = 33,000$ ft-lb

4.18 $D/d = 1.189$; weight saving $= 70.7\%$

4.20 I.D. $= 3.47$ in.

4.22 O.D. $= 2.50$ in.; I.D. $= 2.26$ in.

4.24 $T = 199,500$ in.-lb

4.26 $\dfrac{\phi}{L_1} = \dfrac{2}{G_1 d_1}\left[\tau_{1e} - \tau_{2e}\dfrac{(I_{p2} + I_{p1}n_{12})d_1}{(I_{p1} + I_{p2}n_{21})d_2}\right]$

4.28 The aluminum one, by 0.0011 rad/in.; $T_{\text{optimum}} = 323,000$ in.-lb

4.32 $U = 2.6$ in.-lb/in.^{3}; $\alpha = 0.625$

4.34 $t_{\min} = 0.023$ in.

4.36 $\tau_{\max} = 1337$ psi; $\phi = 0.0192$ deg

4.38 $d = 1.884$ in., 2.52 in., and 2.203 in.

4.40 $\tau_{\max} = 2190$ psi; $\phi = 7.53$ deg

4.42 $a = 0.793$ in.

4.44 (a) $\alpha = 0.309$. (b) $\alpha = 0.265$. (c) $\alpha = \frac{5}{16}$. (d) $\alpha = \frac{4}{15}$

4.46 $\tau_{\max} = 24,700$ psi; $U = 118$ in.-lb/in.^{3}; $\alpha = 0.367$

4.48 $d = \frac{11}{16}$ in.; $N = 7$

4.50 $P = 2332$ lb; $K_{\text{eq}} = 293$ lb/in.; the smaller spring, by 6.18 in.

4.52 0.886:1

Chapter 5

5.2 $V = -300 + 200x$; $M = 300x - 100x^2$.

$V = 700$; $M = 4500 - 700x$.

$V = -500$; $M = -7500 + 500x$

5.4 $V = 1690 - 600x + 50x^2$; $M = -1690x + 300x^2 - \frac{50}{3}x^3$.

$V = -110$; $M = -7200 + 110x$.

$V = -500$; $M = -7500 + 500x$

5.6 $M = -1000$ ft-lb

5.8 V is zero at $x = 4.075$ ft; $M = -2256$ ft-lb

5.10 $x = 2$ ft; $R = 300$ lb

5.12 $R = 2750$ lb

5.18 $M = \dfrac{pL}{2}x - \dfrac{p}{2}x^2$

5.20 $M = \dfrac{pa}{2}x - \dfrac{p}{6a}x^3 + \dfrac{p}{3a}\{x - a\}^3$

5.22 $M = \dfrac{pa}{2}x - \dfrac{p}{2}x^2 + \dfrac{p}{6a}x^3 - \dfrac{p}{3a}\{x - a\}^3$

5.24 $M = \dfrac{pa}{3}x - \dfrac{p}{12a^2}x^4 + \dfrac{2p}{3a}\{x - a\}^3$

5.26 $M = -\dfrac{P(L - 2a)}{L}x + P\{x - a\}^1 - P\{x - L + a\}^1$

5.28 $M_{\max} = Pa(L - 2a)/L$

5.30 $M_{\max} = 3000$ ft-lb

5.32 $M_{\max} = 500$ ft-lb

5.34 $M_{\max} = pa^2/3$

5.36 $M_{\max} = pa^2/6$

5.38 $C = 2000$ ft-lb, clockwise

5.40 $\dfrac{M}{n} = \dfrac{C}{n_1} + C\left(\dfrac{1}{n_2} - \dfrac{1}{n_1}\right)\{x - a\}^0$

5.42 $\dfrac{M}{n} = \dfrac{R}{n_1}x + R\left(\dfrac{1}{n_2} - \dfrac{1}{n_1}\right)\{x - a\}^1 + Ra\left(\dfrac{1}{n_2} - \dfrac{1}{n_1}\right)\{x - a\}^0$

5.44 $\dfrac{M}{n} = \dfrac{C}{n_1} - \dfrac{C}{n_1 L}x - \dfrac{C}{L}\left(\dfrac{1}{n_2} - \dfrac{1}{n_1}\right)\{x - a\}^1$

$\qquad + C\left(1 - \dfrac{a}{L}\right)\left(\dfrac{1}{n_2} - \dfrac{1}{n_1}\right)\{x - a\}^0$

5.46 $\dfrac{M}{n} = \dfrac{p}{n_1}x^2 + p\left(\dfrac{1}{n_2} - \dfrac{1}{n_1}\right)\{x - a\}^2$

$\qquad + 2pa\left(\dfrac{1}{n_2} - \dfrac{1}{n_1}\right)\{x - a\}^1 + pa^2\left(\dfrac{1}{n_2} - \dfrac{1}{n_1}\right)\{x - a\}^0$

Chapter 6

6.4 $M = bh^2\sigma/6.$ $M = b^2h\sigma/6$

6.6 $M = a^3\sigma/32$

6.8 Rectangle should be $(2\sqrt{\tfrac{2}{3}})A$ by $(2\sqrt{\tfrac{1}{3}})B$. Loss in weight $= 40\%$. Loss in bending strength $= 53.8\%$

6.10 $\sqrt{2}:1$

6.12 20I65.4 and 18WF64

6.16 $d = 4$ in.; $M = 32\sigma$ in.-lb

6.18 73.6% by the flanges; 80.6% by the flanges.

6.20 $V_{\max} = 4570$ lb

6.22 72.4% by the stem

6.24 0.1655 V psi as against 0.1745 V psi, or 5.16% too low

6.28 $\tau_{zx} = 354$ psi; $\tau_{yx} = 472$ psi

6.30 $e = \dfrac{3b^2}{h + 6b}$

6.32 $e = 4R/\pi$

6.34 $\tau_{\max} = 0.0117\,V$ psi at 4.737 in. above base

6.36 $h_{\min} = 6$ in.

6.38 10W21

6.40 4900 psi tension and 6860 psi compression

6.42 At quarter points

6.44 $a = 0.293L$; 2.91:1

6.46 2.74 ft; 23,200 lb

6.48 20I85

6.50 (a) $\alpha = 0.25$.   (b) $\alpha = 0.25$

6.52 $P_{max} = 218$ lb

6.54 $b = \dfrac{3p}{H^2\sigma} x^2$

6.56 $p = 1520$ lb/ft

6.58 $\sigma_{steel} = 15{,}990$ psi; $\sigma_{brass} = 14{,}000$ psi; $\sigma_{aluminum} = 10{,}220$ psi

6.60 $\sigma_{concrete} = 690$ psi; $\sigma_{steel} = 14{,}600$ psi

6.62 (a) 3.94 in. from top.   (b) $I_{eq} = 484$ in.^{4} (c) $M = 119{,}900$ in.-lb

Chapter 7

7.2 $\rho = 49.1$ in.

7.4 $\delta_{max} = PL^3/3EI$

7.6 $\delta = qL^4/8EI$

7.8 $\delta = 0.196$ in.

7.10 8W17; $\sigma_{max} = 14{,}100$ psi

7.12 $y = \dfrac{P}{6LEI} [-(L - 2a)x^3 + L\{x - a\}^3 - L\{x - L + a\}^3$

$\qquad\qquad + (aL^2 - 3a^2L + 2a^3)x]$

7.14 $y = \dfrac{1728}{EI} \left[\dfrac{400}{3} x^3 - 500\{x - 6\}^3 + \dfrac{1600}{3}\{x - 10\}^3 - \dfrac{30{,}400}{3} x \right]$

7.16 $y = \dfrac{1728}{EI} [250x^3 - 25x^4 + 25\{x - 5\}^4 + 500\{x - 10\}^3 - 15{,}625x]$

7.18 $y = \dfrac{1728}{EI} \left[-\dfrac{845}{3} x^3 + 25x^4 - \dfrac{5}{6} x^5 \right.$

$\qquad\qquad \left. + \dfrac{5}{6}\{x - 6\}^5 - 65\{x - 10\}^3 + \dfrac{794{,}744}{3} x \right]$

7.20 $y = \dfrac{P}{EI} \left[\dfrac{a}{12} x^3 - \dfrac{1}{120a} x^5 + \dfrac{1}{60a}\{x - a\}^5 - \dfrac{5}{24} a^3x \right]$

7.22 $y = \dfrac{P}{EI} \left[\dfrac{a}{12} x^3 - \dfrac{1}{24} x^4 - \dfrac{1}{120a} x^5 - \dfrac{1}{60a}\{x - a\}^5 - \dfrac{1}{8} a^3x \right]$

7.24 $y = \dfrac{P}{EI} \left[\dfrac{a}{18} x^3 - \dfrac{1}{360a^2} x^6 + \dfrac{1}{30a}\{x - a\}^5 - \dfrac{3}{20} a^3x \right]$

7.26 $-0.336{:}1$

7.28 $y = \dfrac{1728}{EI} \left[\dfrac{245}{6} x^3 - \dfrac{25}{3}\{x - 1\}^4 + \dfrac{5}{18}\{x - 1\}^5 - \dfrac{5}{18}\{x - 4\}^5 \right.$

$\qquad\qquad + \dfrac{25}{3}\{x - 4\}^4 - \dfrac{25}{6}\{x - 6\}^4 - 500\{x - 8\}^2$

$\qquad\qquad \left. + \dfrac{205}{6}\{x - 10\}^3 - 814x \right]$

7.30 Not Eq. 2.7a

7.32 $\delta = 9720/G$ in.
7.34 $\delta = \sigma L^2/4Eh$; $6:5$
7.36 $\delta_{max} = 0.00305P$ in.
7.38 $h_1 = 3.10$ in.; $h_2 = 3.53$ in.; $\delta_{max} = 0.1665$ in.
7.40 $\delta_{max} = 0.951$ in.

Chapter 8

8.2 $n = 2$ (axial forces ignored)
8.4 $n = 6$
8.6 For case in figure, shorten bar an amount $\sigma_e(a - b)/E$
8.8 $P = 6780$ lb
8.10 $\sigma_{max} = 7500$ psi; $\delta_{max} = 0.00583$ in.
8.12 $P_{max} = 12,030$ lb
8.14 (b) $\Delta\phi = 2\tau_e(a - b)/Gd$
8.16 $T_1 = T_2 = C_1$
8.18 $a/L = \frac{1}{4}$
8.20 $\tau_{max} = 3950$ psi
8.22 $d = 2.81$ in. $T_0 = 64,200$ in.-lb
8.24 $M_{wall} = -1.68P$ ft-lb; $\delta_{max} = 1728(9.8)P/EI$ in.
8.26 $M_{wall} = -8.82p$ ft-lb
8.28 $M_{wall} = -11.7p$ ft-lb
8.32 $M_{wall} = -2P$ ft-lb
8.34 $M_1 = -0.96P$ ft-lb; $M_2 = -1.44P$ ft-lb; $\delta_{max} = 1728(4.7)P/EI$ in.
8.36 $M_1 = M_2 = -pL^2/12$; $\delta_{max} = pL^4/384EI$
8.38 $M_1 = -2.712p$ ft-lb; $M_2 = -3.888p$ ft-lb
8.40 $M_1 = -M_0(b/L)(2 - 3b/L)$; $M_2 = 3M_0(b/L)(1 - b/L)$
8.44 $P_1:P_2:P_3 = 3:4:6$, where $P_1 = 10,000/3$ lb
8.46 8WF28, 8WF24, 6WF20
8.48 Raise support $384M/EI$ in.; $P = M/16$ lb; where $M = \sigma I/c$ in.-lb. 12.5% increase in P.
8.50 Raise support $10,620M/EI$ in.; $p = 0.01517M$ lb/ft; where $M = \sigma I/c$ in.-lb. 45.8% increase in p.
8.52 $R_1 = -0.256P$. $P_{max} = 7810$ lb
8.54 $P_{max} = M_e/27$ lb, M_e being in in.-lb
8.56 $R_1 = 5.13p$ lb; $R_2 = 33.11p$ lb; $R_3 = 11.76p$ lb

Chapter 9

9.2 $\sigma = 1600$ psi, 1900 psi, 2025 psi
9.4 $P_{max} = 2566$ lb
9.6 $\sigma = 2110$ psi
9.8 $P = 1423$ lb
9.10 (a) long. (b) long. (c) long
9.12 (a) $P = 1453$ lb. (b) $L = 99.5$ in.
9.14 (a) $\Delta l_2 = 0.01253$ in. (b) $\Delta l_2 = 0.141$ in.
9.16 (a) $P = 23,560$ lb. (b) $C = 1.46$
9.18 $P = 4785$ lb
9.20 $P = 48,530$ lb

9.22 $P/A = 40{,}000 - 3.86(l/k)^2$, $0 < l/k < 72$

9.24 8W-31

Chapter 10

10.6 $\sigma_{\max} = 1284.5$ psi, $\sigma_{\min} = -1727.5$ psi, $\theta_{xP} = 9.69$ deg

10.8 No

10.14 $\sigma_{\max} = 1207$ psi, $\sigma_{\min} = -207$ psi, $\tau_{\max} = 707$ psi, $\theta_{xP} = -22.5$ deg

10.16 $\sigma_{\max} = 618$ psi, $\sigma_{\min} = -1618$ psi, $\tau_{\max} = 1118$ psi, $\theta_{xP} = 31.7$ deg

10.18 $\sigma_{\max} = 15{,}000$ psi, $\sigma_{\min\,\max} = 5000$ psi, $\tau_{\max} = 7500$ psi, $\theta_{xP} = 45$ deg

10.20 $\sigma_{\max} = 2207$ psi, $\sigma_{\min\,\max} = 793$ psi, $\tau_{\max} = 1103.5$ psi,
$\theta_P = 22.5$ deg between two σ's shown

10.22 $\sigma_{\max} = 4000$ psi, $\sigma_{\min\,\max} = 2000$ psi, $\tau_{\max} = 2000$ psi,
$\theta_P = -45$ deg from horizontal

10.24 $\sigma = 2000/3$ psi, $\tau = 3590$ psi

10.26 $\sigma_{\max} = 250\sqrt{2}$ psi, $\sigma_{\min} = -250\sqrt{2}$ psi, $\tau_{\max} = 250\sqrt{2}$ psi,
$\theta_{xP} = 67.5$ deg

10.28 $\sigma_{\max} = 500\sqrt{2}$ psi, $\sigma_{\min} = -500\sqrt{2}$ psi, $\tau_{\max} = 500\sqrt{2}$ psi,
$\theta_{xP} = 22.5$ deg

10.30 $\sigma_{\max} = 1000$ psi, $\sigma_{\min} = -1000$ psi, $\tau_{\max} = 1000$ psi, $\theta_{xP} = 45$ deg

Chapter 11

11.4 $\epsilon_{\max} = 1003 \times 10^{-6}$, $\epsilon_{\min\,\max} = 197 \times 10^{-6}$, $\gamma_{\max} = 1003 \times 10^{-6}$,
$\theta_{xP} = -3.57$ deg

11.6 $\epsilon_{\max} = 1000\sqrt{2} \times 10^{-6}$, $\epsilon_{\min} = -1000\sqrt{2} \times 10^{-6}$,
$\gamma_{\max} = 2000\sqrt{2} \times 10^{-6}$, $\theta_{xP} = 67.5$ deg

11.8 $\epsilon_{\max} = 5303 \times 10^{-6}$, $\epsilon_{\min\,\max} = 1697 \times 10^{-6}$,
$\gamma_{\max} = 5303 \times 10^{-6}$, $\theta_{xP} = 16.85$ deg

11.10 $\epsilon_{\max} = 2000 \times 10^{-6}$, $\epsilon_{\min} = -2000 \times 10^{-6}$,
$\gamma_{\max} = 4000 \times 10^{-6}$, $\theta_{xP} = 0$ deg

11.12 $\epsilon_{\max} = 1940 \times 10^{-6}$, $\epsilon_{\min\,\max} = 60 \times 10^{-6}$,
$\gamma_{\max} = 1940 \times 10^{-6}$, $\theta_{xP} = 86.45$ deg

11.14 $\epsilon_{\text{mean}} = \dfrac{\epsilon_a + \epsilon_c}{2}$; $\dfrac{\gamma_{\text{stat}}}{2} = \dfrac{1}{2}\sqrt{(\epsilon_a - \epsilon_c)^2 + (2\epsilon_b - \epsilon_c - \epsilon_a)^2}$.

$\tan 2\theta_{xP} = \dfrac{2\epsilon_b - \epsilon_c - \epsilon_a}{\epsilon_a - \epsilon_c}$

11.16 $\epsilon_{\max} = 2526 \times 10^{-6}$, $\epsilon_{\min} = -526 \times 10^{-6}$,
$\gamma_{\max} = 3052 \times 10^{-6}$, $\theta_{xP} = 95.45$ deg

11.18 $\sigma_{\max} = 12{,}475$ psi; $\sigma_{\min\,\max} = 6060$ psi

Chapter 12

12.2 $P_{\max} = 2310$ lb

12.4 $b = 2.74$ in.

12.6 M.S. $= 1.02$

12.8 $(P_1)_{\max} = 186$ lb, $(P_2)_{\max} = 86$ lb

12.10 $t_{\min} = 0.041$ in. by either theory. No significant difference.

12.12 None.

12.14 $t_{\min} = 1.895$ in. by either theory
12.16 (a) $t = 1.895$ in. (b) $t = 1.630$ in.
12.18 86.7%
12.20 100%
12.22 (a) $T = 116{,}800$ in.-lb. (b) $T = 115{,}500$ in.-lb
12.24 No, but rather in the ratio $(2 - \nu)/(1 - 2\nu)$

Chapter 13

13.2 $U = p^2L^5/20Ebh^3$
13.4 $U = P_{cr}{}^2\delta^2L/4EI = \pi^4EI\delta^2L/4$
13.10 $\delta = (10^6/E)(1.466/A_c + 1.086/A_t)$
13.12 $\delta = 5pL^4/384EI$
13.14 $\delta_C = \pi PR^3/2EI$; $\delta_{BH} = \pi PR^3/4EI$, $\delta_{BV} = PR^3/2EI$; where $I = \pi d^4/64$
13.16 $\delta = PR^3\left(\dfrac{\pi}{4EI} + \dfrac{3\pi - 8}{4GI_p}\right)$
13.18 $R_1 = Pb/L$; $\delta = Pab/AEL$
13.20 (a) $P/5$, $4P/5$, $P/5$. (b) $\delta = 2PL/5AE$
13.22 $M_1 = -pL^2/8$
13.24 $M_A = 8P/9$ ft-lb; $V_A = 13P/27$ lb; $V_C = 14P/27$
13.26 (a) $H = P/\pi$, $V = P$. (b) $\delta = 8PR^3(3\pi^2 - 8\pi - 4)/\pi^2Ed^4$
13.28 (a) $M_A = \dfrac{PR}{2\pi}(\pi - 2)$. (b) $M_B = -\dfrac{PR}{\pi}$.
(c) $\Delta d = \dfrac{PR^3}{4\pi EI}(-5\pi^2 + 20\pi - 8)$. (d) $\dfrac{PR^3}{2\pi EI}(4 - \pi)$, where $I = \pi d^4/64$

Chapter 14

14.2 $P = 2\sigma_pA$; $R = \sigma_pA/3$
14.4 $T = 141{,}100$ in.-lb; 133.2%; 99.85%; 0.382 deg/in.
14.6 $T_L = 136{,}000$ in.-lb; 0.191 deg/in.
14.8 $F_p = 16/3\pi$
14.10 $F_p = 2$
14.12 $F_p = 1.88$
14.14 (a) $M = 156{,}000$ in.-lb. (b) $\rho = 417$ in. (c) 96.3%
14.16 $P_L = 4M_L/L$
14.18 $p_L = 11.67M_L/L^2$
14.20 $p_L = 23M_L/L^2$
14.22 $p_L = 24M_L/L^2$
14.24 $l/k = 42.3$
14.26 $A = 1.705$ in.^{2}; $\delta = 0.0828$ in.
14.28 12WF27
14.30 18WF50
14.32 AB, AD, and CD: 1.045 in. by 1.045 in.; DB: 2.085 in. by 2.085 in.; BC and AC: 2.197 in. by 2.197 in.
14.34 (a) $p = 4.77$ in. (b) 79%

INDEX

Active coils of helical spring, 103
Active system, 114
Admissible stress values, 355
Allowable stress, 81
Analysis, 54
  definition of, 1
  equations of, 83
Andrews, E. S., 382, 391
Angle between two lines, 326
  of twist per unit length, 82
Anticlastic curvature, 197
Area-moment method, 200, 203, 387
Assumptions in beam analysis, 144
Auxiliary force, 384, 392
Average shear stress, 73
Average stress, 11

Back pitch of rivets, 443
Balanced reinforcement, 190
Bauschinger effect, 51
Beam, cantilever, 112
  compound, 112
  continuous, 112
  curved, 112
  definition of, 112, 113
  overhanging, 112
  simple, 111
  simply supported, 112
  single span, 234

Beam, statically determinate, 112
  types of, 111
  uniformly stressed, 112
Beam deformation, 194
Beam in pure bending, 143
Beltrami, 349
Bending, assumptions in analysis of, 144
Bending moment, 114
  rule for evaluating, 119
Bending-moment diagram, 136
Bending-moment equation, 116
Bending strength, 142
  of a beam section, 147
  of **WF** section, 150, 151
Bernoulli-Euler equation, 198, 199, 200, 203, 216, 261, 269
Bessemer process, 441
Betti, E., 382
Biaxial stress, 291–294
Biaxial stress, Mohr's circles for, 310–312
Bleich, F., 432
Body forces, 3, 18
Bond between steel and concrete, 191
Braced term, use of in axial loading, 65, 66
  in bending, 119
  in torsion, 96

Bredt, R., 109
Brittle material, 48, 56, 348
Buckled column, 278
Buckling, 265, 275
Built-in support of beam, 112
Burr, W. H., 282
Butt joint, 442
Butt straps, 443

Cantilever beam, 112, 237
  uniformly stressed, 179
Cartesian components, 38, 290
  of stress, 306
Cartesian tensors, 290
Castigliano's theorem, 382
Characteristics of force and moment, 4
Checker's equation, 190
Circumferential stress, 369
Civil engineering usage, 56
Clockwise and counterclockwise shear
  stresses, 289, 290
Closure of M-x diagram, significance
  of, 139
  of V-x diagram, significance of, 138
Coefficient of friction, 114
Cold bend, 397
Collapse, 404
Collapse of column, 275
Column, 260
Column behavior, salient aspects of,
  267
Column formula, straight-line, 282
  parabolic, 282, 283
  Gordon-Rankine, 283, 284
Column slenderness, 271
Comma technique, 203
Compatibility, significance of, 25, 26
Compatibility equation, 225
Composite beams, 183, 191
Composite member, axially loaded, 70
Composite shaft, 87
Compound beam, 112
Compression, 51, 52
Compression spring, 101
Concentrated loads, 134
Concentrated moment, 121
Conjugate-beam method, 200, 203, 387
Considère, A., 432

Constraint redundancy, significance of,
  227
Contact forces, 3
Contained plastic deformation, 407
Continuity of elastic curve, 247
Continuous beam, 112
Continuum, 12
Controlled plastic deformation, 404
Correct collapse mechanism, 437
Correction factor in helical spring, 102
Correspondence between stress and
  strain, 329
Coulomb, 349
Cover plates, 443
Critical slenderness, 266, 271, 272, 275
Cross shear stresses, 289
Curvature, 200
  of elasto-plastic beam, 416–417
Curved beam, 112
Cyclic permutation of subscripts, 314
Cylindrical pressure vessel, 369–371

Deflections due to shear, 210–215
Deflections of a beam, 199
  of a helical spring, 103, 104
Deformation of a shaft, 81
Degree of indeterminateness, 221
  of redundancy, 221, 390
de Jonge, A. E. R., 442
Den Hartog, J. P., 76, 98, 314, 371
Depth-to-span ratio, 214
Design, 54
  definition of, 2
  equations of, 83
Design stress, 56
Designer's equation, 190
Deviator stress tensor, 355
Diagonal tension in pure shear, 307,
  308
Differential equations of equilibrium,
  18, 19
Differentiation under integral sign, 384
Dilatation, 354
Dirac functions, 126
Direction cosines, relations between,
  292
Discontinuity in deformation geometry,
  212
Discontinuity stresses, 371

Displacement, 22, 194
Double integration method, 200, 203
Double modulus column formula, 432
Double shear, rivet in, 448
Doublet, 126, 127
Ductile material, 48, 56, 348
Ductility, 397
Duguet, 349
Durelli, A. J., 324

Eccentrically applied load, 255, 260
Eccentrically loaded member, 279
Eccentricity, significance of, 264–267
Eccentricity of load as an error, 271
Effective column length, 275, 276
Effects of forces, external and internal, 3, 4
Efficiency of beam section, 177
of riveted joint, 448
Elastic constants, 340
Elastic core, 407, 413
Elastic curve, 199, 207, 212
Elastic deformation, 404
Elastic instability, 428
Elastic limit, 50
Elasticity and proportionality, 30, 31
Elasticity theory, 31, 401
Elastic-plastic material, 399
Elastic strength of a material, 350
Elasto-plastic moment of rectangular beam, 417
Electric strain gages, 89
Elongation of hanging bar, 67
of tension bar, 45
Empiricism in column design, 282
End conditions, examples of, 277
End-fixity coefficient, 278, 282
End fixity, uncertainty of, 282
End of usefulness, 53, 54
Energy of strain, 353, 375
Energy methods, 200
Energy stored in helical spring, 105
in shaft, 100
in tube, 108
Engesser, F., 432
Engineering approach, 34, 222, 436
Engineering constants in Hooke's law, 340
Equilibrium, indifferent, 265

Equilibrium, neutral, 265, 268
stable, 268
unstable, 265
Equivalent area in beam section, 185
Equivalent column length, 275
Euler, L., 267
Euler column, 267–272, 276, 279
Euler column length, 268
Euler curve, 268, 269
Euler hyperbola, 269, 282, 283
Euler length, 278
Eulerian definition of strain, 51
Euler value, 273
Euler's theorem on homogeneous functions, 380, 381
Euler-Engesser formula, 433
Euler-Van den Broek equation, 433
Existence theorem, 36
External moment, 114
External redundant, 391
External shear force, 114
External work on tube, 108
Extrapolation, 35, 58
in analysis of shear in a beam, 153
of elementary beam formulas, 167
to variable cross section beams, 179
of torsion analysis to helical spring, 101

Factor of ignorance or uncertainty, 55
Failure of column, 281
of material, 348
Felgar, R. P., 357
First moment of area in a beam section, 155
Flow figures, 291
Föppl, A., 125, 203
Force-variation diagram, 66, 67
Form factor, 84, 179
for shear, 212
in a beam, 148
Fracture, 51
Free-body diagram, construction of, 5
Friction force, 114

Gage length, 47, 89
Galilei, Galileo, 181
Gaudard, J., 442
Generalized displacement, 380

Generalized force, 380
Generic equations for V and M, 119
Generic plane, 286, 290
Generic section in a beam, 118
Geometric incompatibility, 212
Geometry methods, 200
Goodier, J. N., 98, 109, 157, 163
Gordon-Rankine column formula, 283, 284
Guest, 349
Guillemin, E. A., 125

Half-parabola, 126, 127
Helical spring, 101
    deflection of, 103
    utilization factor of, 105
Helices on surface of round shaft, 82
Helix angle, 102
Hencky, 349
Hetenyi, M., 368
Hinge, beam support, 112
Hinged-end column, 276, 278
Hodge, P. G., 419, 436
Holl, D. L., 129
Hollow shaft, 85, 86, 410
Hooke's law, 44, 79, 82, 104, 144, 183, 212, 263, 265, 340–342, 349, 354, 379, 398
Hooke's law, description of, 26, 27
    equations of, 27, 28, 341
        for plane strain, 29, 342
        for plane stress, 29, 342
        for uniaxial strain, 342
        for uniaxial stress, 29, 342
Hoop stress, 370
Horsepower transmitted by shaft, 92
Huber, 349
Hydrostatic stress, 298, 351

I-beams, 149
Impulse, 126, 127
Independent variable, 54, 391
Inelastic column action, 428–435
Inelastic instability, 433
Influence coefficient, 379, 382
Initial crookedness, 271
Integration constants, meaning of, 204
Interaction curve, 359, 364
Interaction equation, 359, 364

Intermediate column range, 272
Internal effects, 116
Internal friction theory, 349
Internal redundant, 391
Inverse method, 33
Isotropic point, 298
Isotropic stress tensor, 355
Iteration process, 258

Jeffreys, H., 290
Johnson, J. B., 282
Jourawski, D. J., 155
Justification for sign convention, 201

Key, shear action in, 73, 74
Kist's principle, 437, 440, 447
Knife edge, 112

Lagrangian definition of strain, 21
Lamé, 349
Lap joint, 442
Leaf spring, 182
Least work theorem, 391
Left-handed coordinate system, 246, 310
Limit analysis of riveted joint, 444
Limit strength, 400
    of long column, 431
    of short column, 432
Linear elasticity, 31, 380
Linear strain theory, 349
Load-carrying capacity of a beam, 142
Load-deformation curve in torsion, 89
Load intensity q, sign convention for, 129
Local failure, 450
Localization of force, 4
Localized forces, 62
Localized moment load, 121
Long column, 271
Long column range, 272
Longitudinal diametral plane, 101
Longitudinal fibers, 44
Longitudinal stresses, 370
Long, R. R., 290
Lubahn, J. D., 357
Lüders's lines, 291

Macaulay, W. H., 125, 203

Machine design practice, 56
Main plates, 442
Malleability, 397
Maple, C. G., 129
Margin of safety, 56
Marks, L. S., 30
Maximum deflection, connotation of, 206
how to locate, 206
Maximum material utilization, 57
Maxwell, J. C., 349, 382
Mean coil diameter of helical spring, 101
Mean perimeter of thin-walled tube, 108
Mechanism, 424
Member ductility, 435
Membrane stresses, 368
Metals Handbook, ASM, 30
Minimum energy, 391
Modulus of elasticity, dimensions of, 30
table of values of, 29, 30
Modulus of resilience, 51, 91
in shear, 108
Modulus of rupture in torsion, 90
Modulus of yield in torsion, 90
Modulus ratio as weighting factor, 70
Mohr, Otto, 310, 349
Mohr's circle for strain, 331–334
for stress, 308–320
Mode of failure in riveted joint, representation of, 450
Modulus ratio, 70, 87, 190
Monocoque construction, 106
Montgomerie, J., 442
Moving loads on beam, 176
Multiforce member, 61

Nadai, A., 348, 356
Natural or logarithmic strain, 51
Neutral axis, 146, 196
in fully plastic beam section, 415
Neutral elastic equilibrium, 429
Neutral line, 197
Nominal axial deformation, 62
Nominal stress, 401
Nonhomogeneous beam sections, 183
Normal stress, 13

Normal stress, in bending, 146, 147
on generic plane, 287

Offset strain in torsion, 90
Offset yield strength, 50, 73
Operational mathematics, 129
Optimization, 58, 84
Optimization by purposeful misfit, 71, 191, 227, 232, 240
by varying beam cross section, 178, 179
in bending, illustrative example of, 172
Optimum beam strength, 149
Optimum material utilization, 188, 191
Order of singularity function, 125, 126
Osculating plane, 198
Over-all failure, 450
Overhang in a beam, 112
Overload factor, 55, 56

Panlilio, F., 421, 426
Parabolic column formula, 282, 283
Parallelogram law, 287
Passing a section, 5
Passive system, 114
Permanent set, 281
Phillips, A., 416, 422, 437
Phillips, E. A., 324
Physical length, 268, 276, 278
Physical slenderness, 271
Pin-ended column, 276
Pitch of rivets, 443
Plane strain, 342
Plane stress, 342
definition of, 300
Plastic bending, 413–417
Plastic form factor, 416
Plastic instability, 430
Plastic material, 399
Plastic section modulus, 415
Plastic stress, 399
Plastic structural analysis, 436
Point force, 121
Point moment equivalent to couple, 122
Poisson's ratio, 29
Polar second moment of area, 80
Poncelet, 349

Postbuckling strength, 274
Prestraining in shafts, 88
Prestressed concrete theory, 192
Principal axes of stress and strain, 341
Principal centroidal axis, 148, 268
Principal plane, definition of, 288
  direction cosines of, 298
  major, intermediate, minor, 298
Principal strains, 330–331
Principal stress, definition of, 288
Principal stresses, 298
Proof stress, 50
Proportional limit, 42
Proportional-limit strain, 50
Proportional-limit stress, 50, 73
  in torsion, 89
Proportional loading, 351, 359
Pure bending, 143
Pure shear in plane stress, 307–308
  in three dimensions, 298
  of uniform intensity, 89
Pure shear strain, 328–329

Radius of curvature, 196, 197
Rankine, 349
Rayleigh, Lord, 382
Realizable end fixity, 279
Redundancy of constraint, significance
  of, 227
Redundantly supported bar, example
  of, 225–227
Redundantly supported members, 221
Reilly, C., 442
Reinforced beams, 183
Reinforced concrete beams, 188
Relaxation methods, 254
Relief of load, 405
Reloading, 406, 410
Repeating patterns in riveted connec-
  tion, 443
Residual reactions, 405, 425
Residual stresses, 406, 410
  in rectangular beam, 419
  in springs, 419
Resilience, 51
  of helical spring, 104
  of shaft, 90
  per unit volume, 91
Resisting moment, 113
Resisting shear force, 113

Riveted joint, 441–452
Roark, R. I., 443
Rotating shafts, 92
Rotational displacement in a shaft, 81
Rotational speed of shaft, influence on
  torque capacity, 92

"Safe" stress values, 350
Safety factor, 55
  for columns, 272
Saint-Venant, 349
Saint-Venant's principle, 35, 195
Salmon, E. H., 284
Scale factors for Mohr's circles, 344
Secant formula, 263, 266
Second moment of area, 279
  in a beam section, 146
  in a transformed section, 185
Section modulus, 147
Section stiffness, 198
Shaft, elliptical cross section, 99
  rectangular cross section, 99
  triangular cross section, 100
Shakedown, 436
Shanley, F., 432, 444
Shear center, 162, 163
Shear flow, 106
Shear-force diagram, 136
Shear force in helical spring, 101
Shear force, rule for evaluating, 118
Shear load, 73
Shear modulus of elasticity, 30, 79, 89
Shear pin, 72
Shear strain, 78
  in a shaft, 81
Shear strength of a beam section, 153,
  156
Shear stress, 13
Shear stress on generic plane, 287
Shear stresses in a beam of circular
  cross section, 164–166
  in beams, 155
  in a helical spring, 102–103
  in flanges of WF sections, 160
  on perpendicular planes, 16
  in a thin-walled tube, 107
Shearing-force equation, 116
Shift of neutral axis, 413
Short columns, 271
Siemens process, 441

Sign convention for bending moment, 119
  for curvature, 198
  for load intensity, 129
  for shear force, 118
  for strain, 24
  for stress components, 18
Signs, 37
  of stress components, interpretation of, 289
Simple beam, 111
Simply supported beam, 112
Sine wave, 269, 278
Single shear, rivet in, 446
Singularities, 384
Singularity functions, 125, 203
Singularity functions, differentiation and integration properties of, 126
  graphs of, 127
Slenderness, 265, 271
Slenderness ratio, 266
Small strains, implications of, 324
Smithells, C. J., 30
Sokolnikoff, E. S., 380
Sokolnikoff, I. S., 166, 380
Solid round shafts, 76
Solid shaft, 407–409
Southwell, R. V., 432
Specification-making bodies, 56
Spherical pressure vessel, 368–369
Spring, helical, 101
Spring constant, 104
Statically determinate beam, 112
Stationary values of shear stress, in biaxial stress, 294, 295
  in triaxial stress, 296, 297
Statics, 1
Steel ratio, 189
Stepped beams, deflections of, 216
Stiffness (rigidity) of shaft, 86
Straight-line column formula, 282
Strain, definition of, 20, 21
Strain energy, 31, 32, 375
  of a beam, 377
  of a shaft, 376
  of a tension member, 376
Strain energy theory, 349
Strain gage, 47
Strain gage rosettes, 336
Strain gages, 336

Strain hardening, 398
Strain tensor, its matrix, 24
Straining machine, 275
Strength, equations of, 83
Strength in tension, 41
  of a beam, 142
  of a beam section, 142
  of a column, 272
  of a compression member, 257, 261, 263
  of a material, 349
  of a shaft cross section, 81
"Strength" of a singularity, 129
Strength of a structure, 3
  of a two-force member, 53
Strength or usefulness, 54
Strength ratio, 266
Strength theories, 349
Strengthening eccentricity, 276
Strengthening moments, 276
Stress, definition of, 11
Stress at a point, 13
Stress components, notation for, 14
Stress concentration factor, 401
Stressed-skin construction, 106
Stresses, necessary condition for correctness of, 20
Stress raiser, 401
Stress-strain diagram, 48
  in shear, 88, 89
Stress tensor, 13, 285
  represented by matrix, 16
  specification of, 15, 16
Stress vector, 13
Stretcher strains, 291
Structural shapes, 149
Strut, 260
Superposition, 36, 64, 102, 199, 255, 256, 259, 357
  in analysis of helical spring, 102
  not applicable, 263
  of strain patterns, 334
  of strains, 327, 329
  of stresses, 322
Superposition, principle of, 380
Surface forces, 18, 20
Symmetry argument applied to torsion, 77

Tangent modulus, 49, 432

Tension spring, 101
Tension test, 47
Tensors, 329
Testing machines, 47
Thin open sections in torsion, 100
Three-moment equation, 244–254
Timoshenko, S., 98, 109, 155, 157, 163, 168, 264, 310, 382
Torque capacity, 82
Torque varying in stepwise fashion, 92, 93
Torsion, assumptions in analysis of, 76, 77
Torsional rigidity, 82
Torsional strength per unit area, 85
Transformed area in beams, 185
  in shafts, 87
Transformed section, 189
Transmissibility, principle of, 3
Transmission of load, 72
Transverse plane, implications of, 6
Transverse shear stress, 155
Tredgold, 284
Tresca, 349
Triaxial stress, 294–297
  Mohr's circles for, 312–316
True strain, 51
True strength of column, 282
True stress, 51
Tsao, C. H., 324
T-shaped section, reason for, 183
Tubes in torsion, 106
Twist meter, 89
Twisting moment transmitted, 96
Twisting strength, demand for, 94

Ultimate strength, 51, 56, 73
Uncontrolled plastic deformation, 404
Uniaxial strain, 325–328, 342
Uniaxial stress, 145, 287–291, 342
  Mohr's circle for, 309–310
Uniformly stressed beam, 112, 179
Uniqueness theorem, 36
Unit-doublet function, 126
Unit-impulse function, 126
Unit-load method, 384
Unit ramp, 126, 127
Units, 37
Unit step, 126, 127
Universal testing machine, 48, 73

Upper and lower bounds of collapse load, 436
Usable capacity, 55
Usable strength, 400
Usable stress, 56
Usefulness, end of, 42, 43
Utilization factor, 407
  in helical spring, 105
  in torsion, 91
Utilization factors of beams, 177

Van den Broek, J. A., 267, 271, 274, 282, 435, 437, 440
Van den Broek's principle, 435, 437, 447
Vinograde, B., 129
von Karman, T., 432
von Mises, 349

Wahl, A. M., 103
Wahl correction factor in helical spring, 103
Wang, C. T., 340, 401
Warping due to shear, 211
  of beam section, effect on normal stresses, 212
Weakening eccentricity, 276
Weakening moments, 276
Weighted area in beams, 184
Weighting factor, 70
  in torsion, 87
Weighting multiplier, 186
Wide-flange section, 149
Wire diameter, 101
Woods, F. S., 384
Work-absorbing component, 379
Work and energy, principle of, 200
Work by external forces, 378
Working load, 56
Working strength, 55
Working stress, 56

Yield hinge, 415
Yield line, 350, 352, 356
Yield point, 398
Yield strength, 50, 56
  in tension, 56
  in torsion, 90
Yield surface, 350, 352, 355